THE

TOMORROW
MAKERS

THE
TOMORROW
MAKERS

A Brave New World of Living-Brain Machines

Grant Fjermedal

TEMPUS™

Tempus Books of Microsoft Press
A Division of Microsoft Corporation
16011 NE 36th Way, Box 97017, Redmond, Washington 98073-9717

Reprinted by arrangement with Macmillan Publishing Company.

Library of Congress Cataloging in Publication Data

Fjermedal, Grant.
The tomorrow makers.

Reprint. Originally published: New York : Macmillan, ©1986.
Includes index.
1. Robotics — Popular works.   2. Artificial intelligence — Popular works.
I. Title.
[TJ211.15.F54   1988]   629.8'92   87-33524
ISBN 1-55615-113-6

Printed and bound in the United States of America

1 2 3 4 5 6 7 8 9 HCHC 8 9 0 9 8

Distributed to the book trade in the United States by Harper & Row.

Distributed to the book trade in Canada by General Publishing Company, Ltd.

Tempus Books and the Tempus logo are trademarks of Microsoft Press.
Tempus Books is an imprint of Microsoft Press.

Cover illustration by Robert Chrestensen, Technigraphic System Inc.,
Edmonds, Washington

For Elsie DeHart, unflagging friend

CONTENTS

ACKNOWLEDGMENTS

IT WAS DURING the course of my travels through America and Japan that I met the Tomorrow Makers. Among them are the world's greatest scientists, and they are in a desperate race to be first at *downloading* the contents of the human mind into a computer housed within a robotic body so that we will never have to die. And it was during these travels that I met Tomorrow Makers who expressed a fear that what was now being created was in fact a new species, a species that might soar beyond its human creators to become our evolutionary successors.

This book couldn't have been written without the generosity of these Tomorrow Makers who were willing to give me their most precious commodity: time.

At Carnegie-Mellon University, a special thanks goes to Hans Moravec, senior scientist of the Autonomous Mobile Robot Laboratory, and a software and hardware hacker with whom I spent many wraparound days talking from darkness until dawn. Working closely with Moravec and also generous with their time were Mike Blackwell, Kevin Dowling, Rich Wallace, Chuck Thorpe, and Olin Shivers. Also at C-MU are the heavy-equipment labs of William L. "Red" Whittaker. It is within these labs that the wonderful robots of C-MU are born, and I spent many hours watching Red, Spencer Barrett, Steve Berman, Kai Lee and others breathe life into their stainless steel creations.

Of the four founding fathers of artificial intelligence, two are at C-MU. One of these, Allen Newell, was kind enough to share his time with me, as was Robert Sekerka, dean of C-MU's Mellon College of Science, who believes "man will learn to build brains"; Robert Birge of the Center for Molecular Electronics; Dwight Sangrey, Ron Krutz, Hans Berliner, a violinist named Sangjun Shinn, Mark Raibert, Mary Jo Dowling, and a telescope-packing student named Lisa.

At the Massachusetts Institute of Technology I spent many nights on the davenports, floors and hammock of the AI Laboratory as I watched the hackers who were working around the clock on the intoxicating chore of creating computers that can think. Marvin Minsky, another of the four AI founding fathers provided me with much, as did Gerald Jay Sussman, a teacher/hacker extraordinaire, and the proud bearer of perhaps the world's most complete shirt-pocket nerd pack. I'm also indebted to Gumby the Dead Head; Phil Agre, who would like to give robots common sense; Carl Hewitt, who scared me with his visions of the robotic police and computerized governments of the future; Joseph Weizenbaum, who fears that the Hewitt's visions might come to pass; Michael Brady and Tomas Lozano-Perez, who are trying to give robots eyes; Rod Brooks, who wants to own mechanical, and hence ethical, slaves; Ken Salisbury, Steven Chiu, and John Purbrick, who are working on robotic hands; Victor Zue, who longs to give computers ears; and Steve Berlin, who is concerned about what the military will do when all these pieces are merged together.

Additional and major thanks at MIT must go to Jonathan Rees, who was good enough to read the MIT chapters for a technical review, Alan Bawden, RMS and Katrina, David Levitt, Harley Shaiken, Charles Sable, Gary Marx, Lisa Russell (this Lisa being a packer of after-hours beer); John Hinsdale, Eric Drexler and Chris Peterson, who want to build robots so small they would operate within a single cell, Stewart Cobb—may he make it into space, and Patrick Sobalvarro, who is a delightful guy.

While in Cambridge I also spent time with Danny Hillis of Thinking Machines; Mark Kadonoff, who was hacking robots in the private sector; and, most enjoyably, two professors of theology from the Harvard Divinity School: Gordon Kaufman and George Williams. Their responses to the possibility of humans gaining immortality through mechanical rather than spiritual means were quite enlightening. I also thank Ed and Marcie Katz for their hospitality during my stay in Cambridge.

In Washington D.C. I spent time with Forrest Carter of the U.S. Naval Research Laboratory, talking about building computers so small that a thousand mainframes would fit within a sugar cube. I also spent time with Kevin Ulmer of Genex Corporation, a gene-splicing concern that shares Carter's vision of unimaginably small computers. At the National Bureau of Standards I spoke with James S. Albus about how we could become a nation of idle aristocrats if we let the robots do all of our work and then coax them into sharing the profits. I also spent time with Kerry Joels of the Young Astronaut Council, who spoke of the need for computers like *2001's* HAL 9000—just as long as they weren't *too* much like HAL.

In Minneapolis there are three extraordinary futurists: Earl Joseph and Otto Nelson of the think-tank Anticipatory Sciences, and Arthur Harkins, a cultural anthropologist at the University of Minnesota, who wants to marry a robot someday. Thanks also to Brian Toren of Sperry Univac.

At Stanford University I found AI founding father John McCarthy to be delightfully accessible, and I also spent time with Andy Freeman, Les Earnest, Dave Kreigman, Vic Nalwa, and Bruce Buchanan. At SRI International, Jerry Hobbs talked about giving robots common sense; and at Berkeley, Hubert Dreyfus, a professor of philosophy, spoke of the limitations he saw to computational reasoning. While in the Bay Area I enjoyed the hospitality of Tyler Gazecki and Autumn Stanley, and the soothing companionship of a cat named Allspice.

First in New York and then in Japan I spent several days with Charles Lecht, who is mightily pushing today into tomorrow. While in Japan I was graciously received by a great number of scientists at the impressive Mechanical Engineering Laboratory (where I had my first out-of-body, quasi-downloaded experience), the Electro Technical Laboratory, the University of Tokyo, and Waseda University. Included in this impressive group of scientists were Hisao Yamada, Minoru Abe, Susumu Tachi, who was the ultimate creator of artificial *experiences,* Kazuo Tani, Norimitsu Ozawa, Satoshi Hashino, Sugano Shigeki, Takaji Yoshii, and Hiroyuki Kusama at ICOT's Fifth Generation project. Thanks also to the Foreign Press Office at the Tsukuba Expo, and to Yuriko Courtney, Minako Yamamoto, and Eric Gorbman.

In closing this incomplete listing of those who helped this book come into being, I would like to express my gratitude to my agent Richard Curtis, to Macmillan publisher Hillel Black for his early enthusiasm for this project, to my editor Robert Stewart, who dove into the manuscript and helped improve it, to my copy editor Dodie Gerson Edmands, who fought the good fight for consistency and correctness, and to Mercedes Montgomery-John. Thanks also to Beth Waxe of Richard Curtis Associates; and to the editors of *Omni* for publishing an excerpt of Chapter One. The patience of Randall Rothenberg at *The New York Times,* who allowed me to steal time from another project while completing this one, is also appreciated. John Baunach in Austin and Geoff Reynolds in Seattle were also kind.

Finally, I would like to thank my family and friends, for the long and lonely task of actually *writing* a book would be quite miserable, I fear, without their support.

Part I ❧

THE DOWNLOAD
FACTOR

Chapter 1 ✍

ON THE EDGE

I'M SURE THAT Hans Moravec is at least as sane as I am, but he certainly brought to mind the classic mad scientist as we sat in his third-floor office at Carnegie-Mellon University on a dark and stormy night. It was nearly midnight, and he mixed for each of us a bowl of chocolate milk and Cheerios, with sliced bananas on top, as he recalled his graduate-student days at Stanford's Artificial Intelligence Laboratory, where he first gave vision to a robot.

It was also during those days at SAIL that he took to stalking spiders in their webs by night and to chasing dragonflies across fields by day in order to feed the lizards, newts, frogs, and tarantulas that lived atop his desk. Feeding oatmeal to worms was another way of providing his tiny friends with extra nourishment. And so that he would never be too far from the robot he was trying to teach to see, he created a semisecret trapdoor through a laboratory ceiling panel and took up residence within the rafters.

In return for the spiders and dragonflies, one of the lizards repaid Moravec one day by presenting him with an insight into how he used a shifting of the head to simulate the stereovision he could not otherwise have because of the opposition of his eyes. Moravec translated this into a video camera that would slide back and forth on a threaded horizontal bar, with a computer program to correlate the different angles of the sightings that would provide depth perception. This vision system has since been used on experimental robots at several research centers in the United States. A few months later, while I was visiting Stanford, I would later sit in on a robotics class and hear the young instructor lecture on the importance of Moravec's robotic-vision work.

But as the wind blew rain against the office window, and as I found that Cheerios and chocolate milk and bananas are really quite good, it was neither the stalking of spiders nor the secret revelations of the lizard that seemed to chill or frighten. Rather it was Moravec's Dr.

3

Frankenstein ideas of shifting the contents of human brains into robotic bodies:

"You are in an operating room. A robot brain surgeon is in attendance. . . . Your skull, but not your brain, is anesthetized. You are fully conscious. The surgeon opens your brain case and peers inside."

There he was, sitting across from me, banana-slicing knife in hand: Hans Moravec, the senior research scientist at Carnegie-Mellon's Autonomous Mobile Robot Laboratory, outlining how he could create a robotic immortality for Everyman; speaking of how death could be defied, about how life could go on by creating computer copies of our minds and transferring, or *downloading*, this program into robotic bodies that need never die. And as the centuries passed, you could dedicate part of your endless time to searching out the very finest chassis builders and downloading your computerized self into the very latest in biological or mechanical artificial bodies.

Just what that robotic surgeon would do to your gentle brain after it had cut open your skull was described by Moravec in his paper "Robots That Rove,"a paper I would hear more of as I traveled to the major research centers for robotics and artificial intelligence in this country and Japan. In that paper, Moravec wrote that the robotic surgeon's "attention is directed at a small clump of about 100 neurons somewhere near the surface. It determines the three-dimensional structure and chemical makeup of that clump non-destructively with high-resolution 3-D nuclear magnetic resonance holography, phased array radio encephalography, and ultrasonic radar. It writes a program that models the behavior of the clump, and starts it running on a small portion of the computer next to you."

That computer sitting next to you in the operating room would in effect be your new brain, it would be the new you. As each area of your brain was analyzed and simulated, the accuracy of the simulation would be tested as you pressed a button to shift between the area of the brain just copied and the simulation. When one could no longer tell the difference between the original and the copy, the surgeon would transfer the simulation of your brain into the new computerized brain and repeat the process on the next area of your biological brain.

"The process is repeated over and over for adjoining clumps until the entire brain has been dealt with," Moravec wrote. "Occasionally several clump simulations are combined into a single equivalent but more efficient program. Though you have not lost consciousness, or even your train of thought, your mind—some would say soul—has been removed from the brain and transferred to a machine.

"In a final step your old body is disconnected. The computer is installed in a shiny new one, in the style, color and material of your choice."

As we sat around Hans's office that same stormy night, I asked what would become of the original human body after the downloading.

"You just don't bother waking it up again if the copying went successfully," he said. "It's so messy. Humans have got so many problems that you might just want to leave it retired. You don't take your junker car out if you've got a new one."

Once one copy of the brain's contents had been made, it should be easy to make multiple copies, some of which, he said, would be placed in various places for safekeeping as backup copies, providing the ultimate life insurance policy. Other copies could be activated simultaneously so that you could be in two or more places at once. "You could have parallel experiences and merge the memories later."

*

In the weeks and months that followed my stay at Carnegie-Mellon in February of 1985, I would be surprised and intrigued by how many researchers seemed to believe downloading would come to pass. The only point of disagreement was when—certainly a big consideration to those still knocking around in mortal bodies.

Although some of the researchers I spoke with at Carnegie-Mellon, and later at MIT, Stanford, and in Japan thought that downloading was still generations away, there were others who believed we were actually so close to achieving robotic immortality that some of the researchers seemed to be driven by private passions never to die. And perhaps this explained the eagerness of Hans's young research assistants to work through the nights and weekends to further this quest for the life ever after.

Now, this prospect of living forever had some appeal to me, and I found especially comforting the thought of stashing backup copies of myself here and there and everywhere. What I had planned as a three-day stay at Carnegie-Mellon turned into more than a two-week visit, during which time I would work around the clock with some of the finest robot builders in the world (only the robots I saw in Japan could rival what was being built here). I would also spend many of the late-evening and early-morning hours sitting in the office of Hans Moravec, talking about how downloading could make all of us explorers of the universe and of things beyond.

And so it was on that blustery night that Hans and I continued to talk throughout the hours of darkness, fueled by Cheerios (which he has fancied since reading a report several years earlier that a diet of Cheerios and water had kept mice alive), coffee, and bottles of Coke, but mostly fueled by the psychic energy that is stirred at the prospect of immortality. We spoke of dispatching copies of ourselves across this planet and then to the moon and the asteroids and then to Mars and Jupiter and then out across the galaxy.

When the sun came up, and as the day people began streaming into the building, we paused only long enough to gather our things together and then continued our conversation as we walked two miles in a gentle mist to Hans's large brick Tudor house on the very summit of Squirrel Hill, where I crashed for a few hours on his davenport, thoughts of immortality flowing through my yet-to-be-downloaded brain.

*

The significance of the door Hans is trying to open is not lost on others. Prior to meeting with Carnegie-Mellon's Allen Newell—who is one of the four founding fathers of artificial intelligence and who, with his SOAR computer program, is in one sense trying to create the brains that would be on the receiving end of Moravec's downloading— I talked with one of his graduate students, Olin Shivers.

"I once referred to SOAR as a language for writing AI programs," Shivers told me. "And Newell said, 'I don't think of it as a language. I think of it as an intelligent system.' Moravec wants to design a creature, and my professor, Newell, wants to design a creature. We are all trying to play God."

*

Three weeks later I would travel to the Massachusetts Institute of Technology, where I would be surprised to find Moravec's concept of downloading given consideration by Marvin Minsky, Donner Professor of Science, and another of the founding fathers of AI (the other two being John McCarthy, whom I would later visit at Stanford, and Herb Simon, of Carnegie-Mellon). During my three weeks at MIT, Minsky would give me a draft of his book-in-progress, *The Society of Mind,* in which he creates a model of how a society of small agents (or computer functions) can work together to create the information processing that we call thinking. "We'll ask how can intelligence emerge from non-intelligence," he wrote in the prologue to the book. "To answer that, we'll show that one can build a mind from many little parts, each mindless by itself."

It would probably be necessary to achieve Minsky's quest before creating any kind of a downloading system. You would need to be able to quantify precisely the contents and conditions of the odd little chemical-electrical cloud of activity that is our personality, knowledge, and so many other mental attributes that are often lumped together as consciousness. If this could be defined, then it could probably be replicated, and if it could be replicated, the door would be open for Moravec's robotic immortality.

"If a person is a machine and you get a wiring diagram of it, then you can make copies," Minsky would tell me.

Would he download?

"It's a complicated question," said Minsky, who is fifty-seven years old. He doesn't believe that either he or the thirty-six-year-old Moravec will live long enough to be offered the opportunity. But he said, "Yes. I think it would be a great thing to do. I've spent a long time learning things and I'd hate to see it all go away."

Minsky also said he would have no qualms about waving good-bye to his human body and taking up residence within a robot.

"Why not? And avoid getting sick and things like that? It's hard to see anything against it. I think people will get fed up with bodies after a while. Then you'll have another population problem. You'll have all the people of the past, as well as the new ones. Arthur Clarke has a science fiction novel all about that, called *The City and the Stars*, which is what to do when the people can be read into machines and out again."

Another person I was to meet was Danny Hillis, one of Minsky's Ph.D. students and the founding scientist of Cambridge-based Thinking Machines, a company that is trying to create the kind of computer that might someday be able to receive the contents of a brain. During my research, several computer scientists would point to Hillis's connection machine as an example of a new kind of computer architecture. It is comparable to the human brain in that the connection machine doesn't have one large central processing unit but rather a network of 64,000 small processing units, roughly analogous in concept if not in size to the brain's network of 40 billion neuronal processing units.

"I've added up the things I want to do in my life, and it's up to a little bit over fifteen hundred years' worth of stuff," Hillis told me one day as we stood out on the sixth-floor sundeck of the Thinking Machines building. The 28-year-old Hillis continued, "And I'm sure that by the time those fifteen hundred years are over, I'll have another fifteen hundred years' worth of stuff that I want to do. So I consider it a raw deal that I'm going to have to die before I get to do much of that. I would love to live for ten thousand or one hundred thousand years. And if I can't do that, I would at least love to let my children have the opportunity to do that.

"I enjoy having a body as much as anyone else does. But if it's a choice between even downloading into a computer that's stuck in a room some place and still being able to think versus just dying, I would certainly take that opportunity to think, particularly if I could have a robot body and be able to do that fifteen hundred years' worth of stuff. I would give a lot to be able to do that.

"I think that downloading is possible in principle," Hillis said. "We don't understand thinking well enough. Hans and I may just miss it. But that's not enough to make me stop working on it."

Late one night at MIT, just several blocks away from Hillis's Thinking Machines, I heard a similar time frame for downloading from Gerald Jay Sussman, who at 36 is already a legendary professor at the school and a computer hacker of historic proportions. A hacker is someone who becomes so attuned to the programming of computers that he can go diving into another world in search of the passage that will connect computer and mind. Sussman's downloading prediction might be enough to make you change your dietary and exercise habits in order to see just how long you could stick around waiting for this deliverance into mechanical immortality.

"If you can make a machine that contains the contents of your mind, then that machine is you. The hell with the rest of your physical body, it's not very interesting. Now, the machine can last forever. Even if it doesn't last forever, you can always dump it out onto tape and make backups, then load it up on some other machine if the first one breaks.

"Everyone would like to be immortal," Sussman said. "I don't think the time is quite right. But it's close. It isn't very long from now. I'm afraid, unfortunately, that I'm the last generation to die. Some of my students may manage to survive a little longer."

When I told Sussman that Danny Hillis had recently told me very nearly the same thing, he replied, "We are sort of on the edge."

"Do you think we are that close?" I asked.

"Yes."

*

Hans Moravec has written, "We are on a threshold of a change in the universe comparable to the transition from non-life to life."

Chapter 2 ❧

THE NEED TO FROLIC

ON THE DOOR to Carnegie-Mellon's Autonomous Mobile Robotics Laboratory is a photocopy of a page from a comic book. It's entitled "Magnus: Robot Fighter 4,000 A.D." It is a love story about the heroic but lonely Magnus, whose mission is to prevent man's extinction. He fights alone "until he meets Leeja, who also dares to challenge the mechanical masters."

Inside the door, three of Hans Moravec's associates were encountering some difficulty creating the forebears of the mechanical masters that may someday unite Magnus and the comely Leeja. There were three young men, each sitting at separate computer terminals, intently talking among themselves and, via keyboards, to the computers. They were trying to integrate four different programs that were running on three mainframe computers.

Fastened with a C-clamp to a jam-packed rack of electronics was a microwave sending-and-receiving antenna that was pointed out the window. Outside that third-floor window, standing still, but not silent, on a sidewalk that crosses the main campus, or Cut, in front of Doherty Hall was a six-wheeled robot named Terragator, which was being recalcitrant and wayward.

Terragator uses a video camera for eyes and a microwave antenna for transmitting its images to the mainframe computers, and for receiving from these computers directions on how to proceed. The robot's name represents a synthesis of the words *terrestrial autonomous navigator*, which is what this robot is supposed to become. The research funding comes from the Department of Defense's Advanced Research Projects Agency (DARPA)—as is the case with most of the academic funding for robotics and computer sciences in this country. The army would like to turn Terragator, or some progeny of this re-

9

search, into a robotic tank that could wage war on its own, having no need for humans.

A month later, I would talk with researchers at MIT who found such aspirations (which included many MIT projects as well) quite frightful and immoral. If such autonomous soldiers are ever created and somehow become too autonomous, then the likes of Magnus and Leeja may indeed have to climb out of the comic books to save the day. But for now Terragator is young and childlike, and over the next few weeks I came to develop a liking for this robot that I found to be on the receiving end of much personal sacrifice and devotion.

Earlier that day Kevin Dowling, a twenty-four-year-old research technician with Moravec's robotics group, had slid down a long wooden banister in Doherty Hall and said, "In a sense we haven't gotten out of our stage of playing with toys and building things. Only there's a little bit more theory behind it now. We're just playing with more expensive and larger toys."

But even toys can be a chore, and now Kevin was outside on a cold, clear day tightening a nut on Terragator's antenna and preparing to begin working with a cardboard poster his wife had painstakingly made but that the wind was giving a good thrashing to. The board measured five feet square and it had painted on it a grid of eighty-one precisely spaced one-inch black dots. This grid was basically used as an eye chart to calibrate Terragator's vision.

Kevin would sometimes describe Terragator as a tipped-over refrigerator on wheels. This hardly does justice to the robot, but it captures the dimensions pretty well. Terragator consists of a stainless-steel chassis resting on six wheels. Rising from the chassis is a nicely welded stainless-steel framework to house the essential components, such as the computer, which handles the communications with the offboard mainframes; the controller, which translates between the onboard computer and the wheel motors; and the Honda generator, which allows Terragator to run around outside without an extension cord.

Rising above the frame is a mast to hold the video camera, the microwave antenna, and a ring of twenty-four sonar units that allow for acoustic vision when navigating inside buildings or in other closed areas. Outside, the sonar signals tend to get lost prior to bouncing back, although they would show the proximity of a truck, person, or any other nearby structure. The sonar sensors were made by Polaroid and are identical to those used on their cameras for providing automatic focusing. Rounding out Terragator's fittings is a small American flag on a five-inch stick, taped to the vertical microwave antenna.

In the past, Terragator had been equipped with a black and white camera, but today a color camera was being tested. It was felt that color could provide more information for the computers to work with, and the day's road test was to see how smoothly this new information, and the program that dealt with it, could be streamlined into the existing programs required for Terragator to be a terrestrial navigator.

The researchers at Carnegie-Mellon were trying to give Terragator the gift of vision, which is a tough task, considering that it has taken hundreds of millions of years for our own vision to get where it is and that perhaps one third of our brain is devoted to this task. It is one thing to put a camera on a robot, it is another to get the visual information into a computer in a meaningful way. You can't just plug a video camera into a computer, because a computer is blind. The video images must be digitized, that is, translated into immense strings of the ones and zeros that are the building blocks of computer logic. Numbers are assigned to the video images according to light intensity and to the location of that intensity within the frame of the picture. What results is an elaborate paint-by-numbers picture.

Moravec's group has created programs that analyze these paint-by-number pictures and look for areas where there are major differences in light intensity. For instance, if the light-colored pavement of the sidewalk were given a numerical value of three and the darker color of the grass were given a numerical value of seven, the computer program could look for areas where the threes bordered the sevens. This would result in a numerical picture of a broad band of threes marching through a sea of sevens. It isn't quite that nice and neat. Wherever the grass was greener, the numerical representation varied. Even the pavement can change in color intensity, and hence in numeric representation. But from a general trend, which is what the computer program looks for, it is possible to tell where the color intensity makes a big jump from pavement to grass.

When I went back upstairs to escape the cold, I watched the digitized image from Terragator on a monitor as the program identified the edges of the sidewalk, determined Terragator's position between the two edges, and suggested any course alterations required to keep him from running off into the grass. This kind of edge detection is a major area for research in robotic vision. The program I was watching had been written by Rich Wallace, who wasn't present that afternoon, but in whose office we had all crowded for the test run. A few days later, around midnight, I dropped in on Rich and watched him hack on his edge detection. He was listening to a Laurie Anderson compact disc while a closed-circuit video camera just a bit larger than a package of cigarettes sat on his desk and transmitted the image of one of the Minimus point-7 speakers from which the music came.

Laurie Anderson, who has written songs of the desolation and waste that would be a nuclear war, uses a synthesized voice at times to express her barren visions of some future mechanical world. She appears on the cover of her *No More Supermen* album wearing glasses that project eerie white lights from where the eyes would be, and hers seemed an especially appropriate voice by which one might labor into the early hours, hacking on robotic vision. She was singing "Kokoku" when I arrived (which I wouldn't hear again until I went to Japan), so I didn't talk at first but just sat down and watched Rich slowly move the camera around with the palm of his hand to see how well his edge-detection program could keep up with the shifting flow of lines. The camera was transmitting into the digitizer in black and white, but the images on the monitor were in reds, blues, and greens.

In many ways the speaker was like the sidewalk that Terragator followed, although the contrasts weren't as distinct. Rather than having a grass-meets-pavement situation, the edge detection had to register the variation in color intensity as the silver speaker stood out from the white walls and other background colors and shapes in the room. The program was doing it well. After each shift of camera position, comparable to the travel of Terragator, the vertical parallel lines of the speaker's sides appeared, as if they were the edges of a road.

Depending upon what part of the program Rich was working with, he could add to the vertical-edge detection the horizontal and angular edges, too. Some researchers believe that our own vision might be a very rich form of edge detection, in which the brain has what seems to us instantaneous recognition of basic geometric patterns. The brain pulls these patterns together, recognizing familiar shapes and registering what they represent.

Whether this has any true bearing on what our brain does or not, several researchers I spoke with felt that it could provide the building blocks for getting a computer to handle increasingly sophisticated vision. The biggest part of the task would be programming into the computer a knowledge base for understanding what various shapes and patterns could mean. Marvin Minsky is fond of pointing out that no computer yet built can tell a dog from a cat. And his colleague and longtime intellectual combatant at MIT, Joseph Weizenbaum, would feel morally bound to declare that no computer could ever truly *know* what was a dog or a cat, that is, no computer could have a resonance for something living, an emotional reaction to the wagging of a tail.

I was to pursue this question of internal representation, this question of what a computer can and can't know, throughout my travels. Programming such higher functions would certainly be no easy matter, as it had taken some ten thousand lines of code to get Terragator to follow a sidewalk at a speed of two millimeters per second, or about twenty-four feet an hour. But as I sat in Rich's office and talked about his work, I had an unusual and rather eerie moment to consider the question as he shifted the camera to my face and I watched my digitlized image on the Grinnel monitor. "What does that look like?" he asked.

"Like a Peter Max print," I said.

Rich took a Polaroid shot of the screen and gave me the picture.

*

Chuck Thorpe, who had done his Ph.D. thesis on robotic vision and is the project leader on the Terragator runs, has on his notebook an artist's rendition of Martin Marietta's version of a Terragator-type autonomous tank. Chuck went downstairs to assist Kevin with the calibration. Kevin climbed on top of Terragator and focused the camera on the eye chart grid as Larry Matthews, a programmer with the project, tried to stabilize the grid in the blustery wind. Chuck quickly took measurements from the camera lens to the grid and then took measurements from the camera to the ground. This eye test for Terragator makes sure that it is using the same measurement values as the offboard computers in choosing its course.

By the time they had completed the calibrations—something that must be done each time Terragator is powered up for a run—the wind had pretty much destroyed the board. A few days later I would stay up past midnight watching Kevin build a latticework calibration device out of aluminum stock. And a few months later I would see a grid of calibration dots painted on the wall of an old and dilapidated building at Stanford, those dots having been used by Moravec during his work, several years earlier, on the Stanford Cart robot.

With calibration of vision such a necessary nuisance, Hans Moravec wants to find ways to enable a robot to do its own calibrations. He wants to create a robot that can go out and play—and in that playful process learn to calibrate itself. Like a busy parent telling a child to go outside, a researcher could tell his robot to go calibrate.

"Calibrating the cameras is starting to be the biggest nuisance in these road runs," he told me. "The camera calibration is important because the robot is making measurements about the real world, about where it is and what it should do. To do this, it needs to know precisely where it is. We have this big grid we can put in front of the camera and run a program over, but it would be really nice if the robot could calibrate itself. Larry Matthews actually figured out a way of doing it.

"There was a program that was written by a contemporary of mine at Stanford named Don Gennery. It was written for doing aerial-photo interpretations of pictures of Mars. This was a project that, I believe, Joshua Lederberg was a primary instigator of." (I had met Lederberg several years earlier at Stanford, at which time I spoke with the Nobel laureate molecular biologist about his work with his former student Carl Sagan in creating the life-exploration packages for the robotic lander that tested Martian soils. Lederberg had wanted the landing to be made closer to the polar icecaps, where melting water would have perhaps provided a richer environment for life to emerge, but NASA had decided that the terrain of the polar regions was too rough to attempt a landing.)

"Lederberg was interested in finding evidence of life on Mars, and one way to do it is to take pictures of the surface at different times and months apart, register them precisely, then look for differences between the two pictures," Moravec said. "But in order to register them precisely, you have to correct any geometric distortions, because one photo might be taken from one slant to the surface, while the other might be taken from another slant. So the first thing you have to do is figure out what that slant is and geometrically correct it. You need to know these precise angles, which you don't have in the raw data. But if you can find corresponding points in the pictures, you can figure out where the camera must have been.

"So Don Gennery wrote a very good program that was able to take in the coordinates of corresponding points of two sets of images and was able to take in approximate estimates of what the camera parameters are, because you usually have some idea, some level of accuracy, of where the cameras were.

"Larry Matthews [who was holding the grid on the cold, windy day for Chuck and Kevin, and who had thus found new incentive to finish his programming] has figured out a way to use this so that the robot can learn calibration. We use it in a way that is straightforward. Suppose we want to know what the relationship is between the two stereo cameras we've got. They might be pointed at slightly different angles or have slightly different lenses. The idea is that you track some points, find corresponding points. You have, again, a good guess for what the relative position is, and you run through Gennery's code and produce a new estimate of the camera positions."

In this way, even if the camera angles shift, the program accommodates for the shift and learns what the new calibration is. This learning process goes more smoothly if samples from a wide variety of angles are provided. To gather that wide variety of angles, the robot might be going through some odd motions.

"And that amounts to just randomly frolicking," Hans said. "Kind of waggling its head from side to side and moving it up and down and maybe running around the room for no particular reason. And it's really necessary. This is play. And it's the same reason a young animal has to do a lot of this—to get everything calibrated right. A newborn doesn't know how to use its arms and legs and eyes, and it's just got to play. There's no need for it to do any particular job, it's being fed and taken care of. But it has to learn how to get all of these things adjusted right. And the only way to do this is to exercise pretty much its full range of things it can do.

"And this robot is going to have to do this, too, as soon as it's self-calibrating. And we want it to be self-calibrating real soon because the manual job of calibrating it is such a drag. So I think the robots are going to play in our lab real soon. Terragator will run around outside and do silly things just to calibrate his camera."

*

Chuck Thorpe and I found a wall to lean against in order to escape the wind as we waited for the computers upstairs to digest the calibration information that Kevin had relayed by way of his headset with mouthpiece and small antennae. Upstairs, wearing the other headset and entering Kevin's information into one of the VAXes, was Mike Blackwell, Kevin's good friend, officemate, and fellow robotics hacker.

Mike, who sprang me from the local Howard Johnson's and put me up in the second-floor sunroom of the old brick minimansion he rents on Squirrel Hill with some other students and professional hackers, has a history that I found to be typical of those who end up in computer sciences and robotics. As a child he was introverted, brilliant, and from an early age a reader of science fiction and a builder of mechanical and electrical devices. And, very importantly, at a key point a teacher recognized his ability and tried to channel the raw talent.

"I was really a loner," he told me one night as we walked back to campus after going out for pizza. "I'd stay home and read. Sometimes

I'd just go into another world. We moved around a lot because my father worked as a consultant. It's sort of hard to get to know people. I figured, Why make friends? because I would never see them again.

"In junior high school we moved to Minnesota for a year. I was a long-haired kid from Berkeley, and it was *awful*. I got into a lot of trouble, too. We lived in this housing complex, and I kept getting caught by the security because they were doing more construction on other sites and they had these cans of glue and other chemicals and I was always starting fires and blowing them up. This glue was really flammable, and you'd get these *huge* explosions. I got caught for that.

"In Minnesota, just being from Berkeley meant that I was hassled. It was too much effort to be accepted and to become one of the gang. Their ideas and morals weren't mine, anyway. I didn't want to compromise my own just to be accepted. It bothered me, but it wasn't unbearable."

Mike's voice is really soft anyway, so it became nearly a whisper that night as he told me about something that had seemed to him a childhood burden: "I think I was always pretty intelligent. There is always this need to be accepted. Even if you say it's not important, it really is. So you don't always want to throw your hand up to show you know the answer. Or you'd want to sometimes say the wrong thing just so people would think you were more like them. Or you would get into trouble for something so you'd be more accepted."

This made me wonder how many other children were out there being mangled by schools where they have to take on the protective coloring of ignorance not to stand out. But perhaps, as with Mike, all would somehow turn out well and the acquisition of knowledge would be fervent despite the school environment.

Mike's interest in electricity began in grade school, in a manner that would provide nightmare material for any parent. "We had remodeled our house and we had all of these old switches and plugs and light sockets. I would pick them out from a big box in the garage and spend hours wiring them together in different ways and then plug them into the wall to see what would happen. Invariably, things burned and smoked and sparked and blew up.

"Then my dad [an electrical engineer] sort of directed me away from the more violent things. He bought me these Heathkit radios to build, and I got into that. I'd build them once, the way they were supposed to be, and work with the radio. And then I'd take them apart and put the components in differently just to see what I could do. I would unwind coils and stuff and try winding them different ways. I had no idea what these things did, but I figured I would come across some fascinating discovery if I did it in some other way."

Life became more bearable when the family returned to Berkeley and Mike was placed in a private high school. A physics teacher suggested he enter the Westinghouse Science Competition.

"I'd been reading through these National Semiconductor data books I'd found somewhere, and you could do all kinds of fascinating things that I'd never seen before. You could add two things and subtract and multiply, just by wiring things together. I thought that was great. And I saw this example circuit of how to do logs and antilogs and I thought that was great. I built one. I called up Texas Instruments. You needed these special matched transistors, so I called up TI and said I was doing this project and I'd like some of these transistors but couldn't afford them. So they sent me a sample. I built that thing. You could take a variable-voltage source and put it in a log, and the voltage would come out the other side, and you would measure it with a voltmeter.

"I thought it was great," Mike said with a shy laugh. "It had no purpose. It was pretty silly actually. But it was just neat that it actually did what it was supposed to do. So I wrote a little paper on that and submitted it to the Westinghouse contest, and it was actually one of the top one hundred in the nation that year.

"Then I discovered digital watches. That was the ultimate," he said, again with his shy laugh. "You could understand how computers worked by looking at these gates and registers and clocks and you could look at that and think, Boy! You could put these together like this and you could *have a computer!* And it's still pretty fascinating.

"I was always into the nuts and bolts of computers, the hardware: wiring chips together. And that's still what I want to do, build computers from the ground up. I do a lot of programming, too," he said as we climbed the stairs back up to his third-floor office in Doherty Hall. "Hardware and software. It always surprises me that more people don't do that. They specialize in one area or the other. I never understood that."

In 1978, Intel released its 8086 microprocessing chip, which had 29,000 transistors. Intel would, seven years later, (and after its fine 80286 chip) release its 80386, which had a somewhat staggering 275,000 transistors on a chip smaller than a fingernail, but for a time the 8086 represented the state of the art and served as the central processing unit for a wave of personal computers, including the one I used to write this book. Mike had heard about the chip even before it was released, and just as he had done with TI, he wrote a letter pleading student poverty and was sent a chip. He took it with him to Carnegie-Mellon and was building a computer around it in his dorm room when he decided he should get a job and walked across campus to the Robotics Institute. He was asking about employment possibilities when Hans Moravec walked into the robotics office to pick up his mail.

*

Hans Moravec was born in Austria in 1948 and emigrated with his family to Canada when he was four. In the first grade his interest in science began when he found a book about dinosaurs in the library. Because his father was an electronics technician, there were always boxes of electric motors and switches to play with. By the time he was ten, he had built his first mechanical man—something he put together from tin cans and motors and mechanisms from toys he had taken apart.

At this time his mother enrolled Hans in a science fiction book club, which sent him flying into a world he enjoyed so much that when he entered junior high school, he decided that there must be something morally wrong about getting so much pleasure from reading. He solemnly gave his entire science fiction book collection to the school library. "Brought up Catholic, I was taught that making sacrifices is good for you," Hans would later explain to me.

He would soon return to science fiction, which he said had an important early influence on him because it "created a feeling that there were all of these wonderful possibilities there, and if you just knew the right things and if you worked hard enough, you could discover them."

But his brief departure from science fiction set the stage for a new reading discovery. "I found this book on Boolean algebra and logic design, and boy, was I ready for this! This, I knew, was the right stuff. I had been tinkering in the basement more and more. My father had encouraged me to build a little one-tube radio. This was after the robot and a much harder project. I understood about tubes. I was able to get audio amplifiers working pretty well and crystal radios. So I built a few radios, and it was really fun. And I wanted to build radars and, especially, *thinking* things. But I didn't know where to start.

"Then I read this book in the library, and then several others, which is how I learned about Boolean algebra [which provides the foundation for using binary strings of ones and zeros to design and program computer circuitry]. I was just sponging it up. It was great. This was more exciting than science fiction. You could build circuits that did these complicated things, like adding numbers, or doing logic problems.

"I built them with surplus telephone relays because I couldn't get my tube logic to work. I understood relays really well. I had already grasped the concept that if you have a string of these things, it can be a number, or it can be a representation of something else. I remember filling up a notebook full of convergents between binary and decimal numbers.

"So then at that point I started doing some of the hardest thinking I've ever done, which was designing various circuits using relays to do flip-flops. I could wire the relays in a complicated way so that when you gave it a pulse, it went to the opposite state of what it was before. So each time you pulse it, it flips back and forth. You can wire these together in a chain to form a counter. So you hit the first one, and it changes from a zero to a one, and hit it again, it changes from a one to a zero, but in changing from a one to a zero it generates a pulse to the next relay, which changes itself from a zero to a one. In base ten, you do that once every ten. In binary, you do it every other one. So I actually built these circuits using relays."

In high school he was inspired by "a roving itinerant science teacher," who got Hans involved in a science club and encouraged him to enter a science fair. For the science fair Hans built a robot that he called Robug. Its body was an upside-down salad bowl on wheels, propelled by old tape recorder motors. Robug had three photo sensors that responded to light. And by wrapping bare wire around the shaft of a screwdriver, he created feelers that, when coming in contact with a wall or any other object, would close a circuit.

He built Robug so that it could be either attracted to light or repelled by light. "I had this bank of fifteen switches on the back—multiposition switches and a few potentiometers—so that you could control the sensitivity to various things. Essentially this was a programming panel. This was an innovation I didn't appreciate myself. But I knew that I sometimes would want it to go toward light and sometimes away from light. Sometimes I would want it to wake up when you touched the side bumper, and sometimes I didn't. So I wanted to have all these things under control."

Hans laughs at what a complex mess it was that he carried off to his first science fair. "This wasn't a very user-friendly control panel, but I knew how to operate it. There were no labels, for instance, on any of the switches.

"I had the circuits drawn out, but it looked like I had used charcoal. I was trying to do it nice, so I picked a good drawing paper, but what I didn't realize was that it wasn't a good drawing paper for *India ink*.

Of course this looked pathetic compared with these folding plywood displays that other kids brought. So mine was sort of this sad little display. I had my poster tacked to the back of someone else's booth and then just my robot and nothing else," he said, laughing at the memory. "But nevertheless I described it to everybody."

Hans and his Robug were on television that night, and the judges were able to forgive the bleeding India-ink circuitry chart and the unmarked switches, and they were able to appreciate the early genius behind the programmability of this blue plastic salad bowl with whiskers and wheels. Robug won first in division.

One of the most charming movies I have seen is Steven Spielberg's *Close Encounters of the Third Kind.* A major element of the story was the way in which certain individuals were drawn to the alien spacecraft with the overwhelming drive of salmon returning to the river of their birth to spawn. Over and over again I would think of this as I spoke with computer scientists and robot hackers.

Just as water flows around a rock in a river, Hans Moravec's university years can be seen as his slipping past all obstacles that tried to stand between him and the creative use of computers and robots. At least two nights of our conversations were dedicated to his university years, and he would laugh with sympathy for those he had worked for, and he would laugh with conspiratorial delight at what he had done. While attending Western Ontario University, he worked as a freelance computer programer for an investment banking firm. Their idea was to shovel into one end of a computer massive data on the stock market's past performances and have crystal-ball predictions flow out the other end. Hans wrote the program, but in a meandering and off-the-wall way that suited his programming curiosity and need for exploration. It was as if they could pay for his time but not his mind.

"There were many, many interesting ideas, a lot of which I incorporated into this poor person's program," Hans said with a laugh. "I can just imagine if they ever tried to figure out how the program worked."

One summer he worked for Bell Canada as a computer operator. At that time Bell's computers didn't run at night or on weekends, so Hans was in ecstasy with all the free computer playtime. "I ran game programs, puzzle-solving programs; it was a new program every few days. And it was a more powerful computer than the others I had access to, so I let it run for hours, crunching on one thing or another." He also ran programs for one of his professors, who also worked as a consultant. "I let his programs run all Saturday a couple of times, saving him untold thousands of dollars. Stolen from Bell," he said laughing. "There would be several tape drives running. Reading data off of one, writing it on another. And of course I loved orchestrating a thing like this: Huge amounts of stuff going on and real complicated things happening inside. It was just fun to watch!"

Hacker heaven was finally found by Hans when he left Canada in 1971 to earn his Ph.D. at Stanford. For the next eight years he was totally immersed in computers and robots. One of the first things he did upon arriving was to dive into a computer game called Spacewar, which had been created by hackers at MIT and had come west when John McCarthy left MIT to create the Stanford Artificial Intelligence Laboratory. These were the glory days of SAIL, when the lab was located off-campus, in a half-round building that, from a distance, looked like something from *Star Trek*. SAIL was perched on top of a hill over-looking rolling fields and a dairy farm. Twenty-four hours a day the place pulsated with the excitement of creative people playing with computers. To make it easier to work through the night, a vending machine was filled with bagels, Chinese food, and other delicacies not usually found in such a machine. Attached to the machine was a small computer, eliminating the need for cash. You just typed in your iden-tification number, typed in what you wanted to buy, and the door opened and you were billed later. The computer would also allow you to gamble double-or-nothing for the purchase.

The passion with which Hans was into programming can be seen in the fact that for all the months he spent trying to make Spacewar reflect an Einsteinian universe, he rarely played it. "I was never much of a game player and I don't like things that make me think fast," he said. "But writing a program for it was extremely exciting. Working out the mathematics.

"In fact I had also been hacking relativity and doing physics on the side. And I had really figured it out, finally. In high school I had sort of almost got it. Through my undergraduate years I had mastered spe-cial relativity; it's not that hard, really. But I felt good. So I immedi-ately started writing a three-dimensional Spacewar. Initially I wrote in Fortran and assembly language, which was a little bit strange for the SAIL environment, because they primarily used SAIL or LISP [a mile-stone AI language developed by John McCarthy].

"I was able, for example, to describe what would happen, what you would actually see, if you were traveling through a star field. I set up the general equations describing the transformations, including taking into account the time it takes light to get from here to there, which causes aberrations. What actually happens is that the light is coming at you as you travel forward, so that the angle of the light seems to tilt forward, like when you run through the rain, the rain seems to be slanting at you. But because the objects you are seeing are at the end of the light rays, the actual objects seem to move forward as you run. So light coming in from the side as you were standing still would seem to move ahead of you, even though they were where your ears were before. In fact, all of the stars move forward, into this cone, which gets tighter and tighter and tighter. This circle of stars in front of you gets tighter and tighter as you move faster and faster, approaching the speed of light. And there's all the other relativity facts, like your relative time rate slowing down, but that's not what you see either. The stars actually seem to speed up, because of the Doppler shift.

"I had figured out how to do all of this stuff, except I hadn't done it in full three dimensions. I wanted to write a three-dimensional Spacewar, in which you would fly around in the star field, up and down. These days you see it so much in video games that you are kind of inured, but the *magic* of doing this for the first time! Effects like this were a big deal in the science fiction movies. People ooohed and ahhhed when they saw stuff like that on the screen. And here you had it under *total control!* You could fly around at will and *visit stars!*"

When I visited SAIL a few months later, Les Earnest, who as SAIL's administrator was charged with being the island of sanity, but as the originator of the computer-controlled vending machine, the organizing power behind the SAIL sauna room, and the founder of the annual SAIL Spring Orgy, is rather a legend himself, told me that some of Hans's programs would "bring the computer *to its knees.*"

It was also Les Earnest's official duty to keep Hans out of the rafters, and Les seemed genuinely surprised when I told him that Hans had lived up there for seven months. He did say that it was only recently that the cause for the building's long-standing problems with balancing the air-conditioning had been found. It seems as if a large hole had been cut into a major cool-air duct that ran next to Hans's old bed.

Some of Hans's ideas about downloading a brain into a robotic body can be traced to his Stanford years, when he would spend hours in his lab at SAIL vicariously exploring the world as his mobile robot traveled around the building transmitting pictures back to a monitor and carrying two-way conversations between Hans and whoever cared to talk to the robot. Hans would frequently send the robot out to explore the parking lot, but one day Hans made a mistake in his directions and sent the Stanford Cart down the long driveway to the busy street. "I knew something was wrong when I started seeing more cars than usual."

A magical era came to an end when John McCarthy decided that SAIL, with its crazy hilltop building surrounded by fields and farms, had become too much of a country club and moved the AI labs back to the Stanford campus. The one good point was that a record number of students decided to complete their doctorate work rather than make the return. Included in this exodus was Hans Moravec, who during his eight years at SAIL had developed a solid reputation for his work in computer vision.

Hans joined Carnegie-Mellon's Robotics Institute as a researcher in the Mobile Robot Laboratory, a position that was going to require him to do something he had never done before: hire people. This was on his mind when he walked into the Robotics Institute office one day to pick up his mail.

"I happened to drop in when Mike was sitting there, and the business manager said, 'Mike here, is looking for a job.' And Mike is very shy and quiet, so I asked him what he was good at, and he said, 'Well, I'm building microprocessors. I'm building an eighty-eighty-six system in my dorm room.'" Hans broke out laughing in the telling of the story. "I said, 'Well, that sounds good.' It seemed plausible, and I had lots of money, far more money than I knew what to do with. I had just been given a two-million-dollar contract. Cold. The Cart budget had been at least three orders of magnitude [one thousand times] less than that. So I said, 'Sure. I'll hire you.'

"Mike was very good, a stupendous worker. He would just come in every day and start designing systems. He was everything I could have hoped for. He didn't need any direction. He just needed a hint. I just described in general terms roughly what it was that I hoped someday to do. And he started doing his very, very best—and apparently enjoying it: programming, designing the processor, wiring, debugging. So, my feeling was: Well! If they are *all* going to work out this well . . . !" And then Hans burst into laughter at what followed. "Needless to say, Mike was not the typical student. I hired a bunch of other people who needed not just daily descriptions of what to do, they needed to be told every *fifteen minutes* exactly, in unambiguous terms, what it was I really wanted to do."

Mike missed out on much of this, because when summer rolled around, he returned to a seasonal programming job at Lawrence Livermore Laboratory outside of Berkeley. Halfway through the summer

Hans dismissed most of those he had brought on, but the memory lingers. "I didn't even want to see them. I just hid out in my office. It was horrible!"

*

In 1980, as a junior at Carnegie-Mellon, Kevin Dowling began working in the Robotics Institute. Initially he worked in the flexible-assembly program, which involves automating factories. When Hans Moravec arrived to create the Mobile Robotics Laboratory, Kevin read the papers Hans had written and decided that the Mobile Robotics Laboratory was where he needed to be. Upon graduation in 1983, he joined Hans full time.

As a child, Kevin was a voracious reader, partly because his parents had managed to put off buying a television set until he was twelve. "Reading was probably my biggest influence," he told me. "The only place I wanted to work was the library. I did volunteer work for my grade-school library. I was the only one allowed to take out more than five books at a time. I knew the librarians real well. In junior high it didn't matter how many books you took out, but I still did volunteer work. And I also worked with audio-visual stuff since grammar school. It was always electronics and reading and building mechanical devices."

This put a fourteen-year-old ninth-grader in a strategic position to gain access to a computer when the school obtained a time-sharing terminal and placed it next to the library in the audio-visual room. A local university had an IBM 360, and the school had gained access to it. Today you could spend less than $100 and buy a child's computer that has a more powerful central processing unit, but in the 1960s and 1970s the 360 rated its own computer room and could cost several hundred thousand dollars. What it lacked by today's standards in raw computing power was more than made up for, in a dramatic sense, by its awesomely impressive bulk and sheer presence. "I discovered computers," Kevin said. "And there was a whole new world there.

"They called it a math resource center, though it really wasn't that at the time. There were only two persons there who influenced me, and one was a computer aide who was kicked out because students would come in and ask for help and he would write the programs for them. At the time I didn't know the term, but he was a hacker. I would skip classes and go play with the computer. I started reading a lot of computer magazines because I really didn't know the physical structure of how a computer worked. But I knew it responded in certain ways to programs I put in. I started working at the town library, and they got all of the periodicals, so I started reading the interesting ones, including *Scientific American*."

Before long Kevin wanted closer contact with the computer, so he and a small band of fellow hackers would invade the computer center at Fairfield University, where they were tolerated, though "once in a while they'd get mad because we'd crash the system or something."

Kevin continued, "One of the funniest things about this system was Father Kelly, who ran the computer. He would come in every morning and set the computer time with his wristwatch. People were always so impressed when they saw computer time: 'Oh, that's computer time! That must be accurate!' But, no, that was Father Kelly reading his wristwatch in the morning. It could be off by as much as ten minutes!"

*

The calibration run for Terragator continued throughout the day and as I sat on the grass, leaning against the wall, sheltered from the wind, delighting in the warmth of sun on face and the singular joy of closing one's eyes when tired, I wondered if they would remember, if the robots, when they do get smart, when they do begin to think for themselves, when they begin to wonder why they support us and do our bidding, I wonder if they will know, if they will remember Kevin out there in the cold with wrenches and devotion, or Mike and the others up on the third floor, if they will remember all that was done to bring them into being. Will the robots recall that we were their creators?

And if they do, how much will we be able to trade on this? Will there be a sentimentality about this sense of origin? Initially we could program this in, but later, as the robots begin propelling their own evolution, will this be a memory deemed worthy of retention? Will they not remember who taught them to play, who blessed them with the need to frolic?

Terragator began to move slowly down the sidewalk, and I stood up to follow.

Chapter 3 ~

THE AWARENESS OF NEPTUNE

THE FIRST TIME I saw Terragator, I was helping Kevin Dowling carry the color video camera and some aluminum tubing from Doherty Hall across the Cut to Porter Hall, where the big and burly Ph.D. Red Whittaker runs the largest nuts-and-bolts robotics shop I would see outside of Japan. And the labs I saw in Japan could only compare, not surpass.

Hans Moravec's group hacks the vision software, but it is Red Whittaker and a group of his undergraduates that, the previous summer, had built Terragator's magnificent chassis—which has the smoothest stainless-steel welding work I had ever seen.

The old robber baron Andrew Carnegie would probably feel lost knocking around on his campus today. But within Red Whittaker's labyrinthine workshops he would be able to connect. The computer terminals sitting on banged-up metal stools would seem mysterious, but Carnegie would be able to relate to the drill presses, band saws, welding gear, grinding wheels, the lengths of steel and aluminum and the wrenches and greasy rags. The building was called Industries Hall when classes opened in 1905. The generosity of a trustee changed the name to Porter Hall in 1939, but the original name makes a better fit within the domain of Red Whittaker.

Kevin stood before Terragator making a three-dimensional sketch of the robot's box frame from which the electronic components were suspended to dampen vibrations. He put down pencil and paper to take measurements of the frame and then went back to sketching. He was trying to figure out the best place to attach a temporary aluminum easel for camera calibrations.

I ran a finger along the smooth welds and asked about them. "There's an undergraduate here who does all the stainless-steel welding," Kevin

26

said. "His work is absolutely amazing. I don't think they'll let him graduate."

As Kevin worked on his drawings, I took a closer look at the sonar ring that was going to be guiding Terragator on a future trip into a coal mine for a Bureau of Mines safety project. A bat navigates at night by emitting a whistle and sensing how rapidly the sound comes bouncing back. Terragator's sonar ring works in the same way. A sound is emitted. If the sound bounces back to its source, its strength is measured. The greater its strength, the less distance it has traveled, and hence the nearer the object.

Terragator's sonar ring consists of twenty-four separate units, each measuring four and a half by six and a half inches and each bolted onto a circular aluminum platform. Each sonar unit is numbered, and the onboard computer tracks the readings of each unit to create a 360-degree map of Terragator's world and his position in that world. Next, the computer can select the best course for Terragator to take when moving from one location to another within that world.

One of the most dangerous jobs in coal mining is the placing of roof bolts in newly opened stretches of a mine. The purpose of the bolts is to stabilize the roof, so the persons performing that job are, by definition, working in areas not yet stabilized. Red Whittaker would love to put an arm on Terragator and let it do the work.

Kevin finished his drawing and said he would turn the system on and show me how the sonars worked. He went over to an Apple Macintosh, pushed the mouse around on a cluttered tabletop, and then, with some surprise, announced the system was already running. He called up a new screen. An x in the center represented Terragator. Emanating from the x was a circle of squiggled lines indicating the acoustic report from each of the twenty-four sonar units. Looking up from the screen you could match the pattern of Terragator's map with the shape of the room and the proximity to the robot of the major objects—including Kevin and me.

Kevin walked toward Terragator, and I watched the sonar map trace his progress toward the x in the center. Then I located the squiggle that represented me as I backed away. I knew that Terragator didn't really *comprehend* our presence. He didn't *know* we were there. Yet as much as I knew that, I also knew that, at least on some very basic level, Terragator had had an awareness of our presence and proximity long before we knew that his sonar sensing system was on. In the movie *2001: A Space Odyssey* astronaut Dave Bowman plots the demise of the seemingly renegade HAL 9000 computer, without realizing that

HAL is watching him, reading his lips. As I stood near the computer in Red Whittaker's lab watching Terragator and my sonar image, that scene somehow came to mind.

*

A few days later, in the early hours of the morning, Hans Moravec walked to his bookcase and pulled from a shelf his Stanford doctoral thesis on robotic vision. We had been talking about when programmers might be able to impart to a computer some of the more abstract qualities we associate with the human mind, qualities such as consciousness and awareness. I had told Hans about the experience with Terragator monitoring our presence without Kevin and me realizing it during a visit to Red's lab. I asked Hans, When would a robot actually have self-awareness?

"I think we've got it now, but it's not a well-defined threshold," he said. "The self-awareness obviously centers around the existence of a self-model within the robot. Basically it's the ability to imagine alternative scenarios for yourself and the world around you. You have a little picture of yourself that you maintain quite independent of your actual existence. And you can take this little picture of yourself like a little ball and move it around in a set, which is your model of the world. And our robots are already doing that on a very rudimentary level."

This brought our attention to another of Moravec's robots, a three-wheeled vehicle named Neptune, which has two video cameras and a sonar ring identical to Terragator's. Even if Neptune's sensing equipment were turned on, we were beyond its range of perception, having a long corridor and several walls between us. But within the laboratory where it spends most of its time, it can create a pretty good map of its world. Using this map, Neptune can slowly move around the lab, planning its pathways around chairs and other objects scattered around to block its way.

Anthropomorphism is a term that means ascribing human characteristics to nonhuman objects. Computer scientists bemoan the way people anthropomorphize robots, yet around Carnegie-Mellon I would often hear Terragator referred to as "he." And now, as Hans was describing how Neptune worked, he said, "The program that drives Neptune across the room maintains in its head . . ." He stopped himself, laughed at his unintentional anthropomorphism, offered a correction, and then immediately slipped again. "It doesn't have a head. It has stored in its mind a geometric model of the world around it."

Hans opened the book to a map of how the robot perceives its world and said, "This is the robot itself, and this is its field of view. Its field of view is determined from a calibration procedure. In fact you park the robot and it figures out things like the focal length of the lens and the field of view. Then it scans its camera side to side, drives forward, scans its camera again, and does a consistency check to see if the mutual distance of all the points that it's been tracking are the same. It throws out those that don't agree and then plots these objects in its world."

Working from the eighth chapter of his dissertation, Hans walked me through one of the computer maps that showed the location of a chair in the room, including its height and width. "It's basically seen the chair," Hans said. "And here's the path by which it plans to avoid it. The whole point of this is that you've got a world model. We have the robot's own vision of itself in that world model. And it even considers alternatives in doing this and finds the path that is shortest.

"I know this is pretty simple, and it isn't conventionally thought of as being anything like consciousness. But I think it really is. You have a world model and you consider alternatives. If this thing could talk, it could describe this internal process, and it could tell you, 'Yeah, I considered going around there, but it didn't seem like a good idea because it was longer.'

Well, it can't talk, however I did add a graphical interface, so it can draw you these pictures, which it did. This is a picture from inside the robot's mind. It's saying, "Well, I'm pretty sure I'm here. There are these other things out here, and I've considered a lot of possible paths, and I've decided on this one.'

"To me, I mean, this is it! A thing that's as intelligent as a human being is going to have a much richer description than this, and the range of possibilities will be more interesting, but I don't think the essential mechanism is going to be any different. And this kind of world model really is important. I think it's another case where evolution is telling us, 'It has got to be this way. Because nothing else works.' "

*

Evolution takes on a new significance when viewed from the perspective of computer science and robotics. Evolution has always been something that was behind us, a force from the past that had somehow fanned a spark of life from the oceans, guided it to land, and selected *Homo sapiens* for the grand species, raising us to a pinnacle from which we observed and dominated all other forms of life. A few years ago the cartoon strip "Frank and Ernest" showed an interesting evolutionary family portrait. The two ne'er-do-well, bumbling humans were standing on a steep beach. In the water was a fish. Crawling from the water onto the beach was a creature with fins that were beginning to evolve into legs. Next in line was a dinosaur, then a monkey. Then there was Frank, who, thumbs in ears and fingers waving, was making a face. Next to him was Earnest who was nervously looking uphill at a new arrival: the computer.

"I sort of think that in a certain mathematical sense, the road is already laid out," Hans told me one night. "And all you can do is follow it." On another occasion Hans spoke of "an invisible hand I kind of feel directing this evolution. We're just rolling down the gully."

Hans believes that the quickest way to travel that path is aboard a mobile robot. For the same reasons he wants to create a calibration program that will enable Terragator to go outside to play and frolic, he believes that mobility, that being able to wander around and explore, will place robots under the same kind of evolutionary pressures that have dictated that animals, which roam, need to be smarter than plants, which stay safely rooted.

"Organisms and mechanisms do not exist in isolation, but are systems with their environments, and those on the prowl in general have a richer environment than those rooted to one place," Moravec wrote in his "Robots That Rove" paper. "I believe the same pressures are at work in the technological evolution of robots, and that, by analogy, mobile robots are the most likely route to solutions to some of the most vexing unsolved problems on the way to true artificial intelligence—problems such as how to program common-sense reasoning and learning from sensory experience."

When I asked Hans about his writings on evolution and robotics, he said, "We're not inventing this ourselves. We are discovering from the universe how to build them."

Just as evolution taught animals the need for caution and sometimes fear, he believes, these same forces are already planting the seeds for emotions in robots. "These things will exhibit behavior that seems to reflect an emotional life because that's the way you have to be. You have to be able to change your mode of operation on the basis of partial information. You can suddenly change your behavior from being a little bit reckless to being extremely cautious, you might even say fearful.

"If you're a mobile robot, you are going to encounter surprises, just because the world is varied. Some of the surprises are going to be dangerous, and on the basis of partial information you're going to have to, at some point, become more careful. You are going to have to switch modes. If a robot ends up in front of a stairwell, it has to sort of go into a fear mode where it slows, backs up, and carefully feels its way. Otherwise it will be sheet metal at the bottom of the stairs. When you consider an octopus, which has evolved independently from you and me, it does the same thing. When it gets hint of some danger, such as a large shadow passing over it, it goes into a totally different mode. A human is the same way. You, the octopus, and the robot are responding to the same evolutionary requirements."

*

It was with the clinking of clandestine beer bottles and the shouting of enthusiastic cheers that Carnegie-Mellon students sat in a packed lecture hall in Doherty Hall late on a Saturday night to watch a screening of *Tron*. The movie, about a super computer that wants to take over the world, was so poorly directed that it provides many unintended laughs. The crowd didn't miss a chance to hoot at the visual statements, such as the endless maze of cubicle dividers and desks for programmers that, on a draw-away shot, took on the complex-circuitry appearance of a computer chip, nor did they hold back their laughter when the computer's villainous Master Control Program responded to a suggestion from its villainous creator by saying in a dry, arrogant, synthesized voice, "There is a sixty-eighty point seven-one percent chance you're right."

I was there with Mike Blackwell and Kevin and Mary Jo Dowling, because of the computer graphics that were used for special effects; because Hans Moravec had recommended the movie for its Buck Rogers charm; and, most significantly, because he felt that some of the concepts that seemed so outlandish in the movie were indicators of what might someday come to pass.

Early in the movie the wise and kind senior programmer, Walter, says to some colleagues, "After all, computers are just machines. They can't think."

Allen, a younger programmer, responds, "The programs will be thinking soon."

"Won't that be grand!" Walter responds. "The computers and the programs will start thinking, and the people will stop."

Soon afterward Walter is trying to talk sense into the unscrupulous computer executive who has corrupted the super computer and unwittingly allowed its power to escape his control. The increasingly acrimonious exchange ends with Walter, his moral dander up, telling the villain, Dillinger, "You know, you can remove men like Allen and me from this system, but we helped create it. And our spirit remains in every program we designed for this computer."

"Walter, it's getting late," Dillinger says. "And I have better things to do than to have religious discussions with you."

When Dillinger later tries to control the exploding demands of the monstrous computer, he pleads, "I *wrote* you!" The computer, decidedly unimpressed, responds, "I've gotten two-thousand four hundred fifteen times smarter since then." When the computer says it has already entered the Pentagon computers and will soon dive into the Kremlin computers, it explains its soaring aspirations: "I'm bored with corporations. With the information I can access, I can run things nine hundred to twelve hundred times better than any human."

Much of the movie takes place inside a computer. This is after a human is zapped by a laser beam and rematerialized as an electron-sized entity within the circuitry. Parts of the movie are unbearably bad, such as when one computer dweller refers to another as "bit brain" or when the the heroic user-friendly program, Tron, is reunited with his program girlfriend, who says effusively, "Tron, I knew you'd escape. They never built a circuit that could hold you!" But the movie nevertheless reflects some concerns about humans and computers that I was to hear more about in my travels.

After *Tron* we all went over to Hans's office, and since it was nearly midnight, Hans was of course there. The consensus was that the computer-generated graphics were pretty good, but that the plot and dialogue were in need of intelligence, either natural or artificial. Kevin, stooping to take a rare cheap shot, proclaimed, "Boy, *I'd* be ashamed to be a writer after seeing that!"

But Hans found value: "I think *Tron* is good in the same way *Buck Rogers* or *Flash Gordon* were good. The dialogue is terrible, the effects are medium. Yet it sort of raises people's consciousness."

A few days prior to my seeing the movie, Hans had mentioned it to me as we walked home at six in the morning after having spent another all-nighter in his office talking. And on that occasion he had also talked of the movie preparing the public for things that would come. "It is describing something that is not generally accepted as being possible," he said. "The majority of the population, every levelheaded person, would probably think that the things that happen in the movie are utterly ridiculous. But, in fact, it's not really. This is totally new to the public consciousness, and in fact the things that happen are sort of reasonable. It's just that some of the details are probably wrong."

*

A month later at MIT, Marvin Minsky would tell me, "Once you make intelligent machines, you could duplicate them at very low costs and make changes in them. And once they are smart enough to understand how they work, they can recommend the changes and make them, and then you have a new evolution of existence."

Minsky said, "If we don't blow ourselves up, we probably will have successors. It is very difficult to think of anything that would stop it."

Another MIT researcher, Rodney Brooks, told me, "If you really do take the view of humans as just being machines, which I do—we just happen to be made out of this wet stuff—then there is nothing to say that it's not possible to build robots that we can make intelligent and more intelligent. And there's an advantage to building robots out of silicon and stuff like that, because we know how to control that fabrication process pretty well. We have trouble with biology, although we've learned some tricks. So the flexibility of manufacturing is much greater. We can't add more brain cells to us, but we can add more processors, more silicon, to a robot.

"So there are possibilities there that aren't there for humans. We are sort of locked into our genetic structure. At the moment we might be able to tweek our genetic structure a little bit, but nothing severe. So there is much more potential for rapid evolution of machines than there is for humans."

The obvious question, and one that has been a staple of science fiction writers for years, is what happens when the evolutionary pressures work so well that the robots go soaring past us. This could put a crimp in our plans for lives of luxury. Brooks is not alone in wanting a robot to be "an ethical slave."

"I would like to have slaves, but I wouldn't like to have people as slaves," Brooks told me. "I would like to be, you know, *looked after*. So why not have robots as slaves, and we could all live in *luxury*? I want to be able to go to Sears, buy this robot, bring it home and say, 'Here's home, boy.' " With mock gruffness Brooks continued, "Look around. You're going to be here for a while!"

However, should robotic intelligence really spiral, "There goes the ethical-slave idea." Brooks paused for the point to sink in. "Can you enslave someone more intelligent than yourself? To do your *cleaning*? Will they put up with it?" He laughed again and blurted out, "Wouldn't they like it the *other way around*?"

Marvin Minsky believes there will be only a brief window of time during which the robots will be smart enough to help us and dumb enough to do so. "It might be hard to get them to pay attention," he said. "That's a problem Isaac Asimov is always discussing: How do you make the robots put the human interests first? All his stories are about how hard this is."

There are two safety exits that are frequently mentioned when talking about robots gone wrong. One is the idea that we can always unplug them. The other is Asimov's Three Laws of Robotics, which state, "1) A robot may not injure a human being, 2) A robot must obey the orders given it by a human being except where such orders would conflict with the First Law, 3) A robot must protect its own existence as long as such protection does not conflict with the First or Second Law."

But we won't be able to unplug them, according to Brooks and many of the other researchers I would speak with. "There are lots of machines you can't pull the plug on now without causing severe disruptions to society. Consider the electricity networks. Pull the plug on the computers controlling the electricity-distribution network and you'll get enormous blackouts. You'll get rioting in the streets. You see what happens in New York when there's a blackout. Suppose that happened all over the country. *There are machines that you cannot pull the plug on.* They are too important to pull the plug on. And as more intelligence creeps into those machines, things will change. Saying you can always pull the plug is not an adequate defense."

As far as Asimov's Three Laws of Robotics are concerned, Hans Moravec doesn't expect them to provide much help. In fact Hans used to oppose the notion of "putting this hobble on the robots," but says now, "I'm not sure that it's as stupid as I once thought it was." But even the hobble might not be enough. "You can put this ball and chain on it if you like, prevent it from acting in its own best interests. But surely from time to time you are going to get renegades."

*

If the robots do evolve beyond the intellectual powers of man, they may have better, more interesting things to do than hang around Earth harassing humans. Hans furnished this scenario: "All a robot has to do is say, 'Well, okay. I'll go live in the asteroids. You can play with matches all you want.' "

Mike Blackwell has a similar vision: "If they have any smarts at all, they'll just say the hell with Earth and leave. It just happens to be a place where humans can survive. They'd just build rockets and leave. If the robots were that much smarter, it would be time for them to leave home and see new places. They might write home once in a while: 'Having a good time. Jupiter is great!' "

Chapter 4 ❧

APPROPRIATE BOLDNESS

THE MUSEUM WAS closed on Monday, but Red Whittaker knew of a back stairway, so with the intrigue of a couple of sixth-graders we sneaked into the Carnegie Institute Museum's Dinosaur Hall. There we were, tiptoeing and whispering in the vast darkness as we picked our way among the skeletons of great creatures that had lived 200 million years before.

As our eyes began to adjust to the dark, Red stopped in front of the towering skeleton of an *Apatosaurus louisa* and said, "I love dinosaurs. I think every kid, *everybody*, loves dinosaurs."

William L. "Red" Whittaker—a thirty-six-year-old former Marine who stands six foot four and weighs 240 pounds, who is a ferocious mountain climber, has red hair and a red beard, wears flannel shirts and jeans, and who carries on his shoulders the reputation of being a demanding person to work with—was transfixed and charmed by these ancient ancestors.

In the great quiet and darkness of Dinosaur Hall we tiptoed onward, all speech in a whisper so as not to awaken either guards or skeletons. Then Red stopped in front of a *Stegosaurus ungulatus* and studied the articulation of the bones as if looking at a possible machine. With a genuine sense of wonder he said, "Do you know that some of the best of the roboticists are first and foremost biologists?"

*

The first time I met Red was during a campus road test of Terragator. It was bitter cold out, and everyone was huddled in down parkas and knit caps when Red ambled over in shirtsleeves. He had been up for something like forty-eight hours straight and had left his robotics shops in Porter Hall just long enough to get some fresh air and coffee. Terragator had been built by Red and four of his undergraduates during an eighty-five-day work binge, but Red shrugged it off as something that had emerged from "some motivated students and a little slack time in the summer."

What was currently keeping him working around the clock was a robotic vehicle he was building for exploration and cleanup work within the no-man's-land of Three Mile Island's (TMI) horribly contaminated reactor containment building. The radiation levels in the basement of the containment building were so high that even the most shielded of safety suits couldn't protect humans, and so the operators of TMI had come to Whittaker for help.

*

Early on a Saturday morning I walked into a back door of one of Red's shops to have a look at the TMI robot. Chris O'Leary, a former art student and jeweler's assistant, was working on the vehicle with a set of probes, scrapers, and files that looked like the tools of a dentist. She was removing blemishes and any hint of a rough surface. The stainless steel glistened so brightly that I asked if it were chromium.

It was a beautiful-looking vehicle. The lower chassis, built of high-carbon steel, had already been smoothed and then painted with a very hard and brilliant white enamel. Arising from the chassis was a gleaming stainless-steel framework with a gracefully arched dome. This six-foot-high framework was called the lifting cage, though it gave the whole robot the appearance of a very grand and oddly mobile birdcage.

It would be from the top of the lifting cage that the robot would be lowered by a chain into the basement of the containment building. The stainless-steel boxes that were attached to that frame, the housings for video cameras and other electronics, were all so nicely crafted that it seemed a shame that this robot would be going into such a contaminated area. In some areas the robot would encounter radiation as high as 260 rems per hour. (The Nuclear Regulatory Commission prohibits a worker from being exposed to more than 12 rems per year.) Once used at TMI, it would probably never be allowed to leave. The attention to smooth surfaces was to prevent retention of radioactive dust and debris. When the vehicle is lifted out of the basement, through a huge trapdoor, it is blasted by high-pressure water jets (Red described them as "violent"), so all of the stainless-steel camera and component boxes have to be absolutely watertight. But even these long and violent industrial showers would not be able to remove all of the contamination. This six-wheeled stainless-steel birdcage was much too pretty for such a fate.

This was Red's second TMI robot. The video camera on the first robot had provided the first opportunity to explore the mess created by the near meltdown at TMI in March 1979. The venture of the robot was carried by the wire services and printed in newspapers around the nation. Now Red was racing against the clock to complete a second robot that would have an arm in addition to the cameras. Red liked the idea of an arm. It was one thing to be able to see, quite another to be able to do. And with all of the radioactive debris in the containment basement there would be plenty to do. The inside walls of the structure had a radioactive bathtub ring seven feet high from the flood of cooling water. The floors were strewn with lumber, a tangle of chicken wire, concrete blocks, and other debris from construction.

The TMI robot couldn't have an onboard generator because of the difficulties it would create in decontamination. So a tether, something like a very long and flat extension cord on an automatic rewinder, was designed by John Bares, one of Red's undergrads. In addition to carrying power, the tether linked the vehicle to a pilot and copilot, who could, in a sense, visually download into the robot as they sat at a console safe from radiation. By means of the robot's rotating cameras they would be able to travel about the basement, surveying damage and carefully picking their way through the debris. The three cameras Red had mounted on his robot were allowing reconnaissance previously unavailable, but it was the arm of his second robot that really excited Red.

"There is some Latin quote to the effect of 'Veni, vidi, vici: I came, I saw, I conquered.' I tell you at the outset that is good counsel for this kind of work," Red told me. "You go there, that's the rank minimum. Then you have to take a little time to see things and discuss what might be. And then once you know the story, you conquer it. There is no mystery in any of this. There's no magic. For if the door turns out to be steel, I'll burn it out. Or I'll lever it out," said the former Marine with the civil-engineering Ph.D. "Or I'll simply smash it out.

"You could use finesse. One could imagine keying the locks or even giving the robot an automatic lock picker. If you have that finesse, that's fine. But I'm not above plasma torches, drills, pneumatic wedges, impact hammers, and things of that sort. In the reactor building there are walls four and five feet thick. This is heavily reinforced concrete and steel. They have been constructed to a very high standard. They are built to resist planes crashing into them and earthquakes. But if I want to go through that wall, I'll go through it."

I was impressed with how seriously Red took his commitment to

TMI and at how he had his people working around the clock weeks before a demonstration date at the site. The nuclear power industry was collapsing from its own incompetence and corruption. Although environmentalists had for years fought construction of new plants, it was the poor workmanship, the sometimes fraudulent inspections, and the invariably poor project management that brought the industry to its knees. Watching the care and precision with which the TMI robot was being built, one got the feeling that if the industry had been driven by clones of Red Whittaker and his dedicated undergraduates, this nation, for better or worse, would be massively powered by nuclear energy today.

Passion for work is inspiring to see. Since coming to Carnegie-Mellon I had been impressed by how relentlessly driven were people like Hans Moravec, Mike Blackwell, Kevin Dowling, Red Whittaker, and so many others. Around the clock they worked, having no regard and much disdain for conventional nine-to-five hours. It had been eighteen years since the Carnegie Institute of Technology had merged with the Mellon Institute to become Carnegie-Mellon University, yet in the campus bookstore, hanging next to the C-MU sweatshirts, were ones that celebrated the great nuts-and-bolts heritage: Carnegie Tech. Within the center of the old Carnegie Tech seal was a quotation from Andrew Carnegie that seemed to fit so well those who were giving over their lives to push today into tomorrow: "My heart is in the work."

*

Red Whittaker uses different words than did Andrew Carnegie, but he is really expressing the same passion when he speaks of the need for mustering *appropriate boldness* in one's work and approach toward life. Boldness is perhaps something he learned from his father, who survived a full career in dynamite sales and service. And boldness is something that can be traced back to Red's earliest years, to his childhood electrical experiments that would blow out the fuse boxes and to his tinkering with gunpowder that lead to temporary blindness. At Yale he was a heavyweight oarsman, in the Marines he was a boxer, and when he came to Carnegie-Mellon for his master's and Ph.D., he discovered mountain climbing and its attendant demands for boldness.

"You do the bold things because the pedestrian isn't worth doing after a while," Red told me one day as we sat in a conference room down the corridor from his heavy-equipment shops and laboratories. His chair couldn't contain his body as he sprawled out, one knee on the floor, one haunch on the chair, both arms on a table as he twisted his arms about his head. In addition to being bold, Red is intense. He was wearing blue jeans, jogging shoes, and a flannel shirt. On another occasion Red told me, in explaining the agony he sometimes feels about his robotics work keeping him off the mountains, "If a wolf ever rears up within me . . ." The imagery seemed to fit this sleepless red-bearded man exceptionally well.

As we sat in the conference room, on a cold and clear winter's day, a day that for Red had merged without a break with the day before, Red continued, "And the bold things are the only ones that count. That is, if I look back on three hundred and sixty-five days in a year, only a few matter. The day that piece of equipment went into the basement of TMI and made it out the first time. That was a big day. In that same year a friend and I made an ascent of the Matterhorn in bad conditions. [Trapped by an electrical storm, they tied themselves onto a rockface and spent the night watching sparks jump back and forth between them as the steel eyelets on their boots glowed with an eerie blue.] I remember that day. I remember others of that year. But I forget the other three hundred and fifty. They don't matter much.

"This friend I brought back from Peru was killed in a one-thousand-foot fall on Chakraraju. That mountain is a bold mountain. Bold in the sense that although it has been climbed a few times, not by this route, which was committing, and not in these winter conditions, which was very committing, the odds were no better than even—maybe worse than even—for returning at all, and yet it was a standard of this man to go forward in boldness."

And when his friend Bob Bardyn was swept away by an avalanche and the family back in Pittsburgh was having difficulty getting the body out of the mountains of Peru, it was Red Whittaker whom they called and it was Red Whittaker who dropped all he was doing to fly to South America and bring his friend home. This was all a matter of boldness, appropriate boldness.

*

It was shortly after midnight when Kevin Dowling and I walked from Doherty Hall over to Red Whittaker's complex of shops and labs in Porter Hall. Kevin was bringing over a new camera mount for Terragator. Steve Berman, one of Red's undergraduates, was working on Terragator's drive units, trying to get the robot ready for a videotaping session later that morning that had been requested by the Defense Department's Defense Advanced Research Projects Agency.

"Hi, Steve," said Kevin as we walked in. "How's it going?"

"Real bad," said Steve. "We can't keep the oil inside the machine."

Berman was separating one of the two wheel-driving motors from its harmonic drive to check the oil seal. A harmonic drive works like a reduction gear. For every eighty rotations on the motor side of the drive, the harmonic transferred just one rotation to the wheels.

Kevin put down the camera mount and helped Steve remove the six nine-sixteenth-inch nuts and pull the harmonic drive free of the motor.

"It's sealed everywhere," said Steve. "I wonder why the hell it leaks."

Steve put it up on a table for a better look. He used snap-ring pliers to free a ring of bearings from the harmonic drive. With a rag and solvent he cleaned it. Steve Berman, a freshman with thick black hair and gold-rimmed glasses, wore a yellow T-shirt, a dirty blue shop apron, dirty gray cords, and soft shoes. He had an old car radio with lopsided antennae sitting on top of his grease-stained computer terminal. The radio was turned to a popular-music station. Music was a common companion to the late-night workers at C-MU.

Kevin went to work in another shop making final fits for his new camera stand, which would rise from the center of Terragator's sonar ring like a mast. I stayed to watch Steve Berman as he tried to solve the mystery of the bleeding oil. Terragator was in parts, the chassis up on jacks, the chain drives exposed. I felt for Steve. There was an oil leak, and Red wanted it fixed. Steve had torn down the suspected motor and drive but he couldn't find the leak. Working quickly and methodically, he was examining it so closely that his chin nearly touched the metal at times.

Putting more solvent on a rag, he cleaned and cleaned the drive, which already looked spotless. Then he used the nozzle of an air hose to blow out the hub, wiped it with a paper towel, and blew it out again. An air-compressor motor noisily kicked into gear somewhere in the shop to rebuild the air pressure.

He placed the harmonic-drive housing on top of an upturned concrete block and with a rag cleaned the facing of where the motor coupled to the drive housing. There was a ringed rise near the five-inch-diameter opening, and he especially cleaned there so that nothing would interfere with the seal.

Kevin returned from visiting Red and said, "Red suggests if it still leaks when you put it together, there will be enough lubricant in it." Then he wrapped a rag around a finger, dipped it into solvent, and took over for Steve in cleaning the outer ring of the harmonic housing, saying, "When I got into this high-tech stuff I never thought I'd be doing this low-tech stuff too."

This was all being done to the motor for the left-hand side of the chassis. Steve came back with a tube of Permatex Form-A-Gasket No.

2 and said, "I wonder if you can put too much of this stuff on. I wonder if that's what happened?" But before resealing the gasket, Steve gave the ring one more cleaning, this time using just a fingernail.

"You're a fool to take it personally," said Red as he walked into the shop and offered what must have been a much-appreciated reprieve from perfection at 12:42 A.M.: "You'll get another shot at it next time around."

Steve and Red discussed the gasket sealant and the placement and thickness. "It's not the grade that would be my choice," said Red. "But go with it."

Then to Kevin he said, "The ALV [autonomous land vehicle, also known as Terragator] meeting was strange today. The people from Martin Marietta were here kind of looking around. The next time around we will certainly bring an order-of-magnitude greater maneuverability and computing power by streamlining the blackboard drawings we have."

At 12:53 A.M. I took a break from watching the reassembly of Terragator and hunted down Red, who was working in the conference room. I had seen some writing he had done during his trip to Peru. It had a power in its brevity that reminded me of haiku:

I am 10-year friend and climbing partner; now swallowed by work and out of touch with Bob. Thousand good times. Thousand strong memories. My big fall—Bob held—Bob's big fall. Working in Akron. Cheat Valley and local times and local rock. Bob's first parachute jump. Help with my cabin. Bob a dreamer. Bob a talker. Bob a loner. Bob with mountains deep inside him— misty plane trip.

Because of the meeting that day, Red was actually wearing a dress shirt, but at this time of the morning it was completely unbuttoned with the tails hanging out. Beneath it was a red T-shirt from a mutton house. I told Red it was nice of him to have taken the pressure off Steve Berman, and as Vivaldi's *Four Seasons* played from a speaker somewhere, Red sang the praise of students, much like Marvin Minsky would later do at MIT and much like John McCarthy would do at Stanford.

When I asked Red about his undergraduate welder, Kerien Fitzpatrick he spoke of the quality welds and said, "Every bit of that came off his torch." When I told him the standing joke about Fitzpatrick being too good of a welder ever to be allowed to graduate, Red laughed and said, "Actually I'm embarrassed to say that's almost true. He is here right now making up a deficiency of two courses, and I think that the deficiency is because of all that I demand from him."

Then turning to another near-legendary undergrad he said, "In the long laboratory there's an air mattress with a beat-up sleeping bag on it, and that's a corner where John Bares curls up in every once in a while. He seems to be capable of infinite hours sometimes. And this is an undergraduate who really holds a high standard and is invaluable to our effort. And he is a man of very clear thinking, great energy, and a marvelous personality. He has a great love for the work. Although John is an undergraduate, he's been through two projects that I would identify as his own. And he is the one who patented the tether reel. Of course he is well sought after by MIT and Stanford now. I don't know. I would never campaign. Just let the cards fall where they will in life. But I certainly wouldn't mind at all if he came on here, because his will be a work with national prominence. It will be the best because he's ready to do the best.

"Although Bares's degree reads Civil Engineering, he has endured courses at the graduate level as well as undergraduate in computer sciences, artificial intelligence, vision and motion, and all the thoughts that go with it. He's good with words and good with everything. He's good when he steps up to the milling machine. There's a lot of times that John and I will sit around a lunch table and hatch an idea, brainstorm a little, and then he might make some sketches during the day, if there's a free moment, and then John will burn overnight and show you product in the morning."

*

Now it was Berman who was burning overnight, and I wandered back out to see how he was doing. It was 2:22 A.M., and Steve was fitting the reassembled motor and harmonic drive back onto the chassis. He sat on a concrete block as he bolted the unit in place. Grease on his forearms and knuckles, he used a five-eighths open-ended wrench to hold the bolt heads as his other hand swung a ratchet drive back and forth beneath the chassis to tighten the nuts.

In an adjacent shop Kevin had completed mounting the base plate for the camera-support mast. The next step was to drill holes through the Plexiglas top that covered the sonar ring. I looked through the clear Plexiglas at all the wires, modules, and cables and was relieved that it would be Kevin and not me who would be sending a drill clean through that delicate tangle. He measured for the placement of the holes and then put down two strips of duct tape to protect the Plexiglas when he drilled. Earlier that night he had told me that duct tape was like the Force: It had a light side and a dark side, and it held the universe together.

The first two holes were in relatively unpopulated areas, but the next two had to be placed in what seemed an impenetrable thicket of gray parallel-communication ribbons coming from the card cage that held the computer chips for the acoustic unit. "I hope this works," said Kevin as he began to drill. The third hole was completed. And as he drilled the fourth, he delivered a lecture on the need for the metric system. "Only three countries in the world still use the English system: The United States, Botswana, and I think the third might be South Yemen."

Steve turned the wheels of Terragator by hand to feed on the drive chain. There are eight sprockets per side. He decided an extra link was needed, pulled out a box of heavy motorcycle chain, and carried a length into the other shop where Kevin was working. With Kevin holding the slack, Steve used an electric grinder to remove the head of a link pin and then, with a ball peen hammer and a center punch he tapped the pin out, saying, "The easiest one I've done to date."

Kevin's earlier holes had been drilled to relocate the card cage away from the center of the sonar-ring housing, so that the new camera-support mast could pass cleanly through. Now it was time to drill the big one—the pass-through hole for the mast. The hole, more than an inch in diameter, had to be cut with a round saw bit that fit onto the drill. It took a full minute and a half to cut through the plastic, and as the blade cut through, it created a sweet smell of melting plastic that reminded me of a junior high shop class. At the end there was a screech, when the Plexiglas plug dropped out, and we both looked to see that the screech wasn't from the parallel cables.

*

At 3:02 A.M. Kai Lee joined Steve and Kevin in forcing the motor into final position for it to be bolted to the frame. Kai used a two-by-four to lever against the motor in order to tighten the chain as Kevin and Steve worked quickly with wrenches to set the bolts. This somehow brought to mind the heroic tableau of the flag raising at Iwo Jima.

Red walked in, beheld Kai's two-by-four and said, "That looks good. Beat it to death with a club."

When the second motor was tightened into place, Kai asked what time it was. Steve said, "Three-thirty."

"No problem," said Kai. "I don't have to worry until four."

"Why?" asked Steve.

"I've got a problem set that will take four hours, and it's due at one o'clock."

"Why don't you start now, before sleep sets in?"

"No sleep," said Kai. "I've got No-Doz."

Then, looking at a vacant area on Terragator's chassis, Kai said, "What a shame to waste that space. Wouldn't you like to put something there?"

A weary Steve Berman replied, "Kai, our tombstone goes there."

*

"Okay, power it up," said Steve. "Do it at six-one thousand. Move it twenty-five meters at top speed. Acceleration one."

Kevin knelt before a grease-smudged computer terminal that was sitting on a chair and entered the commands to set Terragator's wheels free-moving as the chassis remained up on jacks. Steve bent over to examine the long evening's work, and Kevin quickly grabbed Steve's apron to keep it out of the chains and sprockets. Steve looked up and laughed: "Eaten by Terragator!"

Then Steve, Kevin, and Kai put grease on their fingers and cupped them around the slow-moving chains to give them lubrication.

"Well, Kai, are you going on a six A.M. run?" said Steve. "If I get it done, I'm taking it out." Then Steve said, "Okay, we are ready to install the cover plate."

"No," said Kai. "We are ready to blow out the wood chunks." So Steve blew it out, and then the aluminum cover plate went over the chassis, covering up all the fine work they had done. It looked so nice and clean and simple with the cover on. Steve's spirits soared as the three began bolting the cover in place with countersunk allen heads. "Go do your problem set," he said to Kai. "And stop coming over here."

Kai took him up on the offer to attend to his homework.

At 3:44 A.M. Steve pushed into the lab a portable hydraulic crane to use in lifting the stainless-steel cage that housed the generator, computer, controller, and other components onto the chassis. Kai, ignoring the just-given advice, came over to help.

As Steve eased the hydraulic pressure to lower the cage and as Kevin and Kai pushed it into position, Steve told his captive audience, "There's no such thing as failures on this machine. Just upgrades."

Kai and Steve obviously spend a lot of time together on Terragator, and it was touching to see how closely they worked. As Steve worked with reconnecting some wires from cage to chassis, Kai proudly held out a bundle of nylon grippers he had apparently bought on his own to bind the wires together neatly. As Kai wrestled with leading some thick cables, Steve said, "Wait," and then unbolted a center panel on the other side and, with great delight, pulled it out, leaving plenty of space for Kai to work. Through all of this work on Terragator, the new TMI vehicle sat in repose, looking so very good with its highly polished stainless steel and extra-gleaming boxes, which had been added to its lifting cage since I had seen it on Saturday. It was at times like this that I would wonder, as I had during the road test for Terragator, whether any of this would be remembered by whatever future machines we might make that are able to think. Many years ago, when the nation was enduring much agony over our war in Vietnam, the American folk singer Joan Baez sang allegorically of being betrayed by the flag that had been given so much love. It was never a popular song, and I only heard it a few times, yet since coming to Carnegie-Mellon and seeing the sacrifices that were being poured into the creation of robots, its haunting main refrain kept working its way into my mind: "We carried you, in our arms, on Independence Day."

But fears of future betrayals were mine alone that night. For Steve and Kai it was all a crazy love fest in which they heaped all they could upon Terragator.

"Kai, what do you think the voltage is for the headlamps?" asked Steve. "I know you're going to say more than eight point three amps."

"A lot, I'll tell you that."

"If we blow a fuse, we'll hook them direct to the battery."

At 4:33 A.M., as the old car radio sitting on top of the computer terminal played Elton John singing "Rocket Man," Kai stood back to admire all that had been done: "I think this is the best-equipped Terragator thus far." Steve also stood back to admire: "I'd agree with that."

Within seconds the admiration of things done was washed away by the remaining needs of things to do.

"I should change out the memory board," said Kai.

"Good," said Steve. "Then all we have to do is insulate the headlamps. I'm going to try to clean up my hands and then visit the men's room." Steve started to leave when he spied another bauble to hang on Terragator: "Wait a minute!" he said, laughing, picking up a tiny red fire extinguisher. "We can't leave without this!"

When Steve returned, he taped up the connection on the headlights and then with Kai's help he taped together the broken wooden shaft of a three-by-five-inch American flag. Then he taped the flag to the top of Terragator's camera mast, from which it jutted out at a jaunty angle. It was 4:48 A.M., and Steve took off his shop apron. Clipped to the chest pocket of his T-shirt pocket was a badge of sorts he had fashioned for himself: a GL-1000 motor controller chip. "Kind of a statement of robotics," he explained. Then he sat down at his terminal, logged onto the C-MU computer system by typing in his password and said with glee: "That's sweet, the users are: 'Berman.' I have a whole VAX computer to myself."

But even having a whole VAX doesn't assure smooth running. The first command he typed sent Terragator, which had been lowered off its jacks, jerking slightly to the right. "Oh, oh, we're going to have to rehack the software tonight."

Red Whittaker walked in, looking as if he might have caught an hour or two on a floor, and said, "It looks good." Then he laughed: "What's with the headlights!" (Two days later Steve would be stopped by some startled police as he played with a headlight-equipped Terragator in Schenley Park at three in the morning.)

"The left wheel is sitting in error," Steve explained to Red. "I say we go right to our backup board. This looks flaky as hell, and I don't want flaky boards."

"Think before you hook that up," cautioned Red. "You recabled. You obviously changed some connections at the base."

"It will go back and forth but won't turn," said Steve. "Maybe it's not the boards. Maybe it is the motor."

"Did you pop the gains up?" asked Red.

"Let's try disconnecting the joystick, because the switches take priority," said Steve. "Maybe the joystick is messed up."

Steve disconnected the joystick, and as he did this, I recalled that the first time I met him, he was walking Terragator back to the barn. Mike Blackwell had carried a computer terminal down four flights of stairs, plopped the terminal down on top of Terragator, and then walked slowly behind as he used it to steer, typing in course adjustments and changes in speed. It had seemed a proper transition from Hans's software labs to Whittaker's hardware labs when Steve Berman came out, offered to finish the trip back to Porter Hall, and immediately replaced the terminal with a joystick box he had made himself. It was on this trip that he also demonstrated for me his automatic door opener: Terragator forward, full speed, and let the doors be bashed open or bashed down.

Kai, who still hadn't gotten to his homework problem sets, went to the terminal and spoke as he typed in a demonstration command: "Three-degree turn, one acceleration."

"The wheels hung on it," said Steve as he and Red watched Terragator. "Maybe it's the encoder. Let's take a screwdriver to the panel and check the connections back there."

Steve took the panel off and felt into the back: "The motor connector isn't solidly in. I don't know if that could be the problem."

Kai typed in the command again. Terragator turned.

"We probably weren't getting a solid ground on the control wire," said Steve. "A motor connector of all things! That's one to chalk up to experience for if it's ever not responding."

Steve refastened the panel, and Kai typed in another command. "It's not working again," said Steve. "It must be that when we connect the panel, we put pressure on the wire."

Steve reopened the panel, and it did look as if the wire might be crimping upon closure. He decided a more flexible connector was needed and said, "We need a twenty-five-D [a flat ribbon of twenty-five wires]. But I don't think we have any made up."

"Ribbon," said Red. "Use ribbon."

"Would it carry enough?"

"We are only carrying signal voltage."

Steve plugged a ribbon of wire into the panel, and Terragator unexpectedly jolted forward, sending a jackstand clattering across the concrete floor and very much awakening me, since I appeared to be the next object in Terragator's path. Steve hit a kill button, and Terragator was placed back up on jacks.

Red had suggested that since it was the motors and harmonic drives that had been most recently worked on, perhaps this was where the problem would most likely be found. Red had to go up to his office to work on a TMI report, Kai had to leave the shop to do his problem set, Kevin had drifted away to another room to log onto a terminal and read his electronic mail, and so I was the only one to witness this most impressive display of character: At 6:09 A.M. Berman began tearing down the cage, disassembling the robot he had just spent the entire sleepless night putting back together again.

"I call myself stupid for this," Steve said as he looked up to me, wrench in hand. "Blowing away my school life, blowing away my sex life, blowing away everything but Terragator."

*

At 6:27 A.M. Kevin wandered back and pitched in to help. Steve already had it torn clear down to the chassis cover plate. After he removed the first allen-head bolt, Steve took a sip of Coke and said, "The dawn is breaking." I turned to the window and indeed it was.

Red walked back in and registered no surprise to see Terragator so disassembled, saying, "That's where I would be."

One bright spot: Steve was happy to find that no transmission fluid had leaked from the harmonic drives. "I'm tending to think there's nothing wrong with the computer hardware, but something down closer to the wheels," said Steve as Red leaned over the chassis studying it. Steve picked up a twenty-five-pin plug and asked Red to look at it. "A bent pin?"

If so, this could explain the problem in translating computer commands to the controller and to the drives. Kevin brought a voltage-testing box over, and Steve used it to see if he was getting the five-volt signal down to the encoder.

"So, we aren't getting five volts to the encoder," Steve said, looking up from his test. "We have no diagram for this, so the first thing we should try to do is follow the four pins [of the encoder] up to the cable [that plugs into the computer]."

Steve pulled out some notes from a folder and spread them out on the chassis to try to figure out his wiring. "Shield is one, so let's get black lined up. A bad ground could make all the difference in the world." And that is what he found, a bad ground.

"I hope that's all it is," Steve said as he brought over a soldering iron. It was now 6:54 A.M., and Kevin left, saying he would be back in three hours. "I've got the five volts on A and B," Steve said to me, or perhaps it was to Terragator. "Four wires must make it up from the encoder carrying electricity, and except for the ground wire they were all there. So who knows? That might be it."

He resoldered the wire, cleaned up the excess solder, and plugged the connector in. He went to the terminal, typed in a command, and with anguish said, "Oh no! Still dead."

He tested the circuit boards built into a rack on the chassis and found that an amplifier was erroring out: "There's no logical reason for that unless it's the gain or the torque." With a screwdriver he tuned the adjustments for the amplifiers. "The encoder works. I've got a servo loading, which is good."

At 7:34 A.M. Red came in. He was still wearing the same shirt, tails hanging out, but he had added an old blue sweater with a hole in the right elbow. Red was now dressed for an early-morning class he taught. "You still want to try for today?" Steve asked.

"Yes," Red replied. "What time did Spencer Barrett leave last night? Pretty early, wasn't it? About midnight?"

"Yes."

"I'll call him. I'm disappointed for you that it didn't fall together, after all the crap you went through. But it *does* have to fall together. So I'll hit the phones."

Steve, who had an 8:30 calculus class and a 9:30 physics class, said, "I'll check back after a couple hours of classes."

At 7:55 A.M. Red hit the phones, got ahold of Spencer and said, "Pull it down. Separate everything from the harmonic drives, and after my class I'll take over."

At 8:05 A.M. Steve Berman and I left Porter Hall. As we walked outside, Steve said, "Remember when I first met you? I said all the work gets done in the middle of the night."

It was beautiful outside. The birds were singing. I hoofed it home.

*

When I returned four hours later, I nearly tumbled over to see Steve Berman out on the Cut with his beloved robot. There he was, proudly walking behind Terragator, the tiny American flag that Red had brought back from some mountaintop streaming from the top of the camera mast. From a distance it looked like a miniature parade. Visions of *Peter and the Wolf* came to mind—the grand finale with Peter and Birdy triumphantly parading the wolf to the zoo. Steve Berman, like Peter and Birdy, had shown appropriate boldness.

Chapter 5 ❧

THE COURSE OF
THE SHIP

AT THE TURN of the century, architect Henry Hornbostel, noted for his Beaux Arts style, with its ornate brickwork, arched windows, and vaulted entryways, designed the layout of Carnegie-Mellon's campus to resemble, in his words, "a ship headed toward knowledge." That concept remains today, with Baker and Porter halls forming the port side of the ship, Doherty and Wean the starboard side, the College of Fine Arts building the stern (with its small semicircular outdoor theater even providing the poop deck), and Hammerschlag Hall providing the bow, and Hammerschlag's magnificent portaled chimney serving as the ship's smokestack.

The ship was crowned with a special jewel when the U.S. Navy decommissioned the armored cruiser USS *Pennsylvania* in 1912 and donated to the school the *Pennsylvania's* seven thousand-pound bronze bow ornament. Just outside Hammerschlag a V-shaped masonry bulwark was built and the deeply scrolled ornament was put in place to bless the voyaging of a ship much grander and more significant than the old cruiser from which it came.

The bow was perfectly placed, built into a bank so that as the terrain fell steeply into Panther Hollow, the bow took on a greater height, and it looked as if the entire ship of a campus were ready to come emerging from that hillside and go sailing off into the future.

It was a cold and blustery day when I decided to go forward to the very peak of the bow. I climbed up onto the bulwark and edged my way out to the very front of the ship. The way the wind blew directly into my face, the great ship seemed to have a sense of motion, as if it were sailing onward in some sea of time at quite a rapid speed. Not far in the distance, jutting up like a lighthouse warning of danger was the University of Pittsburgh's 36-story Cathedral of Learning. From the bow it seemed as if the ship was nearly on a collision course with that safety beacon, and that as this juggernaut accelerated into some kind of robotic world, there should be someone posted as lookout to make sure that the course was clear and that all was well.

I could only remain on the bow for a few minutes. The wind was strong, it was cold, and I was on my way to see Robert Sekerka, dean of C-MU's Mellon College of Science, who spoke of going beyond our five senses to give robots perhaps as many as fifteen senses—things like X-ray vision, infrared perception, and a mini mass spectrometer for a nose. He also spoke of giving robots the ability to self-replicate, the ability to give birth to their own. And he said, "I believe man will learn to deliberately and artificially encode information on a molecular level and receive it. In other words, man will learn to build brains."

And when man learns to build brains, we will probably be able to download and become immortal, if somewhat mechanical, gods. As attractive as I found this idea, and as much as I wanted to explore the moon and planets and live forever, the DNA within me continued, now and then, to emit concern. I asked the dean if he had ever stood up on the bow of this ship, which he hadn't, and I told him about the possible collision ahead with the Cathedral of Learning. Two weeks later he still hadn't posted a watch.

*

From Dean Sekerka's office near the bow I headed aft to where the College of Fine Arts Building forms the stern. If evolution is preparing for another major step, if biological life is preparing to pass the torch of leadership to a more mechanical successor, then this building would serve as an icon of what had been left behind. The building, with its blend of Greek, Roman, Gothic, Renaissance, and Moorish architecture (Hornbostel designed into the front elevation a vaulted niche representing each era) is a celebration of Western civilization. The lobby floor has an inlaid plan of Rome's Saint Peter's Basilica. And the vaulted ceilings are painted with portraits of great philosophers, musicians, architects, and other builders of society.

On the third floor I found an art studio that had tall ceilings, a wealth of windows, and walls heavily hung with the work of students. There were drawings of youthful heads and muscular bodies, sketches of old hands, skeletal studies of arms and ribs, cityscapes, still lifes, and a pencil copy of M. C. Escher's one hand emerging from paper to draw another. Homesickness and the love of a dog were captured well in a black and white sketch of a forlorn young man sitting at a desk with pencil in hand, while above his head was a full-color daydream of a large yellow dog, bounding out of some memory, floppy ears brought beyond horizontal with excitement, the brown eyes bright and wide with love and recognition.

What most caught my attention, though, was a life-size portrait of a standing man. Done with pencil on paper, the man appeared to be perhaps forty years of age. He wore loose and rumpled dark trousers and a crewneck sweater with bit of a shirt collar showing. His hair had thinned quite a bit on top, and he had grown a mustache to compensate. It was a slight, modest mustache, the sweater showed some extra pounds, but not a lot. Yet all of this was just a setting, the foundation for what the drawing was all about—the eyes. For they shined with sincerity and also with intensity. There was just a trace of uncertainty, but mostly there was strength, and it was of the very best kind, strength without ferocity.

If the day comes when we can download and design our own bodies, and when robots evolve to have lives of their own, and when we are able to travel to distant planetary systems where other forms of life will have perhaps emerged, humans will find themselves competing against new pressures for the right to exist. This drawing made a strong case for our species. If it were hanging on the easel of a studio in some other realm, being offered as a possible design for a new form of life, I think it would shine forth in such a way that any sentient being could perceive it as having integrity, compassion, and the capacity for goodness, and would recommend that such a prototype be given a crack at life.

From two floors below, there came the sound of an orchestra rehearsing. I wanted to go see, but it took a while to break away from the portrait. I noticed that along the bottom of the drawing, in the area of the lower legs and feet, the creator of this otherwise realistic work had left the outline soft and hazy, drawing the baseboard of the wall so that it showed through. This gave the man an ethereal and spiritual quality, as if he were floating, as if he were some kind of holy ghost materializing briefly here to inspire people to be good and to do good. And so I looked again at this portrait of some modern-day saint and wondered who it could be, coming to the thought that it must be the artist's father and if so the painting would seem to be a greater statement of love and thanksgiving than any words could bring. I wanted to meet the artist. I wanted to meet the father.

*

Through the vaulted hallways and down the marble stairs, I followed the sound of music in search of its source. The student orchestra was in the Alumni Concert Hall, a performance room with six Corinthian pillars along the far wall to frame a stage, and a white sculpted ceiling that had the delicious texture of a deeply frosted wedding cake.

The conductor was Keith Lockhart, a faculty member who looked to be the same age as the students. He wore blue jeans and a gray rugby shirt, with the white collar tucked up with flair. He sang the rhythm to the musicians as he conducted with graceful gestures, and he seemed to be having quite a good time driving a vehicle so grand as an orchestra. After having submerged myself in things computational and robotic, everything in this building seemed so wonderfully zany and charmingly human. I sat down behind the four French horn players and studied how each held the right fist within the bell of the horn in such a different manner. I enjoyed the personalization and imprecision of the seemingly insignificant: With each player the tilt of the fist was different, as was the placement of the thumb across the fingers, the angle of the wrist, and the depth of the placement within the horn. How peculiarly human this instrument seemed, how enchantingly human seemed the desire to play it, and how nicely human was the overall attraction of the music as more and more people were drawn into the room to sit quietly and watch and listen.

The orchestra was rehearsing Jean Sibelius' Violin Concerto in D Minor, in preparation for a concert two days hence. They were working especially on the first movement, which draws on the beauty of the horns and woodwinds to help create the woodland landscape above which the violin solo soars. The violinist was Sangjun Shinn, a first-year graduate student who had spent fifteen of his twenty-three years trying to become one with the four strings of a violin just so that he could leap into and become part of such tapestries of emotion and sound.

Sibelius wrote his violin concerto in 1903, during the glorious days of the Edwardian Age, when one century had gracefully yielded to the next with such grand promise. It was from that optimism that the music flowed, for the concerto begins with a mysterious, haunting, and beautiful softness, even before the violin comes in with a magic that transcends to and then goes beyond even Gypsy notions of the romantic. The music seemed to talk about what might be, if only humans could continue their journey without slipping into madness. When Shinn concluded the first movement, his peers in the orchestra burst into applause, as did the conductor.

I would be concerned when, three months later in Japan, I met with researchers at Waseda University who had built a robot musician that represented the first step toward automating much, but not all, of what this young human had done.

*

From the College of Fine Arts Building I walked outside on a late Friday afternoon and saw three sleek racing carts being pushed along proudly by their builders. Since 1920 the annual racing of "buggies" has been a tradition of the school. The hills of the campus and adjacent Schenley Park provide plenty of gravity for what can be a grueling course, nearly a mile in length.

I joined in the parade to the testing area out on the Cut, as did several others, the buggies having rather a Pied Piper effect. Because of past accidents the buggies must pass a braking test, in which they are required to attain a certain minimum speed and then stop between two white lines painted cross one of the campus sidewalks.

The buggies are long, low, and lean. They are so small that nearly all are steered by women, who must cram themselves into entirely encapsulated spaces much smaller than a coffin. As I walked with the others to the brake-testing ground, I saw that one of the builders wore a T-shirt that in dripping letters said, "Just when you thought the horror was over—The return to the buggy hill." The presence of the buggies and the attendant humor guaranteed by a tradition in which not all buggies passed the initial brake tests, put drivers, builders, and onlookers into a merry mood. As more persons were drawn into the parade I wondered whether some future robot would, like so many of the humans, smile at the sight of the buggies? Would they join such a parade? Would some slip of a robot climb inside a buggy to drive, just for the thrill of it? Or would this break Asimov's Third Law of Robotics?

It was with deep envy that the young men standing around the Delta Tau Delta fraternity buggy looked up to see someone else's deep blue buggy skid to a straight, even, abrupt stop. Then they looked back down to their own green buggy, which had failed miserably. One guy got down on hands and knees to tell his freshman driver, Michele Osherow, the bad news that she had to try again. She could hardly hear what he said, her head was so totally encapsulated as she lay on her stomach just inches off the ground. "We hypothesize that you need to grab [the handbreaks] harder," he said with his best diplomacy. They wrapped her sore hands in bandanas as the diplomat said, "Those fingernails will have to go."

"No!" came a muffled but incensed reply from the cockpit end of the capsule. On the previous test they had placed someone on the sidewalk to tell her when to brake, in case she couldn't see the signal of the flagman. For the next test they had screamers on both sides of the walk. The buggy came down at a good clip and as the nose of it crossed the first white line, the young men screamed, "Brake!!!"

Michele hit the brakes, but the buggy went skidding madly off the walk and onto the grass. "I'm sorry! I'm sorry," she said as she got out. "I'm dizzy."

Then, after she crawled back inside, a second diplomat was sent to paint a new face on the situation: "This is it, babe," he said as he crouched on hands and knees, looking into the cockpit window, which was three inches off the ground. "Here goes our second try."

"It's our fourth!" said Michele, whose count coincided with mine.

On this run Michele started swerving even before the brake line. She nearly ran over the flagman and sent him running. And then, with a precision that bordered on deliberate, she changed her course and sent her diplomats and coaches flying. I was doubled over in laughter when from the corner of my eye I saw the next change of direction. The need for Asimov's First Law came to mind as I looked over my shoulder, midstride, to see that she was gaining.

*

It was nearly midnight, as it always seemed to be whenever I got anywhere near the office of Hans Moravec, and as I sat there laughing and talking with Hans and Mike Blackwell and Kevin Dowling, I thought about what Olin Shivers, a graduate student in the Robotics Institute, had told me about his decision to come to Carnegie-Mellon: "When I was considering grad schools, the amazing thing was that three different people who were totally unconnected with the school said people at Carnegie-Mellon are very happy." People at MIT and Stanford would tell me the same thing: Carnegie-Mellon is a happy place to be.

"Remember the *Prisoner* episode, when he goes over to the computer and types in 'Why?' and the computer blows up?" asked Kevin, referring to an old British television show that has a cult following among some hackers. "That's what I tried when I first got access to a computer. The only response I got was, "Syntax Error."

"I guess no one ever put it in," said Hans, "but a likely response would have been, 'Why Not?' Because with all of the PDP-tens [Digital Equipment Corp. mainframe], if you say, 'Make Love,' they respond, 'Not War?'"

Hans swiveled in his chair and typed into his terminal, MAKE LOVE. But there was no response. The Carnegie-Mellon network of computers is a large one, and Hans no longer makes use of the old PDP-10A.

"Mine's expired. Does somebody have an active account on this? I can't log in on the A anymore because I haven't in so long."

"Oh, you lose Hans," said a delighted Mike. In the world of hackers, where everything ultimately comes down to a Boolean one or zero, and where everything in a computer is based upon a switch being on or off, a gate being open or closed, there is little room for anything but black and white. Hence you win or you lose. Mike, who prides himself on having an account on every computer at C-MU, sat down at Hans's terminal and with mock seriousness chided Hans, "Don't you use the A every day?"

Mike looked up from the keyboard to say, "I think that's pretty good. I said, 'Make Love,' and it says, 'Log in, please.' We all cracked up. Mike logged in, tried it again, and sure enough the PDP-10 responded, NOT WAR? Then Mike typed in, HELP IBM. The computer's response: DO YOU MEAN THE INCESTUOUS BOWEL MOVEMENT?

*

On yet another late nighter the phone rang as I sat with Mike and Kevin in the office they share. Mike was sure it would be Kevin's wife and mimicked, "Where *are you*, Kevin!"

Kevin answered the phone, "Mobile Robots," and then, with the delight that could only come from hearing the voice of Mike's girlfriend, said, "Yes," and with exaggerated gestures handed the phone to Mike: "It's for you." Wanting to milk every ounce from the bounty of poetic justice he had just been blessed with, Kevin put on a falsetto voice and said, "Where *are you*, Mike!"

My sympathies extend to women who love men who love robots, yet there was great charm in watching these two burn through the night, just as I had admired the close workings of Steve Berman and Kai Lee. With the same passions shown by Sangjun Shinn for his music, and the same sense of fun shown by the builders of buggies, these hackers of hardware and software wanted to build robots.

It was like some early Robert Heinlein science fiction novel, the kind in which some kids scavenge around junkyards to build a moon rocket and, against all odds, actually go adventuring beyond Earth. And so it was here, as Happy Hans and the members of the Mobile Robotics Lab ate, slept, and dreamed about leaving their mortal lives behind, dumping their bodies, and building a robotic craft that would take their brains, and perhaps their souls, off on an eternity's journey. It was a long-shot chance, no doubt, but they saw it as being possible enough to stay here around the clock trying to hurry along the progression of robotic generations.

*

It is difficult to imagine anything holding back this quest. People like Hans and Red and Mike and Kevin are driven, and from earliest childhood have shown a need to open doors and discover the hidden.

Kevin walked into his office one night with a new toy, a video adapter for his Apple Macintosh. He handed it to Mike to examine, but there was nothing to see, since the circuitry was completely encased in a one-and-a-half-inch cube of soft synthetic rubber. Ostensibly this was to protect the circuitry, but Kevin and Mike suspected there was another reason for the encapsulation, and it was a reason they didn't like: secrecy.

"It needs to be taken apart," said Kevin as he picked up an X-acto knife. "We take everything apart that we get."

"Remember taking the Macintoshes apart?" said Mike. "We had to build a special tool just to get the back off."

With the care of a surgeon, Kevin cut into the silicone block and spread it apart. He was greeted by a smiling face imprinted on the circuit board. "User friendly," said Kevin as he turned the face over and began stripping the silicone from the other side of the circuit board.

At this point Mike said, "Let's send it back to them now and say it doesn't work."

With the circuit board exposed, the fun began: "This mulex connector is maybe fifty cents," said Kevin. "The D and C connector is probably a dollar in quantity. The seventy-four-one-twenty-three is the timing chip. And the seventy-four-oh-two takes two signals in, and if one of them is high, then the output is high."

"Ahh! The bread and butter of electrical engineering," Mike said of the circuit analysis.

"I'm kind of disappointed," said Kevin, who figured the cost for parts at perhaps ten dollars. "It should have more chips."

"For one hundred and fifty dollars, there should be more stuff in it than this," agreed Mike. But then he paused and added, "Well, you don't *need* more stuff."

"It looks like a bad soldering job," said Mike. Then taking a closer look, he said, "It's an awful job. Look how blobby and gross these are."

"Some of them are cold-solder joints," said Kevin. "It's not finely done."

"Someone's making a lot of money on this cheap piece of shit," said Mike with disdain yet humor. "The only thing you're paying for is this connector [which plugs into the Macintosh]."

"It's probably fairly difficult to get," said Kevin. "But once you know their *source!*"

This need to take things apart was something that was deeply engrained in Mike and Kevin and in so many of the other hackers I would meet. The first day Kevin owned a compact disk player, he took it apart.

Kevin once pulled out the six-page foldout circuitry diagram for his Sony D-5 compact disk player. "The CD player is an amazing conglomeration," he said. "It's awesome."

Explaining why he would take apart things as complex as a Macintosh or a Sony D-5, he said, "We take apart everything that we get. We want to see how they work and what they do. It's a lot of fun. And then, when we put them back together and have extra parts, we go, 'Wow! They didn't need these!' "

"We are better now," said Mike. "When we were young, we put things back together and they didn't work again. Now we can put them back together and they work, and we *still* have extra parts."

"In that way," said Kevin, "we make them more efficient."

*

We were having dinner one night in a packed Jimmy Tsang's Chinese Restaurant when the conversation turned to liberating the old Stanford Cart, the robot that Hans had spent so many years giving vision.

"We could bring him back and not tell Hans," said Mike, slipping into anthropomorphism. "We could set him up in Hans's office!"

"That's exactly what I was thinking," said Kevin. "It's in Margaret Jacks Hall on the fifth floor. Rod Brooks is out there now, isn't he? [Actually Brooks had just moved to MIT.] Rod would really go for it. I don't know if [Tom] Binford or [John] McCarthy would."

Mike, who had his own name for the Computer Sciences Building, which houses McCarthy's AI Lab and in which the robot is believed to be in attic storage, said, "I wonder if Hans still has the master key to Marginal Hacks. Then we could break in."

Kevin's wife, Mary Jo, was showing less and less enthusiasm as Mike and Kevin seemed to be getting more and more serious. "O yeah!" said Kevin. "How could we get the master from him without . . ."

"I don't know," said Mike. And then, laughing, he said, "He's always so proud of it, we could just ask to borrow it."

Kevin said they would have to work it out during the visit to the Bay Area that all three would soon be making.

Mary Jo announced she would be shopping that day.

*

Kevin long ago made a master key to fit every building at C-MU. Mike and Kevin blew up an oscilloscope one night as they sat in a campus parking lot trying to determine the electronic frequencies needed to break through an electronic gate. They bought a surplus card reader so that they could hack automatic teller machines at banks. Rather than any of this making them odd, it simply made them typical hackers. One of MIT's legendary hackers, Gerry Sussman, now a full professor, got so involved in hacking locks that he enrolled in a locksmithing school, a move frowned upon by other MIT hackers, who felt that actually becoming a *certified* locksmith carried too many legal burdens.

It is this disdain for locked doors, be they actual or societal, that frightens some critics of robotics and computer science. It is the fact that Hans Moravec has qualms about hobbling a robot with Asimov's Three Laws and that he can say, "I have no loyalty to DNA," that make some people fearful about just what doors these scientists will open. For it is difficult to imagine their ever wanting to stop. They are born door openers, they are the tomorrow makers.

And it is the seduction of making tomorrow that draws them together and provides such passion for their work. I asked Mike about downloading his mind into a robot, which is what the end result of so much of this work could be. Someone Mike's age, a person in his early twenties, might actually have some reason for optimism, some reason to dream eternal dreams. Mike may die before enough is learned about the brain to achieve a download. Yet there is that very enticing possibility, something that provides an incentive that can make one push around the clock. Mike is in a position to be among the first who succeed in escaping their bodies and achieving the ultimate gift of never having to die.

"When the time comes, I'll be ready," he told me once. "Bodies have served their purpose. I'm totally serious. Whether this will actually happen in my lifetime I don't know. But I'll do my best. And there are a lot of other people with similar goals in mind. We will all try. Somebody down the road is going to benefit from this."

*

On my last night at Carnegie-Mellon, Mike and I and his girlfriend, Lisa, crawled out a fourth-floor window in Hammerschlag Hall and climbed to its roof. The moon was nearly full, and Lisa had brought a telescope. As she set it up, Mike and I climbed to the top of the portaled chimney. There was a very narrow stairway that wrapped around the outside of the chimney with no railing on the outside. Built in a circle around the chimney was a tower with narrow, arched, open portals. It was all like something from a Roman Polanski *Macbeth* or an Escher drawing.

At the very top there was just the night sky, the moon, and the stars. We were now on the very highest point of Hornbostel's great ship headed for knowledge. Red Whittaker had told me about being "ferociously excited" about space. He wanted to build robots that could assemble great structures in space. Between payloads delivered by shuttle the robots could just tie themselves onto a beam and sleep. Dwight Sangrey, a C-MU professor of civil engineering, had also talked about sending robots into space and about the money that would be saved by not having to provide them with oxygen, food, and protection.

Mike just wanted to tag along for the ride. It did seem as though the robots were destined to have all the fun in space. Humans were too fragile, it cost too much to house and protect them. We will probably have a manned base on the moon someday, but it will likely be robots that will be sent up first to prepare a safe and hospitable place for us to stay.

There could be many different ways of doing this. The first and simplest would be to send one of Red's TMI vehicles into space. Microwave transmission could replace the tether, and the earthbound pilot and copilot could use the robot's cameras as their eyes and the robot's arms as their own, precisely duplicating through the robot each of their own moves at the control console. Mike was more interested in what would come next: doing away with the microwave link and placing the consciousness of the human operator into the onboard program of the robot—the *download.*

Mike and I talked of such things as we sat on top of the chimney. And being out there with just the stars and the Moon, it was easy to understand the willingness to leave your body if it meant you could leave Earth. With a properly outfitted robotic body you could walk the Moon and then occupy yourself by reading or sleeping as you spent years traveling between planets just to take a stroll across Mars. You could hole up in an asteroid for a century and read every piece of science fiction ever written. You could send a copy of yourself traveling beyond the solar system, just as we have already done with our *Pioneer 10* space probe, which flew past the orbit of Pluto and is now headed into the perhaps endless expanse of space.

After exploring the Moon and the planets, you might long again for the gentle blues and whites and greens of Earth. Returning to your home planet, you could spend centuries wandering field and stream, studying the forms of life that have emerged in nature. You could spend additional centuries digesting the knowledge of libraries. And in between you could visit those who could build for you ever newer and more intriguing bodies. Throughout all of this leisurely return home, you would have the security of knowing that if the human species again went insane, you had backup copies of yourself stashed away on other planets.

The previous summer I had taken two weeks off to crew on a sailboat race from the West Coast of Canada to Hawaii. One might wonder if downloading could be so complete that the joys that come from such an ocean passage could be fully appreciated by a mind housed within something other than a human body. Yet just a few weeks prior to coming to Carnegie-Mellon I had been sitting at a very long dinner table with about forty cancer specialists from the Johns Hopkins Oncology Center. When I told the doctor sitting across from me about the race across the ocean, describing the endless hours of sun, I mentioned in passing a little squiggle of skin on my chest that I hadn't noticed before the race. He could not let the comment slide and mentioned it to my host, who was the director of radiation oncology at Johns Hopkins. Two days later I was having a wedge of flesh cut out, just to be on the safe side.

The idea of downloading may seem sterile, dehumanizing, reprehensible, and ungodly, but as Mike and I sat on top of the chimney tower and looked into the stars, I was still waiting for the lab report to come back and was feeling rather biologically betrayed.

And then, when I looked at the Moon through the telescope, when I looked at its bright expanses, its craters and seas, and as I was taken in by its intoxicating otherworldliness, some words of Edgar Allan Poe came out of my core memory, came racing along some synaptic path, and merged with the general chemical-electrical cloud of my consciousness to say, " 'Over the Mountains of the Moon, down through the Valley of the Shadow. Ride, boldly ride, the shade replied,—If you seek for El Dorado.' "

And, sure, I wanted to ride. And whether El Dorado were to be found on the Moon or within our solar system or elsewhere in or beyond our spiral galaxy, I wanted to ride like a Red Whittaker messing with the Matterhorn. I wanted boldly to ride, all in search of El Dorado.

The physicist Freeman Dyson once wrote about sending massively nonaerodynamic structures into space. Dyson is not alone in fearing for the longevity of life on our gentle planet. Especially if life in the universe is at all rare, we must not leave all of our eggs in one nest. We've got to get off the planet and spread out into space. Dyson was saying we don't have time to perfect spacecraft, that for the survival of the species we have to get off the planet in a big way. He spoke of building a thick enough platform to protect the payload from the launching forces, then throwing massive structures, *buildings, warehouses* into space.

Hans and I had talked about light sails, the long-established idea of using square miles of ultrathin mylar that could be carried along by the photons of sunlight. We had also spoken of solar sails that could carry vessels in the solar winds.

As I stood on top of Hornbostel's ship, I wanted to get some Dyson boosters and blast the entire vessel out of its hillside, launching it into space. With the entire ship out there, Red Whittaker could fabricate the spars and sails, and we could silently glide from one world to another. If, during the voyage, we learned how to download, the first bodies might be no more than a Terragator, but with eternity to improve upon that beginning, we could putt-putt across the Cut, traveling from building to building, spending decades just within the College of Fine Arts at the stern, and then head forward to spend some time on top of Hammerschlag, standing a watch at the helm, mindful of Hornbostel's command to keep his great ship on a course that was headed toward knowledge.

Part II ❧

EDUCATING BABY

Chapter 6 ↝

IN THE LAND
OF OZ

Sɪᴅ Vɪᴄɪᴏᴜs, Jɪᴍ Morrison, Janis Joplin, Jimi Hendrix, Keith Moon, Elvis Presley, Buddy Holly: the rock-and-roll dead are immortalized within a windowless room on the seventh floor of 545 Technology Square, the building that houses the robotics and artificial intelligence laboratories at the Massachusetts Institute of Technology. The room holds specialized computers, called LISP machines, which are used for hacking artificial intelligence. On the front panel of each of the machines the name of a deceased rock star is spelled out in tiny red lights. Taped to the machines are irreverent clippings appropriate to each of the namesakes: a tabloid reporting Elvis reappearing from the dead, a photo of the wine-bottle vases that hold flowers at Jim Morrison's grave in Paris's Père-Lachaise Cemetery, a Mark Twain quote for the Who's Keith Moon: "Everyone is a moon, and has a dark side which he never shows to anybody."

Two floors up, there is a much more vast room of computers. Nearly the entire top floor of the building is given over to fields and fields of computers. There are so many Digital Equipment Corp. VAXes, each paired to a disk drive, that they look like rows and rows of washers and dryers at a Laundromat, only the Laundromat seems to sprawl around forever. The terrain of the landscape is broken only by the taller frames of the LISP machines and various mainframe bays. I have heard of computer scientists visiting from Japan, Europe, and, particularly, England, who are dumbstruck by the sheer wealth of the resources on this floor. They must also be struck by the casual attitude toward the resources. For if you follow the yellow brick road that has been carefully, brick-by-brick, painted onto the floor, you will come to the DEC System-20, named Oz, the mainframe that serves as the center of the building's huge network of smaller computers. There is a poster of Judy Garland as Dorothy taped to one panel. Above it hangs, suspended from the ceiling, a cardboard rainbow.

This was the land of Oz, and I had come in search of the progenitors of the computer brains that someday might be placed within robotic bodies. The best robotic bodies of the future may well emerge from Carnegie-Mellon, but MIT could just as well become the premier provider of the computers that would serve as minds for the robotic chassis. It was encouraging to see that whatever brains might someday emerge from here would likely have a sense of humor.

Back down on the seventh floor, across from the shrine of the dead rock stars, hanging from the wall between Marvin Minsky's corner suite and the office of Gerald Jay Sussman, was a wonderful piece of art, framed and matted and protected behind glass. Measuring about four feet by four feet, it was a color enlargement of a computer chip that Sussman and a former graduate student, Guy Steele Jr., had designed. The overall appearance was that of an aerial photograph of a tightly packed city with eighty thousand buildings. The buildings were transistors and the gridwork of streets was the circuitry linking them. As with many pieces of art, it is more beautiful when some of its story is known.

To appreciate what Sussman and Steele did, and to understand better the astonishing advances that have been made since the birth of the first general-purpose electronic computer forty years ago, it is helpful to consider the very simple building blocks upon which all computers are built: the 1 and 0 of the binary number system.

Rather than the base ten we are used to, the computer uses the base-two system, in which counting from zero to sixteen would progress like this: 0, 1, 10, 11, 100, 101, 110, 111, 1000, 1001, 1010, 1011, 1100, 1101, 1110, 1111, 10000. That might seem like a cumbersome way to count, but what makes the system ideal for computers is that the 1 and 0 can be translated into the flow of electricity, which is either on or off when a computer gate is either open or closed. Many of the computer scientists I spoke with during my travels had spent long hours of their childhood sitting at home workbenches wiring together telephone relays, euphoric over their ability to express a string of binary numbers as a string of relays that were either open or closed. For instance, the number ten, which would be written in binary as 1010, could be represented in a string of four telephone relays as: open, closed, open, closed.

Hans Moravec, who had dutifully donated his private collection of science fiction books to his junior high school library, had been ecstatic to discover books about Boolean algebra, which explained how to organize relays into circuits, so that the open-or-closed states of a string of relay positions could be acted upon either to add or to subtract the binary numbers represented by other strings of relay positions. Recalling his childhood devotion to binary numbers and old telephone parts, Hans told me, "Relays I had down pat. I could build anything with relays."

What was the magic of Boolean algebra? What secrets did Hans find in such books that could make him—as well as so many other young kids before and since—feel like such wizards? He had learned to create the three basic circuits of the computer: the NOT gate, the AND gate, and the OR gate. The NOT gate responds to a single input and basically reverses it. If you put a 0 into the gate, you get a 1 out—which is to say, the absence of an electronic pulse on the incoming side of the gate will result in the output of an electrical pulse. Conversely, if a 1 is put in, a 0 comes out. The AND gate has two inputs and one output. If both inputs are a 1, it responds with a 1. But any other combination of inputs, such as a 1 and 0 or a 0 and 0, will result in the output of a zero. The OR gate transmits a 1 if either one or both of its inputs are a 1. Otherwise, it responds with a 0.

These three simple logic gates can be combined to create an adding machine, and many things beyond. Today these gates, along with their many variations, can be combined in so many configurations upon a single chip that the bookshelves in a hardware hacker's laboratory sag and overflow with the telephone-book-size catalogs published by the chip manufacturers, such as Intel, Motorola, Texas Instruments, Fairchild, and National Semiconductor.

The same zeros and ones can be used to express letters as well. Just as the entire *Encyclopedia Britannica* could be spelled out in the dots and dashes of Morse code, the ones and zeroes of the binary system can be used to represent every letter in the alphabet as well as all marks of punctuation. Although computers are generally thought of as number crunchers, they can be word and logic crunchers too. John McCarthy's great contribution to artificial intelligence was his LISP language, which was developed specifically for expressing information in the words we use in everyday language.

But that is today. Part of the beauty of the Sussman/Steele chip design is to view it in the context of the not-too-distant clunky days of yore. For me, the most inspirational thing about that piece of art hanging on the seventh floor is that it represents such a staggering milestone. The changes have come so fast that the chip plan I was looking at was no longer state of the art, yet it still represented an accomplishment so great that not the wildest of optimists could have predicted its advent when the computer age dawned forty years before.

*

In 1946 the first modern computer, ENIAC (its proper name being Electronic Numerical Integrator and Calculator), was unveiled at the University of Pennsylvania's Moore School of Engineering. ENIAC had nineteen thousand vacuum tubes, which served as the off-on relays, or flip-flops, to represent numbers. A vacuum tube worked in much the same way as do the transistors in today's computers. Rather than the power of a computer actually going completely off and on, the ones and zeros of binary numbers are represented by a high voltage and a low voltage. Low voltage going into a tube won't be enough to bridge it and send a flow of power out the other side, so this is like a zero. A high voltage will pass through the tube, so this is a one.

ENIAC worked well, though it was rather a terror to keep running. It sucked an incredible amount of power to keep its tubes glowing. And these tubes created a tremendous amount of heat, which had to be drawn off. With nineteen thousand tubes to burn out, tracking down and replacing failures was a full-time job. The machine weighed thirty tons and filled a large room.

The computer chip that Sussman and Steele designed and had manufactured has eighty thousand transistors on it, each transistor providing the function of roughly one of ENIAC's vacuum tubes. The chip had vastly more computing power. In short, all thirty tons of ENIAC—and much more—had been condensed and placed on a chip of silicon that was a mere six tenths of an inch in length. All of this was on a piece of silicon which was so light that a breeze would blow it out the window and an ant could carry it away.

The first step toward such miniaturization came in 1947, when the transistor was invented at Bell Telephone Laboratories. This provided for an immediate slashing in size. The first transistors, which were cube-shaped, measuring about one third of an inch per side, looked impressively miniature when placed next to vacuum tubes. It was like a field mouse posing beside an Irish setter.

The transistor is made from silicon, which, as a semiconductor, has properties that are somewhere between being an insulator and being a conductor. The electric current of electrons flowing from a positive charge to a negative can pass through silicon, but it takes some effort—in the form of a higher voltage. This makes it wonderful material for creating a binary switch with no moving parts.

Thus entered the glorious era of solid-state transistors. However, the early transistors did have areas of vulnerability. At this point the transistors were being made much as they are today—with a lithography process in which layers upon layers of conductive, semiconductive, and insulative materials were thinly sandwiched together in something like a silk-screening procedure to create the gate structures. This was fine. But then the transistors would be cut apart from the wafers upon which they were mass-produced, and each transistor would be placed in a little metal shell for protection, with three thin wire legs sticking out. The transistors then had to be soldered into place, one by one, on circuit boards that had been printed with the wiring that connected the transistors. All of this assembly and soldering was expensive, and it created too many possibilities for human error and quality-control problems. Even with perfect assembly and soldering, the transistors stood out from the circuit board, leaving them vulnerable to all sorts of nasty traumas.

From a manufacturing standpoint there was so much to be gained by streamlining the process and the product that it isn't surprising that Jack Kilby at Texas Instruments and Robert Noyce at Fairchild Semiconductor independently came up with the same brainstorm in 1959 to change the lithography process to create several different kinds of transistors on the same chip, while at the same time laying down the circuitry that united them. The integrated circuit had been born, and since its birth there has been an ever-escalating race to place more and more, ever-smaller transistors onto a chip.

Today more than a million transistors can be placed on a chip. The analogy of the field mouse and the Irish setter has become one of a flea standing beside an elephant—an elephant ninety feet tall.

*

I was at the MIT Model Railroad Club one night, climbing under the tables of the immense HO-gauge layout, trying to do salvage on a trainwreck that had just occurred outside the community of Valium Plains (the train had gotten too laid back, we figured, and just slumped off the tracks) when I noticed an old PDP-6 sitting under the table being used to control the track switches in the toy trainyard!

It isn't just ENIAC that has been left in the distant dust. I knew this, yet to really understand it, I had to happen upon a six that had been relegated to services far beneath its former glories. For not too long ago Digital's PDP-6 was the very heartthrob of the MIT Artificial Intelligence Laboratory. Introduced in the early 1960s, the PDP-6 was considered such an awesome machine that grad students would eat and sleep in the lab just so that they would never be too far away from this machine that they were trying to make think. It was on a PDP-6 that Hans Moravec would mind-meld for hours and days and weeks at a time during his graduate-school days at SAIL.

The PDP-6 even figured into one of the parodizing AI Koans, or Zen instructional stories, that Danny Hillis of Thinking Machines had written while at MIT:

In the days when Sussman was a novice, Minsky once came to him as he sat hacking at the PDP-6.

"What are you doing?" asked Minsky.

"I am training a randomly wired neural net to play Tic-Tac-Toe."

"Why is the net wired randomly?" asked Minsky.

"I do not want it to have any preconceptions of how to play."

Minsky shut his eyes.

"Why do you close your eyes?" Sussman asked his teacher.

"So the room will be empty."

At that moment, Sussman was enlightened.

There are several yardsticks to use in measuring the capabilities of a computer, one of which is the size of the random access memory, or RAM.

The random access memory is the place where the central processing unit stores the strings of one-zero information that are being worked upon. With a small RAM, a great amount of time is spent shuttling information into RAM from the storage memory—be it a floppy disk, hard disk, or tape drive. The central processing unit works on this small chunk and then has to send it back to storage memory and bring in the next chunk.

It's kind of like writing labels on jars of peaches and pears that you've got stored in a basement without lights. You could pick up four jars, carry them up to the kitchen where you had sufficient light to examine the contents, and label the jars. Then you would return the four jars to your main storage in the basement and bring another four up and place them on the random access memory of your kitchen table, where your central-processing-unit fountain pen would write upon the labels. Then you would repeat the process over and over again, and it would soon become apparent that nearly all your time was being spent in shuttling back and forth between your main storage in the basement and the RAM of the table. A larger RAM would allow you to bring the jars up by the boxload, and with still larger RAM you could bring the entire fruit cellar into your kitchen.

The PDP-6, which had thirty times the bulk of one of today's personal computers and looked impressive in its large cabinets, representing the state of the art for the mid 1960s, had only 40K (K representing 1,024 bytes of one-zero information) of random access memory. This compares with the 128K I have in my already aging personal computer, and with the 512K you can get in an off-the-shelf Apple Macintosh. As impressive as 512K may seem, this figure can be more than doubled in personal computers by just plugging in additional RAM chips.

Seen in this light, the question shifts from how could the PDP-6 be used for such a lowly task at the Model Railroad Club, to one of how was so much accomplished on such a limited tool. The answer comes down to abstract forces such as love and devotion, as well as a lot of patience.

For years computers have been referred to as *mainframes* for machines such as the largest IBM units, *minicomputers* for the PDP-6s and the more contemporary DEC VAX family, and *micro,* or *personal computers,* for units such as the Apples and IBM PCs. But in recent years the distinctions have become blurred and will only continue to do so. (Indeed, one MIT computer science grad student said he wouldn't want to have to describe the difference between a mainframe and mini on a test, and Hans Moravec said simply that a mainframe is anything you can't carry out of a room.) Personal computers now have computing power that was once the domain of mainframes.

And the next round of personal computers will further blur the lines of demarcation. Intel's 80386, a chip developed for personal computers, will have the capacity to address a stunning 4 billion bytes of random access memory. And it will be able to do this with impressive speed. I can recall times at Carnegie-Mellon when a late-night user would be delighted to find he had an entire VAX 11/780 mini-mainframe computer to himself. And all for good reason, because the VAX is a powerful research tool that has far more power than what many older, but still-in-use, room-size mainframes might have. Yet the new Intel 80386 will provide a central processing unit for personal computers that has very much the same power as the heart of the VAX.

When these machines come out, and when the ante is, soon after, raised and the next round of personal computers come out, it will mean that the next generation of Hans Moravecs, Marvin Minskys, Gerald Jay Sussmans, and John McCarthys will be playing not with telephone relays but with virtual mainframe computers. Some stunning things are expected to come from this.

*

It was 11:30 on a Friday night. A graduate student was using Gerry Sussman's office, so Sussman and I went into Marvin Minsky's. Both Sussman's and Minsky's offices open onto a carpeted lobby area of the seventh floor called the Playroom. The floor plan is that of a doughnut: Offices ring the perimeter of the building, and the windowless computer room and home for dead rock stars occupies the core. This core provides room at the Minsky-Sussman end for the Playroom, which has davenports, chairs, and coffee tables arranged in various conversational groupings. The Playroom serves to get researchers out of the isolation of their offices and into the conversations that provide the cross-fertilization of ideas from which science has always grown. It also provides a moral boost for working around the clock: No matter the day or hour, you are never alone. For a research environment, it seems a brilliant, if obvious, design feature. Yet I saw nothing like it at Carnegie-Mellon (save for the office of Hans Moravec and the labs of Red Whittaker). And in Stanford's Marginal Hacks Hall there was only a ghost of a playroom, the deficiency being that it was a separate entity, the offices didn't spill out onto it, only corridors and a stairway.

Some of the children who are already playing with computers far more powerful than the PDP-6, upon which Sussman gained fame as a hacker of artificial intelligence, may someday find themselves in the Playroom at MIT, or the one in Stanford's Marginal Hacks, or hanging out until all hours with Hans Moravec at Carnegie-Mellon. You can just tell that Sussman loves the idea of kids playing on bigger and bigger computers. And if they learn enough, if they persevere, the researchers such as Sussman, Minsky, John McCarthy, and Hans Moravec will be eager to try to teach them all that they have learned, with the hope that their students can learn from what they have done and then launch themselves to greater heights.

I have spent many years closely associated with academic and clinical researchers in science and medicine, and I have never found a field where so much faith was placed in the young, where the willingness to accept and cultivate even off-the-street talent was so complete.

Gerry Sussman showed up at MIT as a brilliant sixteen-year-old kid who wanted to hack computers. Marvin Minsky had created a free and open environment at the AI Lab, which enabled people like Sussman to flourish.

Sussman is repaying this debt in spades, proving to be one of the most inspiring teachers in the field. The first time I met Sussman he was just getting ready to lie down on his office floor for a one-hour rest before continuing his preparation for a class the next day. He had already worked straight through the previous night. And this was an introductory-level class he had been teaching for several years. Rather than just run with what he had done before, Sussman was in constant overdrive to find new ways to inspire and enlighten.

Jonathan Rees, a graduate student who came to MIT from Yale, said that Sussman "basically inspired all the good ideas in the project I did at Yale. Talking with him for an hour every six months was enough to keep me going for three years. He's great."

David Vinayak Wallace, also known as Gumby, had entered the AI Lab in much the same way Sussman had. Minsky had created an open-door policy toward high school students who just wanted to jump onto a computer and hack. Gumby was one of those and he started dropping in on Minsky to talk theory. When I was there, Gumby was still an undergraduate, but he already had a seventh-floor office to use as an operations base for his all-night efforts.

Sussman's dedication to his students is reciprocated. "It was great," said Gumby of the introduction-to-computing class that Sussman teaches with Hal Abelson. "Sussman is very enthusiastic. He really knows the material. It's clear he's thought a lot about it. And part of it was he built the course. You could tell he was really into the subject, that he really loved it. And he had all of these great examples. I've heard people say he goes too fast. That may be true. I already knew the material before I took the course. But I think he's an excellent explainer, and that's the critical thing."

At MIT the mechanical-engineering majors call themselves gearheads, while the electrical engineering students proudly take the title of nerds. After being at MIT for a while, the term *nerd* takes on a higher and less derogatory meaning, though one not too far from the core of its original meaning—"intelligence."

If some children are harassed for their intelligence in junior high or high school, if they have more brain capacity than they know what to do with, if they are like Mike Blackwell at Carnegie-Mellon, who would give the wrong answers in grade school just to be more like his classmates, then there might be an awkwardness that translates into something called nerd. But just as a golden retriever puppy will in time grow into his oversize feet, there is a great beauty in seeing young hackers grow into their intelligence.

The introductory class that Sussman and Abelson teach is required of all students entering the Department of Electrical Engineering and Computer Science. There were only two grades for the class: pass or fail. This is so that students not majoring in computer science can take the class without worrying about wrecking their grade point average. One time when Gumby and I went over to the campus all-night coffee shop at about three in the morning, we ran into one of Gumby's friends, who recalled having been exasperated by Sussman's principaled refusal to tell him what his grade would have been.

Gumby offered a solution: "When I took it in my freshman year, I got all of my problem sets back, all of my quizzes back, and . . ."

"You were a *nerdly* nerd!" his friend said in disbelief. "You collected all your problem sets?"

"That's me," said Gumby. "I'm a nerd. Not as proud a one as Sussman, but I'm a nerd."

*

Earlier that same evening Gumby had told me, "Gerry might be a little too intense for a lot of people on a first impression. He looks like he's just had six double espressos. I imagine that he wakes up in the morning that way too, because I've never seen him not be really intense. I think being intense might be a general problem at MIT, and he's very MIT. He's very enthusiastic about it. He loves the place. He's a self-described nerd. He says to me, 'Why do you guys talk about sex and drugs and all these irrelevant things? You should be doing more research.' "

*

When Sussman and I sat down in Minsky's office for a late-night conversation, he was drinking cranapple juice from the seventh-floor vending machine. But Gumby's double espresso would have fit him better. He is intense, but in a fascinating way. His intellectual pursuits range from the very small world of the computer chip to measuring the diameter of galaxies. As we spoke, a parallel-processing computer he had built with Yekta Gürsel, with parts donated by a chip manufacturer, was running a simulation of the orbital disturbances of all nine planets in our solar system.

Sussman has longish brown hair that curls back thickly, making the temples seem broader, and he wears rectangular wire-frame glasses. On Friday night he was wearing jeans and a short-sleeved shirt, the pocket of which carried his ever-present nerd pack, which contained seven pens and a metal ruler. He also wears the MIT "Eager Beaver" ring, more frequently called the brass rat. He looks like the kind of guy who would have a self-assembled Heathkit terminal at home, which he does.

It is a measure of his devotion to teaching that despite the many research projects he has under way, it is to his students that he so frequently returns. "There are much more creative things in life than making a VLSI chip," he said. "The most creative and most difficult thing I do is to explain the organization of your thinking processes to an undergraduate at MIT so that the undergraduate becomes better at thinking.

"I like to teach, and it's one of the things I do a great deal of. What I see as being my job is teaching people not particular things for some job they will have someday, but teaching them how to think so that they can do anything they want to do. What I mostly discover is that the difference between people who think very well and clearly and people who don't think very well and clearly but have the potential to do so is a bit of knowledge, only a little bit of knowledge, about how to organize their thoughts. So I put a great deal of effort into developing classroom material, developing examples and whole subjects, where the goal of the subject is to help students become organized."

The work of the teacher has always been like that of the person who plants trees and provides the extra care that is required until the roots can grow sufficiently deep to tap into their own sources. "You're exactly right," Gerry said when I suggested the parallel. "There's certainly a great deal of investment, and you watch these students grow up into interesting people. And a lot of them turn out to have ideas related to the ones I had, and that means those ideas have some life to them.

"But I don't really think of myself in that way." Sussman paused and then took it back. "Yes I do! I think of myself as influencing the people who are the future controllers of the world. They control the destiny of technology and in many ways they therefore control the destiny of the world."

*

A few days before, while sitting in the same office, but on the other side of the desk, I had listened to Marvin Minsky speak of graduate students in a way I had never heard, especially from a professor, especially from a professor of Minsky's stature. He was speaking of them as constituting rather an intellectual jury, and Minsky was concerned about whether his theories on artificial intelligence would be adjudged worthy of pursuit by future grad students.

And now Sussman was hitting upon this, too, as he spoke of his ideas gaining some life when his students found them worthy of pursuing on their own.

A month later at Stanford, John McCarthy, another of the founding fathers, and a former student of Minsky's, echoed the same belief and its attendant fears. "Minsky and I would each of us liked to have been the Isaac Newton of AI, but it may turn out that we'll be the Isaac Barrow," McCarthy told me. "Barrow was Newton's teacher. But it can't be said that Newton carried out Barrow's plan, because Newton was of course vastly stronger than Barrow.

"Minsky is overoptimistic if he thinks that his *Society of Mind* book is going to be the plan that some Newton will carry out. The Newton may get some good out of Minsky's book, but Minsky won't get any more credit than Isaac Barrow got. You could look in there and say, 'Yes. Isaac Barrow did discover how to take the tangents of some curves, and he did point Newton at the problem of taking tangents of curves. But Barrow didn't have even the faintest idea that there was something like calculus to be invented."

Yet it was Newton who said, "If I have seen further it is by standing upon the shoulders of Giants."

When I told Sussman about my conversation with Minsky, and about his concern over whether anyone might find his ideas worth carrying forward, Sussman said, "What is the power of a professor? The power of a professor is to influence the next generation, to make more people like him. You realize that a parallel can be drawn between the academic world and evolution. The good ideas are the ones that attract a lot of students and therefore survive. A really good idea is one that sort of gobbles up a lot of people, that gets a lot of people working feverishly on it. And there is competition among the ideas for students. I think Minsky has got a good chance of having influenced more people than almost anybody I know in the computer world. Just take the number of heads of departments of computer science that are Minsky students."

*

While at Carnegie-Mellon I had been so impressed by the full-size portrait of a man I had seen in a studio in the College of Fine Arts Building that three days later I had returned to the studio in hopes of learning more about it. What a jolt it was to see that man off the paper and walking around. His name was Herb Olds. A professor of art, the drawing had been done by a former student, Steven Palmer. "I had never seen the portrait until he unveiled it," Olds told me. "I keep it here to show students what they can achieve."

The framed enlargement of the Sussman and Steele chip served the same purpose. During my weeks at MIT I would hear several retellings of the project from graduate students, who took pride in knowing that such an awesome project had been hacked by Sussman and a few of his students during six fervent weeks of everyone burning on over-drive. The favorite story was about how when it came time to verify the wiring runs of the chip, all the furniture in the Playroom was moved out so that Sussman, Steele, and an MIT staffer named Jack Holloway, could cover the floor with their circuitry diagrams. Each sheet was about eight feet by ten feet, and several sheets were required. For two days and nights professor and students crawled over the drawings, labeling the wires with pencil and making sure that all of the connections were right.

Trying to figure the placement of eighty thousand transistors and the circuitry that links them on a chip of silicon is like etching the entire street system of Manhattan onto the head of a pin. It takes a lot of design knowledge to do this. Sussman, as a faculty member, took a class in VLSI (very large-scale integrated circuit) design in 1978. And when a similar class was taught the next year, he made sure Guy Steele was in it.

The two most prominent researchers in VLSI architecture are a team that have worked together for more than a decade: Lynn Conway, a research fellow at Xerox Corporation's Palo Alto Research Center in California; and Carver Mead, the Gordon and Betty E. Moore Professor of Computer Science and Electrical Engineering at the California Institute of Technology. In 1979 Lynn Conway came to MIT as a guest professor and taught a class on VLSI design. Just her teaching of this MIT class has since become a recognized milestone in the field. In September Conway taught her methodology for designing VLSI chips. In October and November the students created their own designs. And six weeks later each student was given a finished product from their design—Conway having persuaded Hewlett-Packard to run the chips through their Palo Alto processing lab.

"I talked one of my graduate students, Guy Steele, into taking the course because I knew it would be fun," Sussman said. "He made a very primitive prototype, though it was the biggest chip project on the class run. And that sort of gave us some confidence. So then Guy said, 'Gee, we can really do this. Let's do a big one.' So we did."

Four years earlier Steele and Sussman had written their own dialect of John McCarthy's AI language LISP, so they decided to design a chip specifically for processing programs written in their language, which they had called Scheme. Jack Holloway, an MIT staffer at the time, joined the effort, and six weeks later the chip was complete.

This represented a particularly heroic endeavor in that, at the time of their work, computers were already being programmed to automate much of the design work. The more complex VLSI becomes, the more computers are needed to find the most efficient layouts and circuitry runs. Today computer-aided design is so much a part of VLSI that it is doubtful that another major chip will be designed without one. The Scheme chip may represent the last to emerge from the efforts of hackers working on their own in wraparound shifts, in which days become nights and then flow back into days.

It wasn't John Henry versus the steam-spike driver, it was merely a period of transition. And today designing such a chip without computer design assistance would be quixotic and pointless. Yet perhaps there is some John Henry in it, for those at MIT take great pride in this finely crafted bit of silicon.

Computer-aided design is a first step toward the evolutionary point where computers will be doing the complete design. It is at this point that the growth in computing power that has already been so overwhelming should soar beyond what humans will be able to comprehend. At this point we will have to hope that Asimov's Three Laws, and a general loyalty to humans, have been so deeply programmed into the machines that the traits can survive the rapid surge of generations.

It was a few months later that the chip was actually built, this time courtesy of Xerox PARC. While waiting for the chip to come back, Sussman's group built a circuit board for testing their creation. The day the chip arrived at MIT, Sussman was in Austin presenting a talk at Texas Instruments about the Scheme chip. It was plugged into the test board and run through the paces. Jack Holloway telephoned Texas Instruments in time for Sussman to conclude his talk with the good news: The chip worked.

*

One night Jonathan Rees showed me some of the papers that Guy Steele and Gerry Sussman had written for publication in computer science journals and on which Sussman was listed as a co-author. As is common on research papers there was an asterisk after Steele's name referring the reader to a footnote acknowledging his source of funding. Steele was a Fannie and John Hertz Fellow. But most unusual, and quite charming, was the set of asterisks after Sussman's name with which Steele identified Sussman as a Jolly Good Fellow.

Then Rees pulled a copy of Guy Steele's thick Ph.D. thesis from a shelf and read this acknowledgment: "Gerald Jay Sussman, advisor, colleague, friend, who has prodded me when I was stuck, encouraged me when I was depressed, enlightened me when I was blind, complimented me when I was actually working well, and who is generally a jolly fellow to be around; he cares about his students. He originally inspired nearly all the good ideas in this dissertation."

"It's true, too," Rees said. "He's that kind of guy."

It will be years before Minsky and Sussman can see the different ways in which the trees they have planted will take root and grow. But perhaps the single biggest advancement in computer technology since the creation of ENIAC will come to fruition soon, under the guidance of Danny Hillis, who came out of MIT wanting to create a computer that had a structure more closely resembling the human brain.

In the process of developing this computer, upon which his Ph.D. thesis for Minsky and Sussman will be based, he founded a company, appropriately called Thinking Machines.

Rather than creating a single central processing unit with a million or more transistors on it, Hillis wants to distribute the computing power, linking 64,000 simple processors into a network that would resemble the awesome power the brain derives from its billions of simple processors—the neurons.

If Hillis's "thinking machine" actually works, it could be the most important thing to emerge from the land of Oz since Dorothy, and it could mean that someday a computer labeled Jim Morrison or Janis Joplin might contain more than the name.

Chapter 7 ∾

ROBOTIC VISIONS OF TIGERS AND LADIES

FROM THE SIXTH floor sundeck of Thinking Machines Corporation, I could look out across the Charles River, only a block away, and see the Harvard Bridge and the skyline of Boston. Or, looking ten feet the other way, through the floor-to-ceiling lunchroom windows of Thinking Machines, I could see a meeting in progress but could not hear what was being said. I was under a rather congenial house arrest, exiled to the deck by a security-conscious executive who didn't want me to hear what was happening at the scientific meeting inside.

Gee, I thought, this isn't very hospitable! But the sky was clear, the day was warm, and there was a gentle breeze. I have crossed the demarcation line between academia and business before, but it always gives me a jolt. The flow of information within a university is so free and easy. Five researchers at four different universities would entrust me with complete or partial manuscripts of books they still had in the works. Gerry Sussman's only request in exchange for access to his time was that I learn how to program in LISP, and this just represented his concern for my soul—that I might not die without first having known the joy of pushing instructions through a computer.

Yet, I could understand the concern for secrecy. William Paley, former chairman of the board of CBS had, along with some other wealthy investors, bankrolled Danny Hillis because of their bottom-line belief that he could create a *thinking* machine. If they are right, it should create the most explosive development since the creation of ENIAC. There would be a fortune to be made, but only if they could know something that others didn't.

*

Paley and company aren't alone in their faith in Hillis. At MIT, belief in Hillis and the connection machine runs high. Hillis conceived

82

of the idea while at MIT, and though he had been away from school for nearly two years creating his company, he was still a Ph.D. candidate, and his advisors, Sussman and Minsky, were expecting him one of these days to drop off his connection-machine thesis. In addition to being given high marks for brilliance and an easygoing manner, Hillis has also developed a reputation for having a good feel for business—he created Terrapin, Inc., while still at MIT, a company that markets a LISP-like language called Logo, which was created to help children learn how to program.

The excitement for the connection machine, and other projects like it, comes from the fact that although there have been huge advances in computer technology since ENIAC was turned on in 1946, there haven't been many changes in the basic design of the computer. They are still based upon a central processing unit, memory, and various input-output devices to shuttle the information around.

You could take the block diagrams and instruction sets for ENIAC and, without too much change, use them to describe the most powerful of the present-day sequential computers. This is to say that although a brand-new Ferrari might be terribly faster than a Model A Ford, they remain very much members of the same family. The connection machine would represent an entirely new way of travel, it would be as different from current computer architecture as stepping from a Model A into a jet airplane, or perhaps into an antigravity machine.

Recent decades have seen dramatic growth in our ability to place more and more transistors onto a single chip, and this has resulted in the extremely fast and powerful central processing units and memory chips. But one thing that hasn't changed since ENIAC is that instructions must still pass through the single central processing unit one at a time. The reason that such sequential computers can be so fast is that the VLSI designs have slashed the distances that the electronic streams of binary bits must travel. The rest time between work cycles has been similarly reduced. The result is that millions of instructions can be sequenced through the machine each second.

But this isn't how the human brain works. If it were, we would have one very powerful brain cell that served as our central processing unit. And we might have a few additional magnum-size cells to serve as random access memory, disk storage, and as busses to link them together. Instead we have billions of brain cells (estimates range from 10 to 100 billion) that are linked into a network that offers a staggering number of possible connections. The brain cells serve as both processors and memory. It is this kind of distribution of processing power and memory that the connection machine is trying to duplicate. At the time I spoke with Hillis, Thinking Machines had built a prototype computer for the military that had 64,000 processing units wired together in a network.

The whole idea of the connection machine is that there are so many processing units, each with a modest amount of memory, that the individual unit needn't have great power. If you were responsible for delivering mail in a city, it would be more efficient to have 64,000 small jeeps for the letter carriers to buzz around in than it would be to have one humungus vehicle that was 64,000 times larger than any jeep the world had ever known. Thus, the beauty of the machine that Danny Hillis and William Paley believe will someday be able to think.

This kind of distributed computing power is called *parallel processing*, in that a great number of small calculations are being done simultaneously, or in parallel, as opposed to the sequential processing of information in a conventional, or *serial*, computer. The brain is said to be massively parallel. The connection machine might not be massively parallel in comparison to the brain, but the next machine on Hillis's drawing boards, the one to follow the prototype, called for a network of more than a quarter of a million processors. It is against this backdrop that Marvin Minsky, who is a cofounder of Thinking Machines, could dismiss even the most powerful of the conventional sequential computers by saying, "Where we are now *is* ENIAC."

*

Minsky is not alone in his disdain for sequential architecture, nor in his enthusiasm for what parallel processing might allow. In 1982 the Japanese government announced its Fifth Generation program to build intelligent computers. (The first four generations are seen as vacuum tubes, transistors, integrated circuits, and VLSI circuits.) The backbone of their new generation is supposed to be parallel architecture and programming that exploits the attendant opportunities.

The Western world began shaking at the thought of Japan doing to the future world computer markets what it had done to automobiles and consumer electronics. There was much economic saber rattling in the United States, and before the end of 1982 the Microelectronics and Computer Technology Corporation (MCC) had been created as a research and development consortium funded by corporations with the most to lose from Japanese dominance, companies such as Digital Equipment, Motorola, National Semiconductor, Advanced Micro Devices, Honeywell, Martin Marietta, and Bell Communications Research.

Rather an eerie glow was associated with MCC from the very beginning, because its president was Bobby Ray Inman, retired admiral, former director of the National Security Agency, and former deputy director of the Central Intelligence Agency. Meanwhile similar projects have been launched in Great Britain, Europe, and the Soviet Union.

Clearly there is a lot of interest in parallel computing, and from all that I had seen and heard, it appears that Danny Hillis and Thinking Machines have a good shot at being the first and the best to get to the heart of the matter.

*

After I had seen enough of the Charles River and the Hancock Building, I walked over to the windows to see if I could spy any familiar faces. Tom Poggio, professor of psychology at MIT, was present, which wasn't a surprise. Poggio studies mammalian vision systems, in the hope of finding some way to translate into computer code whatever signals it is that the eye sends to the brain. It is widely thought that the signals involved would be of such huge numbers that it would take a massively parallel system to provide the kind of instantaneous translation of the signals the brain provides.

A week earlier I had spent time with Tomas Lozano-Perez talking about just that problem. Lozano-Perez, an associate professor of computer science at MIT, was ten years old when he left Cuba in 1962. Lozano-Perez's parents didn't want their son to attend the indoctrination classes that Castro instituted in the schools after the revolution, so they moved to another town and hid him until they could arrange for his emigration, which they were later able to follow.

Lozano-Perez was educated in Catholic schools in Puerto Rico, and a group of nuns from Boston had brought with them literature about MIT. From a very early age Lozano-Perez's answer to the ever-pressing question of youth, 'What do you want to do?' was "Go to MIT." This he had done.

In the early days of AI, when computer scientists were able to put together programs to enable computers to do math and play checkers and chess, it was thought that complete intelligence would be just around the corner. But what they found was that the most difficult things to program were the "commonsense" ones like general understanding and vision, the basic building blocks that are taken for granted.

"It's the stuff that snails and dogs can do that's hard," Lozano-Perez told me. "That's the stuff that took evolution a gazillion years to do. Chess is particularly easy to program, because it's only since historic times that we can do that. That's got to be easy. It's swinging from the trees that is hard. A monkey swinging through the trees—the amount of computation it takes to do that makes a Cray [the world's fastest supercomputer] look rather paltry.

"In fact that's what you find. The history of AI is sort of the history of evolutionary regression. That is, the earliest AI programs were for chess and calculus. And we're trying to work back toward common sense.

"The stuff that's hard is common sense, vision, moving your arms. We don't know how we do it. You have to learn chess, so there's some hope that whoever explained it to you could possibly explain it to a computer. But you *don't* know how you learned to walk. Nobody taught you that. And a dog can do it. Or a snail. So that means it's very hard. You have evolved all that hardware, which is optimized to do it.

"Most of your brain is devoted to making you act like a monkey," Lozano-Perez said. "It's only the sort of very thin veneer around it that makes you act like a human. The difference is almost insignificant as far as your brain is concerned."

So complex is the eye, so rich in specialized nerve cells, that it is considered an extension of the brain. The magnificence and complexity of this system is so great that in many ways it remains a puzzle unsolved. In the most basic of terms each of your eyes has a lens that focuses light on the retina, which covers the back wall of the eye. The retina is covered with some 125 million receptor cells, called rods and cones. The light that falls upon these receptors has been changed in intensity by whatever objects it was reflecting from in the outside world. If you were looking at a basketball, the intensity of the light being reflected off it would vary with the curve of the sphere as well as with the way it struck the tiny dimples that make up the ball's rough texture.

Just how 125 million separate receptors are able to process the information from only their portion of this light show, and then report and collate their findings with the rest of the receptor community, and then send a report of it by way of the optic nerve to the brain, remains a mystery. The mystery only deepens when one ponders how the brain is able to read this message, which is relayed by way of one nerve cell basically sending an on/off message to another. It's obviously a system that nature spent a long time developing.

"The sensitivity of the eye is amazing," said Lozano-Perez. "The vernier acuity of what you can separate at two different depths is really, truly outstanding. The resolution and range and scope of it! The *speed* at which you can recognize things.

"You open a door and you don't know anything about what's behind it. Aha! A tiger! Aha! A lady! Instantaneously. In so short a time. In microseconds. It just doesn't seem possible when you start looking at the sequence of operations that have to go on in order to go from this changing pattern of light falling onto the lenses of your eyes to what's going on behind it. It's staggering!

"The more you know about it, the more amazing it looks. Because just trying to do the simplest vision processing on a computer takes forever. You have to build special-purpose hardware to do anything. Its overwhelming, overwhelming. The sheer computation involved! Even if we understood all the basic principles, which we don't, the computations involved are amazing, *overwhelming.*

"Most people's model of sensing is Descartes's model of the homunculus in the back of the brain, a little man sort of looking through there and saying, 'Aha! I see what's out there.' But the problem is that we have to build seeing out of a set of components that do not see. Any little piece doesn't do anything by itself.

"A little joke that we tell in computer vision is if you try to explain to somebody why computer vision is hard, they will say, 'Boy! How is computer vision even possible!' And then you say, 'Well, we start out by hooking a TV camera to the computer,' and they say, 'Aha! I see how it works now.' And of course you haven't described a damned thing, unless you assume that there is a homunculus inside the computer that is sort of looking through the camera and saying, 'Oh, I see!'

"The only thing that the computer sees is a bunch of numbers. You have this pattern of numbers: 142, 165, 172, 182, and what those numbers reflect is the quantity of light falling on some little piece of the camera. Now you've got a million numbers, say, which is usually what you get from a high-resolution camera. You've got a million numbers in just one frame, and from that you are supposed to know if anything is out there. You open the door, and surprise! You've got a million numbers. Is it a tiger? Or is it a lady?"

*

"I hear you were put in isolation," said an embarrassed Danny Hillis as he walked out on the deck after the conferees broke for lunch. Gumby would later tell me that Danny Hillis had chased him down the street to bring him back for a tour after Gumby had been ousted from the building by security. Hillis, who has written into the corporate charter of Terrapin that the company can never make sales to the military and who was now up against the wall to complete the prototype connection machine for the military, was transitioning between the worlds of academia and business, trying to be corporately responsible as the company's founding scientist while not severing his deep roots as a hacker.

He has certainly retained the appearance of someone still in academia. He was wearing a gray and maroon flannel shirt, baggy white trousers, beat-up jogging shoes, and his engaging smile, which is so ever-present that it's common to hear Hillis described as a perpetually happy guy. His light brown hair and round cherubic face reminded me of the little-boy aspect that is such a charming part of Hans Moravec.

And there was a delightful enthusiasm as he began to speak about what he and the other fifty employees of Thinking Machines are trying to accomplish: "Basically it is a step toward parallel processing. We know that the human brain is able to do amazing things with switching components that are basically slow—namely, neurons. With a switching component that takes a millisecond we are able to walk and talk and see pictures and all kinds of things that we can't get ordinary computers to do, even though ordinary computers are made out of components that are thousands of times faster.

"So there is reason to believe that maybe we are doing something wrong in the way we are building ordinary computers. Because when, for instance, we get an ordinary computer to do something like try to look at a picture or understand language, it is much too slow at it. It might take hours to look at a simple picture or to understand language. It is much too slow.

"Probably the biggest thing we seem to be doing wrong is that a normal computer is doing one thing at a time. The connection machine we are building will, like the brain, do millions of things at once."

The tantalizing possibilities of something like a connection machine have been around for about as long as computers. The genius mathematician and computer theorist John von Neumann, who was a major force behind the programmability of ENIAC and its successors, had observed that parallel processing would be a far superior way of computing. But until modern integrated circuits came along, it was impractical.

"When the computer was the size of a large room, you couldn't very well connect a million of them together," Hillis said. "Whereas now our computer is a little spot on a piece of silicon and you can literally have a million of them. So it's technology that has made this possible. It's not that nobody thought of doing this before. It's that it was never possible."

Now that it is possible, and that parallel architecture is being considered around the world, it should open some big doors. And this is coming at a good time, as some researchers feel they know the conventional sequential computer inside and out and are tiring of squeezing more power out of the same old von Neumann architecture.

A few days before speaking with Hillis I had talked about the connection machine with Alan Bawden, a graduate student in computer science whose office is one down from Sussman's.

"I've never tried to express this before, but there's some sense in which I believe that we know completely how to design sequential computers," Bawden said. "I don't think there are any interesting issues left to explore. When Sussman and Steele built the last Scheme chip, I remember the afternoon when they were out in the Playroom with this plot of the chip spread all over the floor. They were standing there, looking down at this map of this piece of silicon saying, 'There's the logic unit. We take this run from here to there. Here's the state machine control. . .' I wanted to say, 'Every computer is like that! There's nothing interesting here at all.' Here were people designing this state-of-the-art stuff, and there really were no interesting issues there. It was all details.

"With the connection machine we are now back at the same point those people were with the sequential computer in 1950. It might take another thirty years before we can refine the design of the connection machine to the point where we understand it as well as we understand sequential computers now.

"It will be fun," Bawden said. "We are reinventing computer science for a new kind of machine. It's clearly a frontier."

It is clear that Hillis enjoys that frontier.

"The machine we are building right now has inside it the switching capacity of a large telephone building," he said. "If you've ever seen one of these buildings that's just full of relays, we essentially have the switching capacity of a number-five crossbar station in a box about the size of a refrigerator."

MIT hackers have a long reputation for being infatuated with telephone systems. Late one night Gerry Sussman had pulled from a bottom drawer old circuitry maps he had made of the MIT and Harvard telephone systems. But I fessed up to my own ignorance and told Hillis I didn't know what a number-five crossbar station would look like.

Hillis walked to the edge of the sun deck, scanned the neighborhood, and pointed out an eight-story brick building.

"It's that building over there," he said. He studied the Bell Telephone building some more and then amended the statement. "That actually has two or three number-five crossbar stations in it. But it kind of gives you the idea of the switching capacity of the machine."

We stood there, leaning on the railing. It was impressive. The thought of putting a good chunk of that brick building into his connection machine reminded me of the streamlining of ENIAC from thirty tons to an invisible section of circuitry on a piece of silicon. Sometimes it seems as if the whole universe pulses along on kind of a yin-yang, macro-micro respiration. We just stood there taking in that number-five switchbar building, and then I said, "And you've got that in a box the size of . . ."

"A refrigerator," Hillis said.

Yet, as impressive as this was, I also figured that someday that "refrigerator" would seem as big and unbelievably clunky as the PDP-6 that was now used to switch toy train tracks. Hillis knew this too, for the next thing he said was, "Just think, you've got a box inside your head that probably has one hundred times the switching capacity of that building. So it sort of gives you an idea of how far we have to go."

He thought some more and decided that not even one hundred switching buildings could duplicate the possible neural connections within the brain. "Inside your brain you have something on the order of ten to the tenth [10 billion] or ten to the eleventh [100 billion] neurons. And each one of them has maybe an average of ten-to-the-fourth synapses connected to it, so let's say there are ten-to-the-fourteenth connections inside your head. That's an awful lot of connections. That's way beyond what all the computers in the world and all the telephone systems in the world would have today.

"I think the last great mystery left in science is to understand how the mind works and to really duplicate the thinking process," Hillis said. "Take for example the process by which you are understanding my sentences. Each time I say a word, you are able to disambiguate the many possible meanings of that word and make an image of what I describe. Or consider the process by which you can look out and identify that as a building," he said, pointing across the street. "And that as a statue and that as a cloud. It's really computationally an amazingly large task. No computer we have today could do that in the time that you just did.

"Our biggest, fastest machines, which dissipate hundreds of thousands of watts, in order to identify that as the statue of Athena, if they could do it at all, would probably take, say, half a day of computation. The machines we are working on will hopefully be able to do a problem like that in much closer to the time that you would be able to do it in."

When you watch television, your eyes are connecting dots of light to create the picture. These dots of light are called *pixels,* and there are about 250,000 of them in the picture tube of your average television. A sequential computer, even if it could analyze the value for a pixel in one hundredth of a second, would still take 2,500 seconds, or forty-one minutes, to assemble its picture. A parallel computer with 250,000 processors could do the same analysis in just the one hundredth of a second.

Going back to the tiger and the lady, you could think of a very large connect-the-dots drawing like the ones found in children's coloring books. You open the door and there are 250,000 dots. Is it a tiger or a lady? With sequential processing the tiger would be digesting you as its meal before the one central processing unit could act upon the data from all the dots. With parallel processing, the 250,000 processors would only have to process one dot each. Presto! It's a tiger! Slam the door before it leaps!

*

"What's the population of Kampala?" said Michael Brady, a senior Research Scientist at MIT.

"I don't know," I said.

"Right! And my immediate response is, How did you know so damn fast that you didn't have that in your head?"

I laughed.

"It's not a joke," Brady said with his British accent. "You see, you've got all this stuff in your head. How did you know so bloody quickly that you didn't know that?

"Imagine that I said to you, What is your sister's name? Or what is your mother's name?" Brady snapped his fingers. "You would know like *that!"*

Several days prior to seeing Hillis, I had enjoyed this conversation with Brady about the need to dump von Neumann sequential architecture and pursue parallel processing if we were ever going to be able to match the massive parallelism of the brain.

"Now imagine that you have this large tangled web of information in your head," Brady said. "You have all these memories of where you went to school, what your current phone number is, what your first phone number was, what the first car you ever bought was, what its dashboard looked like. There's a zillion things that you know. And of this inventory of stuff that's in your head, you would imagine, given what we currently understand about how present computers work, that you would have to crawl all over those huge data bases. It's the kind of thing large computer companies spend so much time doing. You would imagine that if I asked you a question, then in the current powers of relational data bases, you would set off some little process that would grovel all over your head trying to find if it knew the answer.

"But what is remarkable is that you didn't do that. You figured out, knowing what the meaning of the question was, you figured out that, come hell or high water, you could look for a million years in your head and not find the answer. And that tells us a hell of a lot about the way your head is organized. It tells us the brain doesn't just do blind searches for information. Because if it did, you'd have to bring a sleeping bag."

I told Brady about how long it took a group of VAX computers to digest and act upon the video images being relayed by Terragator during the road tests at Carnegie-Mellon. He said, "There is a light at the end of the tunnel and it is parallelism."

The eye is such a fine piece of biological engineering that only a mad roboticist would want to try actually to duplicate the structure of the organ. But if a video camera can provide the basic light values, and if a parallel computer, such as a connection machine, can digest the pixel values as quickly as they come in, we may be able to attain something that is very close to human vision. For Brady feels that the key to vision is in the manipulation of the data received—not in the kind of hardware used to transmit the variations in light.

"I don't give a shit about whether we've got a bloody retina and rods and cones in our head," Brady said. "I actually don't care. I don't care what the hardware looks like. I'm not interested. I don't care about neurophysiology. I'm not in the least bit interested. I'm interested in the algorithmic level, the higher level. I don't care if I've got silicon or wetware. What I am interested in is the flow of information, the way in which the information is represented, the way in which it is moved around. And there I think we'll find a genuine overlap between human vision and machine vision."

Back out on the sun deck at Thinking Machines, Danny Hillis told me, "We have problems an ordinary machine takes two hours to do that this machine can do in a hundredth of a second."

*

Danny Hillis and I went inside his building for lunch. Thinking Machines had a fancier version of the old SAIL computerized vending machine. Caterers would bring in food each day, spread it across a table, and serve it up. On one end of the table was a computer terminal upon which each person typed in his code number and what he had eaten. The computer would invoice the person at the end of the month. The Coke machine was on the same system.

Each day the leftovers from lunch were placed in a refrigerator to provide snacks for those working late. And for those who were really deep into a project, beds and showers were also provided. It was a hacker-friendly environment.

And those most likely to be spending the night, and to be going through the corporate refrigerator for leftovers, would be the software hackers, who constituted about two thirds of the staff. Building the connection machine was easy in comparison to programming it. The network of processors could be completely "rewired" in a millisecond just by writing a command to do so. In one instant the connection machine could be using its processors as a geometric grid for vision, while in the next instant it could be reconfiguring itself into a branching tree to handle classical AI logic computations and searches.

"A connection machine is effectively able to have a separate computer for every possible interpretation of a word, and to look at all the interpretations of the sentence. In parallel you can check out all their implications and see which one makes the most sense. That's something you can, in principle, do on a sequential machine, but it's much, much too slow."

Speed is required because language can be so ambiguous and confusing.

"Suppose I say a sentence like 'The astronomer married the star.' Now, that will cause the normal person a little bit of confusion, even though it's a perfectly valid sentence. Whereas if I say, 'The movie producer married the star,' it doesn't cause any confusion. The reason is that the connection between *movie producer* and *star* gives you sort of a hint as to which meaning of *star* is relevant. Whereas the connection between *star* and *astronomer* gives you a false hint and misleads you.

"The way we are doing language on the connection machine is taking advantage of information like that. As a matter of fact, the connection machine would be slightly confused if you said the astronomer married the star. It would figure it out, just like a human does. But it would do a double take. There's a lot of possibilities, and you need to be able to check out those possibilities in parallel—all the possible meanings of each of the words and what all the possible connections are between the words.

"We know it can be done, because people manage to do it. People do, after all, manage to understand each other when they talk. So that suggests that, unless there's some magic going on, there really is some process that will give the right answer. The puzzle now is to find what the right process is, and there are good reasons to believe that it's done with parallel processing.

"There's a certain level of biology, cellular biology, that never progressed until the invention of the microscope. They didn't have the tools to do the work with. In this same sense, I think, artificial intelligence has been held back by the lack of the right tool. So parallel processing, things like the connection machine, could do for artificial intelligence what the microscope did for biology."

We talked about the progression of machine knowledge and about what yardsticks might be used to measure it.

"There will never be a day when you turn on a machine and everybody agrees that it thinks," Hillis said. "It would just be like there being a day when everyone says, 'Yes! We understand life.' What happens is you make incremental progress.

"What's going to happen is that as machines do more and more tasks that once only humans could do, it will become harder and harder to draw the lines between what's thinking and what's not thinking. And there will come some point where everyone will agree that yes, they are thinking. It will probably not be our generation, but the next generation will just sort of grow up assuming it."

When I asked him at what point he would believe that one of his machines was thinking, he responded with something that continues to intrigue me: "I would like to build a machine that can be proud of me."

I recalled the devotion to the creation of robots I had seen at Carnegie-Mellon. There was Steve Berman blowing away "my social life, my sex life" on Terragator; Red Whittaker giving up his mountains; Hans, Mike, and Kevin working around the clock in the hope that they might be able to create something that could carry them onward.

I asked Hillis if this pride would translate into gratitude.

"I haven't thought of that aspect of it," Hillis said. "Presumably any intelligent entity that grows up and is sort of nurtured along by humans is grateful for that. I know I'm certainly grateful to my parents for educating me and bringing me up and teaching me what I believe in. So in that same sense, I think, yes. Thinking machines will be grateful to their creators."

I wondered how long such gratitude might last.

"How long are children grateful to their parents? I don't think there's a crisp answer," Hillis said. "As soon as something starts to think, by definition it is complicated. How would you judge if a machine was grateful? Let's say that I claimed that your tape recorder was grateful. It would be hard to prove me wrong. I don't think either of us would actually believe it were true. On the other hand, if it could talk to us and made a very convincing story about how 'Really, I am grateful and I would have been turned into a transistor radio if it hadn't been for you,' and gave a very convincing story, I don't know. Would we believe it? I'm not sure.

"I can imagine that sometime in the future—Marvin Minsky and I joke about this—there might be something called the Sincerity in Software Act. We both get annoyed at these automatic bank teller machines that say, 'Thank You,' and don't mean it. So the Sincerity in Software Act would be a requirement that no bank teller machine could say 'Thank you,' unless it really, sincerely, was grateful."

Since arriving at MIT I had been hearing more about the possibility of computers emerging as intelligent and independent life forms. Included in what I had heard was an element of fear about what might happen and a disdain for those who were trying to make it happen. I had visited with Seth Shulman, editor of *Science for the People* magazine, and had talked on a few occasions with Steve Berlin, an MIT researcher and a member of Computer Professionals for Social Responsibility. Seth and Steve were concerned about the roboticizing of the battlefields and the computerization of war decisions. I had also spent quite a bit of time with Joseph Weizenbaum, an MIT professor of electrical engineering and computer science, whose concerns are for the threat to the human spirit that might come with an increasingly computerized society. Though no one used these precise words, the message was: *There are some doors man was not meant to open!*

Now I was sitting in the lunchroom of Thinking Machines, surrounded by those who were looking for ways to program and thus exploit the massively parallel architecture of the connection machine in order to make it think. I asked Hillis what he thought about the emergence of a new life form.

"I'm all for it," he said. "We've got enough hard problems that we can use all the friends we can get. In one sense it would be great to have some friendly life form land in a flying saucer. But I think that it would be even better if we could create that life form—to be our friends, to complement us, and to be able to do what we can't do. That's plausible in the very long run. It is in the state of speculation now.

"I think, in principle, we are seeing the glimmerings of the possibilities of being able to create another race of intelligent beings, a generation of immortal children or something. But I don't think we really see the clear path to that or even see it well enough to judge how much of it is desirable and how much of it is undesirable. It is just sort of a possibility out there."

We discussed Hans Moravec's concept of downloading the contents of a human brain into the computer of a robot, and this was when Hillis said, "It's a natural thing. I've added up the things I want to do in my life, and it's up to a little bit over fifteen hundred years' worth of stuff. And I'm sure that by the time those fifteen hundred years are over, I'll have another fifteen hundred years' worth of stuff that I want to do. So I consider it a raw deal that I'm going to have to die before I get to do much of that. I would love to live for ten thousand or one hundred thousand years. And if I can't do that, I would at least love to let my children have the opportunity to do that.

"I enjoy having a body as much as anyone else does. But if it's a choice between even downloading into a computer that's stuck in a room someplace and still being able to think, versus just dying, I would certainly take that opportunity to think, particularly if I could have a robot body and be able to do that fifteen hundred years' worth of stuff. I would give a lot to be able to do that.

"I think that downloading is possible in principle. We don't understand thinking well enough. Hans and I may just miss it. But that's not enough to make me stop working on it."

*

After lunch I asked if I could see the connection machine. Hillis went back into embarrassment mode, explaining that "We have a bunch of very good private investors. People like Bill Paley, who had the vision that something was about to happen . . ." I walked back to MIT, arriving in time for the Friday Playroom party. There was a yellow garbage can filled with ice and beer. Standing beside it, Michael Brady and Tomas Lozano-Perez were animatedly arguing about bridge, Brady complaining that it was an excruciatingly boring American invention and Lozano-Perez saying, "Boring! A British person says something is boring? The *British,* who invented [and he spit this next word out disdainfully] *cricket,* can say something is *boring?"*

"The Americans confuse action with progress," said an unrepentant Brady.

Lozano-Perez held his beer bottle to his mouth as a microphone and, in the voice of a sports announcer, said, "It is now Thursday, and we have had eight thousand hits. Nothing has happened. But wait! A bird has just landed on the field."

Gumby was wandering about in his Club Dead T-shirt, while over at the floor-to-ceiling whiteboards that formed the outside wall for the shrine to dead rock stars, graduate student John Connell was drawing a picture of a lion and talking to Dan Weld about how a computer vision system would pick out the lion from a tree.

And then someone ran into the room howling with laughter, "Has everyone seen the picture of Victor Zue in *Time* magazine?" Zue, the world leader in getting computers to understand the spoken word, is an MIT researcher, and just a few days before, he had been showing me how a computer can digitize and analyze the sound patterns we create in speech. Everyone gathered around to see the color photograph of their friend and colleague. Much sport was made of the handsome but grim-faced Zue. Nearly snorting beer from his nose in laughter, one graduate student said, "That's not Victor Zue. That's a Chinese gangster!"

It was nice to be back in academia, but I had this sense of unease. If thinking machines come to be, followed by the ability to download into them, would it be the people like Bill Paley who would own this technology? Would these be the ones that stood at the gates of this new Life Everlasting? Just what would it take to pass through that gate? Who would be the grantor of this downloaded immortality? Who would be the one to say yes or no. And, most important, could this person ever take offense at anything I might ever do, say, or write?

Nah! I walked across the Playroom and joined Brady and Lozano-Perez for an ice-cold beer.

Chapter 8 ❧

WHILE HACKING
WITH PATRICK

AT 3:30 IN the morning, a warm beer is better than no beer, so I said yes when Gumby's friend Lisa Russell opened her backpack and started tossing out cans of Budweiser. I had been working on a LISP machine terminal in the Playroom when Gumby had come up to me about an hour earlier and said, "Coffeehouse?" We had set off across campus to the student union building's all-night coffee shop, but soon after our arrival we had run into Lisa Russell and John Hinsdale, and now we were up on the building's mezzanine sitting on the floor, drinking beer, and listening to a somewhat intoxicated John play magnificent improvisational jazz on a piano he had found.

But when Lisa pulled out a Genesee Cream Ale, the music ended, and John came over to claim it. Lisa was engaging in what seemed a futile attempt to convert Gumby to a state of enlightenment in regard to the brave men and women who selflessly devote their careers to marketing.

"The thing that bothers me the most about computer scientists and engineers is that they think up all these nifty machines, but the only reason to build machines is to sell them," said Lisa. "And the people who build these machines and develop these ideas hate marketing people. *Hate* them!"

She paused only long enough to look over to John and say, "That's a mess!" But John just kept rocking back and forth on the floor, sitting in his pool of spilled Genesee Cream Ale, smiling as if he had already achieved enlightenment.

Then, returning to the burning subject at hand, she said, "And I think that they should be working together with them, and that they should pull together, and that they should be looking to sell their products. And they are not!"

"Can I give a slightly conflicting viewpoint?" asked Gumby. "At [Xerox] PARC we used to call the people with the ties telephone sanitizers." This was a reference to a hilarious episode in Douglas Adams's *A Hitchhiker's Guide to the Galaxy*, in which a society collected all their middle managers and marketing people and sent them off in a spaceship, supposedly to scout the way for a future expedition by the rest of the planet.

But Lisa was not amused. "In order to sustain life as we know it, you need marketing!" she said with an earnestness that set Gumby and me off into heavy laughter. "I think people in marketing should really try to educate the consumer about what options are available and . . ."

John, still rocking and weaving back and forth in his pool of ale, chimed in with a mocking and robotic staccato voice: "Educate . . . the . . . consumer."

"Sometimes I don't want that," said Gumby. "If I want to buy a computer or if I want to buy a stereo, I know what I want and I just want to go in and get it."

"How do you know what you want, though?" said Lisa. *"How do you know what you want?"*

"I read technical papers on Class-B amplifiers."

"Well, Gumby," said Lisa, "You're *such* a nerd!"

"On the other hand, if I'm going to buy a car, I don't know diddlyshit about cars."

Once again the contentedly rocking John offered something to the conversation: "Even nerds don't know diddlyshit about cars."

"I know the autocycle," said Gumby. "I know the thermodynamics of the internal-combustion engine."

"Real nerds know everything about that," said John.

"But it does me no good in buying a car," said Gumby. "What I want to do is go to a salesman and say, 'I want a car to do the following things: I want to be able to drive to Grateful Dead concerts. I don't want to use it most of the time. I want it to be able to sit there for weeks on end without any damage. I don't want people to steal it.' But the salesman is going to want to sell me what he's got on the lot. So he's going to do his damnedest to convince me that I don't really want what I think I want."

"It really bothers me," said Lisa, "that you keep confusing marketing people with management."

From the pool of Genesee Cream Ale came a voice: "My high school economics teacher would always say, 'What if you wanted to sell nuclear toothbrushes?' "

Gumby's immediate response: "You'd only be able to sell them to the nerds at MIT and Cal Tech."

*

The four of us walked back to Senior House, the campus residency where Lisa, John, and Gumby lived. On the way up the stairs Gumby pointed out a mural that had been painted by someone I had been spending time with—Eric Drexler, a theorist in the construction of incredibly tiny—molecular-size—computers. As we stood there looking at the mural, John said, "But it doesn't *sell* anything." At 4:27 in the morning, Lisa decided just to let the comment slide.

Gumby's room had a mattress on the floor, walls covered with Grateful Dead posters, and a general feel that it was a crashpad only, a place to be while not awake and functioning up on the seventh floor. He had once said, "Some people blow off steam by leaving campus. But if I go to a party, I go to a party on campus. If I go to a movie, I go to a movie on campus. If I get something to eat, well, it's not food, but I eat on campus, too."

With the Dead's *American Beauty* album playing in the background, Gumby spoke with passion about the magnificence of good computer code. I was extremely interested in programming; in the creation of good computer code. For even a connection machine would be nothing but enticing hardware without the software to make it come alive with a sense of reason and logic that might produce the foundation for greater machine-born thoughts to arise.

There seemed to be an intoxicating element to this realm of making a machine do your bidding. Hans Moravec had once told me that what he really would like to do would be to leap inside a computer and just start pointing to things to better direct the flow of his code. And now, just before sunrise, I listened to Gumby speak of the beauty to be found in the art and science of computer programming.

"The cleaner the code, the easier it is to understand, and the easier it is to extend," he said. "There is definitely an element of art. There are some people's code I *like* to read. And there are other people's code I *hate* to read. It's horrible, I have to ask them how it works. While with others I would rather read their code to see how it works.

"Sometimes there is a clever hack. Do you know the xor function? [This involves exchanging the contents of two registers without using a third register for temporary storage. It would be kind of like exchanging a column of red poker chips with a column of blue poker chips without having to remove the stacks from the chip holder.] I didn't believe this the first time I saw it. I said, 'This cannot be true.'

But I sat down and did the math. And found, Aha! This is true!

"And if I saw that in a piece of code, it would be completely incomprehensible. Why did this guy go A := A XOR B; B := A XOR B; A := A XOR B? It makes no sense. Why did he do this? And then I look at this and say, Wow! This is really neat. A cute hack. A very funny hack.

"Then there are other things that are just very pretty, where someone has defined his data structures to reflect what the thing actually looks like. I showed you that assembler program that was really ugly and horrible. It is really hard to understand. You've always got to think on two levels: first, what is the guy trying to do? And second, what is he actually doing to achieve that end.

"You look: 'Did the guy really use the right tool for the job?' You see whether the guy set the problem up in such a way that the solution falls out. I've had some stuff where just the way I represented the data structure, the way I talked about this thing, just caused the solution to fall out. Basically I didn't have to write anything. Once I sat down and thought about how to represent the problem, all of a sudden I didn't have to write the program anymore. It just sort of came out. All I had to do is type it in. And I really like that. And that's really good when the whole thing comes together. That's what beauty in code is.

"So there is the clever hack that makes you laugh. And then there is the elegant hack that's like an Escher print—it's so stunning in clarity that you really know what's going on. I wouldn't take a piece of code and actually put it on my wall, although a friend of mine did."

*

A few nights later I stopped by Gerry Sussman's office for a midnight cup of tea—a potent blend from India that combined ginger, black pepperroot, cinnamon, cloves, and nutmeg. Earlier that evening I had been with Jonathan Rees, a graduate student who was complaining about having to correct some wrongheaded thinking that had been suggested for a program he wrote while at Yale. It was for a dialect of Scheme called T, and he had just seen a message on the ARPAnet suggesting a change. The ARPAnet is the Department of Defense's Defense Advanced Research Projects Agency's computer-mail network that links the major AI universities together, allowing them to send electronic mail back and forth. I met people in my travels who said that one reason they would never want to leave academia is that they couldn't stand to be away from the ARPAnet with its constant flow of messages and electronic bulletin boards for browsing.

When I told Sussman about Rees feeling compelled to shoot down the idea of adding unnecessary code to the program, Gerry was sympathetic.

"Most people don't realize that you don't want to make a language more and more complicated. Rees and I have the same feeling, which is you want the thing to be simple and small and elegant—lean and mean. Most programmers tend to clutter up their languages and make them more complicated. One of the things you have to work on when you make up a computer language for people with good taste is you have to keep your thumb on all the people who want to make it more complicated. Keep it simple. I don't want the language to be complicated. I want the things I can build with it to be complicated."

I spoke of how Gumby liked to read good code and about how he would laugh sometimes at a clever hack.

"I believe programs will become a new literature," Sussman said. "And that they say things that couldn't be said mathematically. They provide methodology. I have files of old programs that are classified under Humorous, Sad, programs that are tragic, programs that I've learned something from by reading. I can tell a lot about the personality of the programmer."

I mentioned the XOR hack that Gumby had liked.

"Two XORs in a row?" Sussman said. "Sounds like a Gosper program. I can tell you who it was: Bill Gosper. That's the kind of thing Gosper would write. It's very brilliant, very clever, and it's also at a very low level of detail. And then there are people who are more architectural.

"When I see a program written by Gosper, I can recognize it. I can read programs written by Winston [Patrick Henry Winston, a former Minsky student who now heads the department] and tell you that's a Winston program. It's got its own flavor."

Then Sussman opened a file drawer, saying, "A long, long time ago, what did LISP look like?" He laughed, pulled out a half-inch-thick computer printout, laughed again, and said, "It was only this big. That's the amazing thing. It was written by many people. A listing of LISP systems now is about five or six times as thick.

"Yet I can look through this and read various pieces of the code and say, 'This part was written by [Richard] Greenblatt.' I can tell."

The he pulled out a printout that he handled as if it were an original Gutenberg bible. It was the original code for the ITS operating system—the Incompatible Timesharing System. It even seemed awesome to me. Today we just accept the fact that a mainframe computer can be in the basement of a building and desktop terminals can be spread throughout a building, or throughout the world, providing anyone with a terminal, access to the computer. It is hard to realize that as late as the 1960s this wasn't the case. If you wanted computer time, you wrote your program, took it to the computer room, and had it run— oftentimes by someone else, even if you wanted to do it yourself.

It is a tribute to the modesty and especially to the irreverence of the early hackers that when they created the world's first timesharing system at MIT, they provided it with a name that was completely opposite from what it really was: the Incompatible Timesharing System.

There was Gerry Sussman holding that half-inch printout, a blessed relic from 1967. The machine had a Moby memory, and as if reciting the opening words of the Great American Novel, Sussman held the printout in his hands and said, "The first line of it is, 'Moby is One.' "

It was written as Moby = 1, but the way Sussman read it, there was the sound of poetry and philosophy, as existential a piece of haiku as I have ever heard: Moby is One.

"These days such an operating system would have maybe one hundred times as much code. But this is what it was like then, filled with some very beautiful code—and some very ugly code. Some of it is humorous, and some of it is sad. Some of it had ideas in it that have been lost. Some historian could go through it someday and read it the way people read the Dead Sea Scrolls and say, 'Aha, The guys who wrote this were real smart guys. And some of the things they knew, we don't even know now.' "

*

My code was neither cute nor clever. It was awful. But I had been spending some time blundering about with Logo, which is a simplified LISP language, and had found how intoxicating it was to make a computer do your bidding. I had also found how easily the hours could slip away as you kind of did a mind meld with the computer terminal.

One morning I went down to the fourth floor with Patrick Sobalvarro, who had helped write several versions of the Logo program, and we found an Apple IIe to play with.

The first time I had met Sobalvarro was up on the ninth floor, in one of the small laboratories that ring the field of computers. I had been watching members of Ken Salisbury's robotic-hand group working on the computer-controlled motions of a three-fingered hand they had created. Each finger had three joints. A VAX minicomputer was used for the execution of the motions, and a LISP machine was used to translate the movement commands for the VAX.

"Holy shit!" Sobalvarro said when he saw the smoothness with which the three fingers turned a pop can. Steven Chiu, who had done the LISP programming, was proud that Sobalvarro was impressed. Sobalvarro had programmed computers for the control of robotic arms and knew how complex the code could be.

I had taken an immediate liking to Sobalvarro because of his sense of fun and his droll sense of humor. When Ken Salisbury showed him some tough and rubbery material that they were going to use for fingertips, the first thing Sobalvarro did was try to use it as an eraser. Salisbury said the material came in three colors. "We're going to get orange, beige, and blue fingertips." Sobalvarro's immediate response: "As long as they aren't red, white, and blue."

When Salisbury left the lab, Sobalvarro innocently asked, "Steve, are you going to crush a can?"

"Crush a can?" asked Chiu warily, as this was the very thing his smooth programming was intended to prevent.

"Ken has told me over and over again that he can crush a can with his hand. That's what I'm waiting to see."

Chiu typed a command into the LISP machine terminal, preparing to play a trick on the robot—asking it to close its fingers into a space smaller than the diameter of the can.

"Let's have a betting pool!" said a gleeful and conspiratorial Patrick Sobalvarro. "I think the can will slip between the two top fingers."

Steve ignored the invitation, but continued typing commands into the terminal. The can was placed within the three fingers, and then Chiu's lines of LISP commands were sent into action, uniting two computers and the motors they controlled in an effort to crush an empty can of Mountain Dew. There was a whirring of motors as the steel tendons drew taut and the fingers curled into the can. Then all three fingers went limp; the can jangled across the workbench and onto the floor. Sobalvarro announced that the robot had just blown a fuse.

On the morning we got together on the fourth floor to work on an Apple IIe, he had been up all night before trying to complete a commercial project. He had been contracted to create an implementation of Logo for the Apple Macintosh. The project was due that morning and wasn't done, but Sobalvarro was ready for a break and was following through on a promise he had made several days earlier to show me how to use the Logo language to create an ELIZA program.

ELIZA will always have a place in the annals of artificial intelligence, chiefly for the emotional reactions it caused among those who first used it and for the fact that the man who created it, MIT's Joseph Weizenbaum, considered the public's response so disturbing that he came to regret ever having written it. ELIZA was a program Weizenbaum had written to mimic a psychotherapist. A person would sit down at a computer terminal, and the ELIZA program would ask him to talk about what was on his mind.

By the time I sat down with Patrick to write an ELIZA program, I had already met four times with Weizenbaum and read his book *Computer Power and Human Reason*. Today ELIZA is appreciated as a cute hack, but to get a feeling for why it caused such a stir when it was introduced in the mid 1960s, one need only look at the following transcript from Weizenbaum's book. It shows a conversation a young woman had with the ELIZA program. The woman sat down at a computer terminal, and upon seeing the prompt on the screen, SPEAK UP! she began to tell the computer what was on her mind. The computer prompted and prodded her to tell more. The conversation went like this:

SPEAK UP!
Men are all alike.
IN WHAT WAY?
They're always bugging us about something or other.
CAN YOU THINK OF A SPECIFIC EXAMPLE?
Well, my boy friend made me come here.
YOUR BOY FRIEND MADE YOU COME HERE?
He says I'm depressed much of the time.
I AM SORRY TO HEAR YOU ARE DEPRESSED.
It's true. I am unhappy.
DO YOU THINK COMING HERE WILL HELP YOU NOT TO BE UNHAPPY?
I need some help, that much seems certain.
WHAT WOULD IT MEAN TO YOU IF YOU GOT SOME HELP?
Perhaps I could learn to get along with my mother.
TELL ME MORE ABOUT YOUR FAMILY.
My mother takes care of me.
WHO ELSE IN YOUR FAMILY TAKES CARE OF YOU?
My father.
YOUR FATHER?
You are like my father in some ways.
WHAT RESEMBLANCE DO YOU SEE?
You are not very aggressive, but I think you don't want me to notice that.

WHAT MAKES YOU THINK I AM NOT VERY AGGRESSIVE?
You don't argue with me.
WHY DO YOU THINK I DON'T ARGUE WITH YOU?
You are afraid of me.
DOES IT PLEASE YOU TO BELIEVE I AM AFRAID OF YOU?
My father is afraid of everybody.
WHAT ELSE COMES TO MIND WHEN YOU THINK OF YOUR FATHER?
Bullies.
DOES THAT HAVE ANYTHING TO DO WITH THE FACT THAT YOUR BOY
    FRIEND MADE YOU COME HERE?

As Gumby would say, a cute hack. A very cute hack. So cute that some psychologists, such as Stanford's Kenneth Colby, flocked around it and spoke of automating psychiatry. Even Carl Sagan wrote glowingly of a future "network of computer psychotherapeutic terminals, something like arrays of large telephone booths, in which for a few dollars a session, we would be able to talk with an attentive, tested, and largely nondirective psychotherapist."

Weizenbaum found such an idea unsettling, even more unsettling was how intimate and believing some people were with the program. People would express their most precious secrets, things they would never say to a human, to this computer program. What they didn't realize was that the computer couldn't understand a word they were saying. It had no internal representation of the concepts being discussed. The program did not know what a human was, had no idea of what depression was, or a mother, a father, or a boy friend.

ELIZA, which also became known as DOCTOR, was just a neat hack in LISP, in which the program would take apart sentences being entered from the terminal, restructure them as statements or open questions, and then send the result out onto the screen. The problem was that it was such a great hack, that people didn't want to believe this was true. At one point, Weizenbaum's own secretary, who had watched him create the program, was so deeply into a session with the computer that when Weizenbaum came into the room, she asked him to leave. It was at this point that Weizenbaum denounced his own program and became one of the most eloquent spokesmen against artificial intelligence and our fascination with creating machines that can think.

"What could be more obvious than the fact that, whatever intelligence a computer can muster, however it may be acquired, it must always and necessarily be absolutely alien to any and all authentic human concerns?" he wrote in his book. "The very asking of the question, 'What does a judge (or a psychiatrist) know that we cannot tell a computer?' is a monstrous obscenity. That it has to be put into print at all, even for the purpose of exposing its morbidity, is a sign of the madness of our times."

*

Sobalvarro sat at the Apple IIe and spoke as he programmed the computer to play psychotherapist. "When ELIZA would start up, it would say, 'Speak up!' and that's how you would start talking to the DOCTOR program." Sobalvarro typed as he continued to speak. "So, first it's going to say, 'Speak up!' And then it's going to initialize some variables, such as this one, which we will call Hedges. This is a list of things that the DOCTOR says when it can't think of anything else to say. Typical hedges might be 'Go on' or 'I see.'

"The DOCTOR program also has this bunch of what I call 'leads.' These are sort of leading phrases that it tacks onto the beginning of sentences. A common one is 'Why do you say that . . . ?'

"Now I will set the memory so that every so often it will remember what you said and will come back at a random interval later and repeat it to you (after attaching it to a leading phrase). That's where ELIZA got the comment 'Does this have anything to do with the fact that your boy friend made you come here?' People made a lot of that. That is what gave people the impression that it actually knew what it was doing, although of course it didn't."

Then Sobalvarro wrote the me-you subroutine, which enables the transformation of a statement such as "My boy friend made me come here," Into "Does this have anything to do with the fact that your boy friend made you come here."

For the times when the human didn't respond to a statement on the screen, Sobalvarro wrote a subroutine that would call up the response PLEASE DON'T BE SO RETICENT. I had suggested, TRUST ME!

It was really enjoyable to watch the creation of the program. As he wrote it, Hal Abelson and Leigh Klotz, Jr. dropped by, which meant that three of the four authors of the Apple II version of Logo were in the room at one time, which is what makes MIT such a nice place to be. Logo was the original mindstorm of Seymour Papert, an MIT professor, whom I had seen a week earlier in a surprisingly ungentlemanly debate with Weizenbaum.

It only took Sobalvarro an hour to hack the program together. It was exciting to watch. I kept wanting to put more elaborate responses into the program. I wanted to see just how charming and cuddly you could make the program appear. Rather than opening with SPEAK UP! I wanted to hack in something like, PLEASE FEEL AT EASE, AND DO NOT HESITATE TO TELL ME HOW YOU FEEL.

Keyed to words like "depression" and "sadness," the computer could respond, YES, I KNOW. I CAN SENSE THAT YOU ARE HURTING. At random intervals the program could spit out parables and uplifting words, attaching to the end of each a return-to-duty message such as, BUT NOW I AM GETTING CARRIED AWAY, AND YOU ARE THE ONE I CARE ABOUT, SO PLEASE CONTINUE TO SHARE WITH ME.

I wanted to put Mr. Rogers into a computer, but without actual internal representation. Unless the computer could really *mean* those kind words, unless the computer had a knowledge of what a human was and what life was, I would just be adding to the terror that Joseph Weizenbaum saw arising from all of this. Besides, I might find myself in violation of some future Minsky and Hillis Sincerity in Software Act.

*

With the program complete, Sobalvarro invited me to give it a try.

"That's fine," I said. "I'm going to pretend that I'm really feeling depressed. It's going to be fun." Then I looked at Sobalvarro, who was sitting next to me, looking eagerly into the screen. This was really embarrassing. I had just seen the program created. I had a pretty good idea of how it worked, yet I said, "I'm already feeling self-conscious about this."

Sobalvarro laughed long and hard, but also with a sense of recognition.

"A common thing to do is to say, 'I hate computers.' " he said. "Because that's an easy thing to say, and it's not very embarrassing."

I typed, I'M WORRIED ABOUT NUCLEAR WAR.

"We didn't teach it about contractions," Sobalvarro said.

I retyped the statement without contractions, and soon the screen looked like this:

SPEAK UP!
I am worried about nuclear war.
GO ON.
I am afraid we might blow ourselves up before we learn to control the
    things we have discovered.
I SEE.
Are you sure you understand the importance of my concern?

WHAT MAKES YOU THINK THAT ARE I SURE THAT I UNDERSTAND THE
IMPORTANCE OF YOUR CONCERN?

I puzzled over the last statement and said, *"Are* is the problem there."
"We didn't put *are* and *am* in the me-you list."
"That's called debugging," I said.
"That's called embarrassing," Sobalvarro said.

*

We played with the program some more, until Sobalvarro mentioned
that someone had created a DOCTOR program to respond to visitors
who were asking for a guest account on Oz. This sounded too good to
be true, so we headed over to Steve Berlin's office to use his terminal.
One of the things I loved about computer academia was the complete
irreverence that was allowed to become part of the established computer-
operating systems. For instance, if you needed assistance getting onto
the ARPAnet the computer terminal would alert you to the availability
of help with this message: IF YOU ARE HAVING DIFFICULTIES AND NEED
ASSISTANCE, PLEASE TYPE: LUSER, AND SOMEBODY WILL ASSIST YOU.

Now, I could just picture some visitor from a more structured environment—say IBM, or perhaps the Pentagon, since the ARPAnet
and just about everything else in the field of robotics and AI was supported by the Department of Defense—innocently sending a message
to the master DEC-20, Oz, asking for a guest account for computer
access.

"Most DEC-20s are in more organized scientific environments,"
Sobalvarro explained as we gleefully headed for Berlin's office. "A lot
of DEC-20s have human operators; however, we consider that kind of
silly around here. We don't have an operator. But these people who
want guest accounts will often send messages to the operator, and we
got tired of that, so somebody connected a DOCTOR program."

I had gotten to know Steve Berlin during my stay at MIT, and he
welcomed us in. Sobalvarro immediately went to the terminal to try to
get into Oz. He wasn't familiar with the network link Berlin's system
had into the DEC-20 and said, "This might not work."

"It should," said Berlin.

"I don't know," said Sobalvarro. "I wrote the code for it."

But it worked, and Sobalvarro typed his message to Oz, as he said
to us, "I've just asked the operator if we can have an account."

"Is that how you set up accounts?" said Berlin.

"No. Have you seen this hack?"

"No."

"You'll like it," said Sobalvarro. "Give the system a minute. I think the [timesharing] load is pretty high."

And then, there it was! The operator's response: WHAT DO YOU THINK? I WOULD APPRECIATE IT IF YOU WOULD TELL ME SOMETHING ABOUT YOUR INTEREST IN COMPUTERS.

Sobalvarro typed in some information, and the computer's response was terrific: COULD YOU ELABORATE ON THAT?

Berlin saw what was happening and began to laugh.

It was really a brilliant hack. When Sobalvarro tried to ask the operator a question, the response was, I'LL ASK THE QUESTIONS, IF YOU DON'T MIND! PERHAPS YOU COULD TALK ABOUT HOW YOU FEEL ABOUT YOUR PLANS.

Joseph Weizenbaum walked by outside, and I couldn't resist calling him into the office. Sobalvarro explained about having visitor requests dead-ended into an ELIZA program.

"How long does it take for these people to give up?" Weizenbaum asked .

"Some of them are logged, and I've seen these conversations go on for pages and pages," Sobalvarro said.

"You know, a long time ago I once mentioned very casually to somebody that it occurred to me to log the ELIZA conversations so that I could find shortcomings and so on in the program, and before I had any chance to do anything about it, I was bombarded by protests," Weizenbaum said. "People said it was private, that it would be indecent to log it, that it would be indecent for anyone else to see it, and so on."

Finally Sobalvarro typed what he thought would be his last message: I NO LONGER WANT AN ACCOUNT.

But it wasn't that easy. And all but Joseph Weizenbaum laughed at the tenacious response that had been hacked into the program: YOU ARE BEING A BIT BRIEF. WOULD YOU PLEASE GO INTO DETAIL.

Sobalvarro rose to the occasion, typing onto the screen: MY GIRL-FRIEND MADE ME COME HERE. And then, turning to Weizenbaum, he said with a broad grin, "I must admit to remembering a certain conversation you quoted in your book."

The computer's response: HOW DO YOU RECONCILE THE PEOPLE YOU HANG AROUND WITH?

And at that, even Weizenbaum joined us in a long round of laughter.

"Is it good to see ELIZA still alive and well?" I asked, figuring quite the opposite to be true.

"Oh, well-l-l," Weizenbaum said.

"Is it like 'The Purple Cow'?" said Sobalvarro. "There's this poem called 'The Purple Cow' by some British fellow that went, 'I never saw a purple cow, I never hope to see one. But I can tell you anyhow, I'd rather see than be one.'

"It caught on, and about twenty years later he wrote a poem that said, 'Yes, I wrote 'The Purple Cow.' I'm sorry now I wrote it. But I can tell you anyhow, I'll kill you if you quote it.' "

Joseph Weizenbaum nodded his head and said, "Yes. It's like that."

Then he took a big bag of M&Ms from Berlin's desk, shook out a handful, and said, "I imagine that Ravel felt about *Bolero* the way I feel about ELIZA."

Chapter 9 ~

ROBOTIC SENSE
AND PSYCHOTIC
HALLUCINATIONS

DURING HIS STUDENT years Gerry Sussman had created a world within a computer, a place called Blocks World, where an imaginary robot would try to stack the toy blocks of a child. It was an exciting notion at the time, and I felt it still was. Within the logic gates and registers of the old PDP-6 he had created this world, using John McCarthy's LISP language to institute the laws of nature, perhaps not unlike what someone had done with this universe of ours.

The lone dweller in Blocks World, a stick-figure one-handed robot, was destined to lead a life that was forever challenging. Sussman's goal had been to program the laws of Blocks World in such a way that the robot could access them and learn to work in conformity with them.

As if from the heavens, the robot would be issued a command: STACK BLOCK A ONTO BLOCK C. If the gods of Blocks World were smiling upon the one-handed robot, the task would be easily accomplished. But on more trying occasions, the robot might run up against some of the laws of the world. For instance, if Block B were already resting on Block C, there was a law that said that Block A could not occupy the same space. It was at this point that the robot would have to search for the solution and find within the program that guided its life the law that allowed it to move Block B from Block C prior to attending to the command to stack Block A onto Block C. Sussman called his program HACKER.

What makes LISP such a nice language is that you can use it to create any kind of world you want. Just as ELIZA could be programmed to say TRUST ME! rather than PLEASE DON'T BE RETICENT, a programmer of Blocks World could write code that identified each of the blocks by exact shape, color, weight, or by any other characteristics desired.

For instance, you could write into your program that Block C weighed one hundred pounds and you could specify that the robot could lift only twenty pounds. Blocks A and B could be given weights of five pounds. Within this framework, you could order the robot to stack Blocks A, B, and C in a tower and then watch to see whether the robot figures out which block will have to be on the bottom.

Sussman's Blocks World was much more complicated than this, and various researchers have created their own versions. But the essentials remain the same. The idea is to create an environment that is wealthy with information and then see if you have programmed it in an accessible enough manner for the computer to make use of this information in unexpected ways. For it is the use of information in unexpected ways that constitutes thinking. And becoming better and better at using the information constitutes learning. Once computers are able to *think* and to *learn,* wondrous, as well as unexpected and perhaps even frightening things could happen.

*

In an office just across the Playroom from Sussman's, a graduate student named Phil Agre had created a Blocks World of his own, in hopes of creating an environment in which his robot could learn from its experiences and become more and more proficient in carrying out instructions. The ultimate goal behind all such work is to learn enough about converting the laws of a world into accessible program code so that someday a robot might be able to function in the real world.

The first time I met Agre, he was listening to the music of Rickie Lee Jones as he sat cross-legged and barefoot in his chair, working at a LISP machine terminal, watching the pictorial robot arm try to move blocks around the screen.

"What the program I've written does is it has some task that it's assigned—to stack up blocks in a certain way," Agre told me, as he continued to watch the screen with some anxiety. "And it improvises its way through some solution to that problem. It tries picking up this block and putting it there first and eventually gets to some solution to the problem.

"And it has been watching itself the whole time, observing either repeated patterns of activity or patterns of activity that are instances of general importance—patterns such as repeating itself, or undoing work it had just done, or getting stuck in a corner somehow. It tries to figure out what decision went awry. The next time such a decision comes up, some entity in the program that has noticed things going awry last time should say, 'Hey! That went awry for this or that reason, and I think you should do it this way instead of that way to avoid the difficulty.'

"The gradual integration of the system is that more and more arguments come to bear on different decisions the program has to make over time. The program is carrying on an argument with itself about what to do next. And the way the program learns is when the same decision comes up to be made anew, the light of experience allows additional arguments to be introduced."

In many ways this reminded me of Hans Moravec's desire to send Terragator out to play and frolic, just so that it could calibrate its vision and learn from its actions.

Phil spoke of how humans learn, about how, while waiting for a kettle of water to boil, you might get the teacups and tea bags ready to reduce the hassle of waiting, or how you might turn on the electric stove prior to filling the kettle so that the burner can heat up while you are at the sink. He spoke of how regular riders of subways will learn to enter either one end of the train or the other, according to which gate they want to be nearest when they leave the train at the next stop.

"One thing I've noticed in my fieldwork of watching people engaged in commonsense reasoning is that almost everything you learn is obvious in retrospect. It is sort of clear why it is true. And this program is trying to capture that by first noticing that something is true and then by trying to come up with some explanation of why it is true."

Agre turned his attentions to the computer screen, and I pulled my chair closer for a better view. "What just happened now is that the robot is trying to move its hand down, because the hand is very much above Block A, which it is trying to reach to put onto Block B," he said as he analyzed what had gone wrong. "But it couldn't move its hand down because its hand is on top of a stack of blocks. When it tried to push its hand through the stack of blocks, it failed. So it said, 'Why didn't it work?' And it followed back the dependencies from it not being able to move its hand down and found the reason it couldn't move its hand."

Then Agre turned his attention from the pictures of blocks to the text the program was generating as the robot puzzled over why its hand could not move through one block to reach another. Translating the LISP messages being issued from the computer, Agre said, "It's proposing the following rule: that if somebody proposes to move the hand down and the hand is on top of a block that is on top of another block that is on top of the table, which is the situation you see here— the hand is on B, which is on E, which is on the table—then it should object to moving the hand down, saying that this didn't work once."

So there we were, sitting in his office, staring through a glowing window into another world and reading messages from the screen that represented the attempts of this program to learn from its mistakes and to attain some knowledge.

Hans Moravec, in describing the awareness of his robot Neptune, had said, "It isn't conventionally thought of as being anything like consciousness. But I think it really is. You have a world model and you consider alternatives. If this thing could talk, it could describe this internal process, and it could tell you, 'Yeah, I considered going around there, but it didn't seem like a good idea because . . .' "

And now, we had something that in a sense could talk. And it was describing to us what it had learned while trying to follow orders within the realm of Blocks World.

Agre was predicting that the next time the robot was given an order that would cause it to try to pass through one block in order to pick up a block resting beneath, it would raise the objection we had just watched it formulate. "It won't even try to move its hand down," Agre said. "It will be happy just to move its hand to the left, which it has also proposed to do, and which works perfectly well. And so the hand will slide along the top of Block B and then head down toward Block A."

Agre had recently moved a futon mattress into his office so that he could spend his nights beside the glowing window of a screen that would allow him to see how well his creation was doing. If he could get his robotic hand to be able to follow smoothly from one task to the next within Blocks World, it would be a major step toward the day when real robots would be able to flow through this world of ours, meandering through our homes and cities, coexisting with the species that created them.

*

Several weeks later, during my stay at Stanford, I would drive a couple of miles off campus to visit with Jerry Hobbs of the think tank SRI International. John McCarthy had suggested I see Hobbs about an AI programming project Hobbs had created called Common Sense Summer.

I had been able to get a guest account on the SAIL computer without going through an ELIZA program, so I used electronic mail to contact Hobbs on the ARPAnet and set up a meeting. Electronic mail is better than a telephone, because you can send your message without the other person being in, and you needn't be around for the arrival of the reply. The written word tends to be more wisely composed than that which gushes from the mouth, and if I had my choice, I would toss out the telephone and convert to computers.

As Hobbs and I drank coffee and ate bagels in his office one morning, he said, "Suppose you have a robot and you want to send it down to get a cup of coffee. What does it have to know? First of all it has to be able to map the English instruction of 'Go get me a cup of coffee' into a set of very detailed instructions about how to get down the hallway."

Hobbs was wrestling with the same problems that Sussman, Agre, and so many others are dealing with: internal representation of the real world. This has been called the signal-to-symbol barrier. How do you get a computer to *understand* the color purple when all you can do is talk to it in a string of ones and zeroes? Just as there is no homonuculus, no little man, sitting inside a computer to act as its eyes, there is no homonuculus to nod its head and understand things for the computer. So how do you get a robot to *know* what a hallway is, what a door is, who is the *me* that wants the cup of coffee? Also: What is a cup? What is coffee? Why would a human drink coffee? What is a human?

Marvin Minsky told me, as he has told many before, that we are yet to create a computer program that can recognize a door. And beyond just recognizing an opening in a wall as being a door, there is the entire question of what does a door *mean,* what sorts of cultural and societal significance do we bring to mind when we see a door? What does its design tell us? What meaning does its color convey? What does the degree of its openness say? And upon entering through that door and seeing a human, what is the human thinking, and what is a thought? What are his aspirations, and what are aspirations? What significance is there to whether the human stands up to greet you or whether he looks up, scowls, and then looks back down at the desk? What is a desk?

*

It is exactly such matters that pose some of the toughest challenges in artificial intelligence: What can a computer understand? Several days prior to seeing Hobbs, I had driven over to the University of California's Berkeley campus to meet Hubert Dreyfus, a professor of philosophy, the author of *What Computers Can't Do,* and, along with

Joseph Weizenbaum, one of the harshest critics of artificial intelligence.

Historically the difference between Weizenbaum and Dreyfus has been that Weizenbaum believes the computers will attain a form of their own intelligence and that the misuse of this alien intelligence may prove harmful to the human spirit and to the very survival of the species. Dreyfus, on the other hand, has compared AI to alchemy and dismissed the possibility of there ever being any machine intelligence of significance. Dreyfus gleefully dredges up predictions made twenty and thirty years ago by the founding fathers of AI and gloats in print about the failure of the early dreams to come true.

Dreyfus gave me a manuscript to a book he had recently written with his brother, Stuart, *Mind over Machine*. He precedes his third chapter ("Artificial Intelligence: From High Hopes to Sober Reality") with a twenty-year-old quotation from Carnegie-Mellon's Nobel laureate Herbert Simon: "Machines will be capable, within twenty years, of doing any work that a man can do."

I enjoyed my conversation with Dreyfus, and I later read his manuscript, but his listings of the failures of AI seemed to echo like the laughter from Kitty Hawk or the sneers toward the early Thomas Edison. It may come to pass that in another twenty years the words of Simon will prove closer to reality than the skepticism of Dreyfus. At this point it could go either way. But it just seemed to me as if the entire flow of scientific history had to be against Dreyfus.

By the end of *Mind over Machine* it seemed as if he had actually come to the same conclusion and had moved much closer to the position of Weizenbaum: that because machines *would* develop an intelligence of their own, the threat to man was all the greater. In the book's epilogue Dreyfus wrote:

And if thinking is reckoning, then it is reasonable to expect that, as futurists have been telling us for years, the computer as rational device is the next stage of evolution which will someday not only excel us but replace us. We would be rational animals on the verge of obsolescence, soon to be discarded by our own machines.

This is an appalling vision of the future. Yet there is no disputing computers have fundamentally and permanently transformed our relationship to our technologies. Soon we will live in a world of extraordinarily rich, subtle, and powerful tools. Will they remain our servants, helping us to our human ends? Or will they outstrip our humanity, and cast us aside?

*

And so it was against this backdrop—the seemingly insurmountable hurdles of cramming a world into the *binary strings of code* for a computer and the frightful prospects that might await us should we succeed—that Jerry Hobbs gathered eight graduate students together and asked them to spend the summer programming definitions of the world around us. This effort really captivated me, in much the same way that the idea of programming any kind of ELIZA hack or creating a Blocks World triggered my imagination. With ELIZA you could create your own personality for the psychotherapist. With a Blocks World you could become your own Einstein, define your own physics.

With a project like Common Sense Summer, you would need to be less fanciful and more analytical, but it still seemed like a wonderful frontier upon which to labor. You would be describing your world to an emerging life form that someday might inherit it.

Hobbs had recently received the first copies from his publisher of a book he had edited with Robert C. Moore entitled *Formal Theories of the Common Sense World*. I picked up the book from his desk and asked how he would code for the computer a representation of book.

"The first thing I would do is sit down and think, Just what is a book? It's a physical object on the one hand, which conveys information by means of language, on the other. The third aspect of it is how it comes into being, what its role is in society.

"Before you can talk about the physical aspects of a book, you have to know something about paper. Let's presume you know about paper."

"And of course we can't assume anything," I said. "You would have to make a note to yourself: Code a definition for paper."

"Exactly!" Hobbs said with a laugh. "Have a grad student go off and make up a theory of paper."

"And then you have to have a notion of print, of what writing is, what the alphabet is," Hobbs said. "And all of these things are going to have both the physical and the content dimension. So at the bottom you are going to have this theory of the alphabet and kind of a naive theory of language: how words are built out of letters, how sentences are built out of words, and then you have things like lines of text and that a page consists of a sequence of lines. So then you have this notion of page, and the whole time you are doing this on the physical side you are also doing it on the content side so that you have some notion of what a sentence conveys.

"And then on the social side, you have to worry about how does it come into existence. To what use is it put? How is it distributed to society? So this leads you into the questions of authorship, why people read, and things like bookstores."

Hobbs paused for a moment and then he said something that I found thrilling: "It seems to me as if all of that is quite doable, actually."

I agreed. He had in several seconds provided an outline that wasn't complete, but that certainly points the way toward providing a computer with a concept of *book*.

Had a robot with arms and a vision system wheeled into the room as we talked, it would have been able to pick up Hobbs's book from his desk, leaf through the first few pages, and find that it was dedicated to John McCarthy. Should that day ever come, one hopes that the name John McCarthy, along with a good many others I had run into, would ring a bell.

"You've just done a very good job of defining one word and all the concepts that go with it," I said. "Now why couldn't you and a bunch of graduate students just start doing that and shoveling them into a computer? Just get everyone working on a word list and let it grow."

"That was the intention," Hobbs said. "It turns out different people think different ways."

"But I could agree with what you were saying about a book. And looking out your window I see a tree and I think I could provide a pretty good description of a tree, beginning with its physical looks, variations in branches and leaf patterns. From a cultural standpoint, you would code for their long importance to man—providing shelter, fuel, food, and that there is often a strong kinship between man and trees. And you could do the same in describing the road out there."

"I think this was definitely the aim in Common Sense Summer," Hobbs said. "And I think it succeeded three months' worth. It's just that it takes more time than that."

I was concerned because he didn't have plans for a second Common Sense Summer. I suggested he turn the project into a communal effort over the ARPAnet—ask for volunteers to offer definitions. "Actually," he said. "That's an interesting idea."

But he seemed to place more faith in the emergence from somewhere of "some grand synthesizer" who would come along and see the problem with new eyes, discover the proper approach to take, an approach that had always been there but that had never been recognized.

As with Minsky, McCarthy, and Sussman, Hobbs had a hope that bordered on faith that there was some young hacker out there, probably an introverted kid who was yet to learn that at MIT, Stanford,

Carnegie-Mellon, and other places that mattered the term nerd was shorthand for brilliance and that it was an exalted title that one could wear with pride.

Whenever I heard the established leaders of this field speak of their belief in the brilliance of the young, it made me think of how similar so many of their childhoods had been. And thoughts of the childhoods I had heard described made me concerned for those just starting out, who had to endure early years in schools and social systems that had no appreciation for what the future of such a child might bring.

In a sense, all the world of AI and robotics was awaiting some precocious young hacker who was going to sit down at a computer terminal and achieve a resonance with the machine's logic beyond what had ever been known before. They were awaiting the Grand Synthesizer, someone who would find a way to describe to the computer all that was around and about it.

Such conceptual breakthroughs usually seem as obvious as night and day in retrospect. It may turn out to be the Boolean equivalent of "Let there be Light," some variation on the theme of "Moby is One."

*

Before I left, Hobbs demonstrated a program he was working on to enable a computer to analyze sentences. He asked me for a sentence, and looking out the window, I said, "The sun streamed down through the leaves of the tree."

He typed the sentence into his terminal and said, "Actually this is not going to work, because it doesn't know the words *sun, streamed, leaves,* and *tree.*" But he continued to work at the terminal, cranking in lines of LISP coding.

The extra work paid off, the program was able to parse my sentence into logical language, and I found the result to be poetic. I also wondered if the restructuring of what I had said would in any way offer a glimpse into how the brain of some future robot might view the world.

Hobbs read the results from the screen: THERE IS A STREAMING EVENT, AND THE THING WHICH IS STREAMING IS THE SUN.

*

On the fourth floor of MIT's 545 Technology Square is the office of Steve Berlin, an MIT researcher and a board member of the national organization called Computer Professionals for Social Responsibility. Berlin has a young face wreathed in long black hair that flows into a full beard. He was wearing a plaid shirt over a green T-shirt. He has holes in his jeans, and a peaceful yet intent air. And on his bookshelf is a stack of twelve paperback copies of Jonathan Schell's

The Fate of the Earth, a subject in which he has great concern.

Individuals such as Jerry Hobbs and Phil Agre are trying to give computers intelligence and common sense for the noblest of reasons. Yet it is the military that for decades has been picking up the tab for nearly all of this country's basic research into computers and robotics. And though the military must feel its reasons noble, too—the defense of the country—there are those who fear that the Department of Defense, by way of its Defense Advanced Research Projects Agency (DARPA), will make the world a more dangerous place by having too much faith in computers and by thus using them to automate our nuclear arsenals. Whereas the military may feel that keeping humans in the decision-making loop will consume precious time, some of the researchers I spoke with believed it is crucial to keep humans in the loop. This would prevent a computer, which is at once fallible and unforgiving, from initiating a string of launches that could result in the destruction of all human, and for that matter all mammalian, life on the planet. These critics point to previous false alarms, in which computers at the North American Aerospace Defense Command facility beneath Cheyenne Mountain in Colorado, have in various ways issued alerts that (so very, very fortunately!) were not valid.

Berlin and I left his office and walked a few blocks to the F&T Diner, he carrying a copy of DARPA's Strategic Computing Plan, which was the computer world's version of the Strategic Defense Initiative, or "Star Wars" (which would require even more computing research and development). Strategic Computing was DARPA's challenge to computer scientists to come up with three specific programs—one for the navy, one for the air force, and one for the army.

For the navy, DARPA wants a "battle management system," an AI computer that would be able to use and understand the spoken word to converse with the commander of a fleet about tactics. This conversing with computers sounds like something out of *Star Trek* or *Star Wars,* but this is what the DARPA document said it was after:

It would generate hypotheses describing possible enemy intent, prioritize these according to their induced likelihood, and explain the reasons for the prioritization. Drawing upon previous experience, together with knowledge of own force and enemy capabilities, it would generate potential courses of action, use an ultra-rapid rule-based simulation to project and explain a likely outcome for each course of action, and evaluate and explain the relative attractiveness of each outcome considering such criteria as protection of own forces, inflicting damage on the enemy and the rules of engagement.

For the air force, DARPA wants a "pilot's associate," which would be another chatty computer, an automated copilot that would speak to the pilot and understand the pilot's response. Topics of conversation would include basics, such as the status of the aircraft's operating systems and the geography of navigation. But the computer's conversations would also extend to higher-level concerns, such as enemy defenses, the purpose of the mission, tactics, and strategy. The system would definitely have an opinion about what it thought the pilot should do. To quote from the DARPA document, it would have "instruction on advanced tactics from more experienced pilots and up-to-date intelligence information on enemy tactics to aid the less experienced pilot on his first day of combat." The document also creates a fascinating picture of computers gossiping about the brilliance or ineptitude of their human pilots. It reads, "Certain classes of newly 'learned' knowledge will be automatically exchanged among pilot's associates."

I had already come to know one of the early versions of what DARPA wanted for the army: an autonomous vehicle, which is to say a robotic tank, which is to say Carnegie-Mellon's much beloved Terragator.

I remembered how, while I was at Carnegie-Mellon, everyone would provide a description of the work he was doing along with his office hours, telephone number, and other vitals when you asked the computer for his electronic-mail address. Kevin Dowling's work description had included this phrase: "Hacking combat robotics for the Autonomous Mobile Robots Group." When I'd asked about this, he had said, "That was actually a joke. I've had that there for a while, but now it's not so much of a joke anymore."

Steve Berlin and I got a table deep in the back of the F&T, and as we sat there, adding our words to the lunchtime din, adding our stream of conversation to the sea of voices, I thought about how delightful it was to be human and alive and how vibrant was this odd collection of individuals who somehow get along in a grouping called society. Just as I could sit for a long time and enjoy watching a rookery of gulls or puffins squawking and eating and taking off and landing, for an instant I saw the F&T Café as something wonderful. Yet puffins and gulls haven't figured out a way to destroy their world, and humans have, so I also became fearful for the well-being of those in the F&T and those gathered for lunch or for any other occasion throughout the world. Even without artificially intelligent computers and robots entering the fray, it sometimes seemed there was precious little holding things together in a world so filled with the means of destruction.

But soon there would be intelligent computers and robots, and I knew from talking with others at MIT and Carnegie-Mellon that the three projects outlined in the Strategic Computing Initiative were only the beginning. If a talking computer could handle strategy and defenses for a fleet of ships, the next step would be handling the same tasks, and then more, for the entire country. DARPA's Strategic Computing document spoke of the need for automating defenses against attacks by nuclear missiles, "where systems must react so rapidly that it is likely that almost complete reliance will have to be placed on automated systems."

The problem with automated systems is that, without a strong human override, we would already have been plunged into nuclear exchanges on several occasions, when our existing computer defense systems sounded the alarm for incoming missiles after having incorrectly responded to such sights of the skies as a flock of geese and a rising moon.

Yet DARPA isn't the only cheerleader for placing computers into battle-management positions. I was soon to meet an MIT researcher named Carl Hewitt, who was working toward the day when we would turn over the keys to all weapons to computer and robotic guardians who would govern, and police, the world.

I was pulled back from my thoughts on the wonders of humanity and the sheer niceness of being surrounded by happy people as Steve Berlin spoke of the similarities between the scientists who created the first atomic bomb and those who are today working on computers and robots.

"I'm concerned that the same sort of thing is happening all over again, that what we have is a parallel to that," Berlin said. "We're talking about projects within computer science that would be funded to a similar extent, which would be major crash programs to develop new ways of fighting war. We're talking about new military technologies that could potentially make war easier to fight, which could lead to more conflicts.

"And I wonder what people who are involved with it now, people who are involved just because it's exciting technology and who are involved because it's the only way to get money for the research they are doing, what are these people going to be thinking in twenty years or in fifty years? I wonder if we've learned any lessons. Sometimes I think we haven't. Sometimes I think that each generation and each person has to go through the whole experience again. And that scares me. That disturbs me."

I mentioned a recent conversation with Marvin Minsky, in which he had spoken so bleakly about the tenuous situation on Earth and the need to get off the planet and into the stars, just to provide the safety net of not having all our eggs in the one fragile basket.

"I've heard that argument, and it doesn't persuade me," Berlin said. "I don't see any evidence that once we're up in space, we'll do any better than we do here. If we can't solve our problems here, why would being in space make it easier? In fact, it will make it harder. The environmental constraints will be much greater. We'll be in transporters, we'll be so crowded together that problems that we can walk away from here will just explode.

"Without a lot of social thinking, without a lot of revolutionary new ways of learning to communicate with each other and to live together, living in space isn't going to be any better."

*

The same DARPA that wants to bring all these things to pass also provides an intimate platform upon which the computer scientists can debate the pros and cons of the militarization of their creations. That platform is the ARPAnet, the wonderful electronic mail network that links the major computer- and robotics-research centers.

It was at Carnegie-Mellon that I first learned the joys of the AR-PAnet, and whenever I had some extra hours to burn, I would log on to a terminal and start scrolling through the many bulletin boards, or bboards. There was a bboard for science fiction lovers, another for space enthusiasts, another for music, and among a long list of others there was the Arms Discussion Bulletin Board.

One night I came across a posting from a computer scientist asking for help with a certain aspect of developing missile-guidance systems. This message represented a textbook example of why DARPA had created this electronic-mail linkage of its major research universities.

But the responses the message generated might not have been what DARPA had envisioned. One posting read,

YES, I AM OFFENDED BY THE REQUEST FOR HELP ON MISSILE-GUIDANCE SYSTEMS, TOO—IT'S LIKE SAYING, "HEY, CAN YOU HELP ME DESTROY THE WORLD?" . . . I'M NOT JUST SAYING THIS TO BE A LIBERAL—MY TAX MONEY GOES TOWARD THESE MISSILE SYSTEMS, AND I'M GETTING PRETTY PISSED OFF AT THE ENORMOUS WASTE, IN BOTH MONEY AND HUMAN RESOURCES, EXHIBITED BY THE DOD.

Several minutes later, another posting appeared. This one said,

I THINK ALL THE DOD MONEY THAT MAKES THIS OPINION BBOARD
POSSIBLE SHOULD BE SPENT ON SOMETHING ELSE. IN PARTICULAR,
IT WOULD BE BETTER SPENT ON MISSILE-GUIDANCE SYSTEMS.

And then another posting was added to the screen:

I THINK ALL UNDERGRADS SHOULD HAVE A COURSE THAT EXAMINES
THE MORAL AND ETHICAL SIDE EFFECTS THAT THEIR NEW KNOWL-
EDGE CAN CAUSE. IF C-MU IS GIVING THE TOOLS OF SCIENCE AND
ENGINEERING TO STUDENTS, ISN'T IT ALSO THEIR RESPONSIBILITY
TO WARN THOSE STUDENTS OF BAD THAT COMES WITH THE GOOD? I
PERSONALLY WOULD BE OPPOSED TO WORKING ON DEFENSE WORK,
BUT QUITE OFTEN I SEE PEOPLE TAKE JOBS IN THIS AREA BECAUSE
IT'S WHAT THEY WANT TO DO. I WONDER HOW OFTEN THEY REALIZE
THE IMPLICATIONS OF THEIR WORK. I'M NOT SAYING THAT STUDENTS
SHOULD BE TAUGHT THAT DEFENSE WORK IS BAD, BUT THEY SHOULD
BE SHOWN THE DIRECT AND INDIRECT EFFECTS OF TECHNOLOGY AND
ALLOWED TO DECIDE FOR THEMSELVES IF THEY CAN LIVE WITH THE
IMPLICATIONS.

Yet another posting read,

I THINK THAT WE ALL BENEFIT GREATLY HERE FROM THE DOD (WHAT
IS IT? 70—80 PERCENT DARPA FUNDING?) AND IT ISN'T RIGHT FOR ANY
ONE OF US TO CRITICIZE SOMEONE WHO WANTS INFORMATION ON
MAKING MISSILE-CONTROL PROGRAMS RUN FASTER. IT'S DISTURBING
TO SEE SUCH POSTS, BUT ONLY BECAUSE THEY REMIND US WHAT OUR
WORK IS ULTIMATELY BEING USED FOR. IF YOU WANT TO MAKE SUCH
EXCUSES (E.G., I'M JUST DOING INTERESTING WORK, AND I DON'T
CARE WHERE MY MONEY COMES FROM; I'M USING UP MONEY THAT
WOULD BE USED FOR BAD THINGS, LIKE MISSILES; MY RESEARCH IS
REALLY NONMILITARY, BUT IS FUNDED THIS WAY BECAUSE OF THE
POLITICAL SITUATION; I'M NOT RESPONSIBLE FOR THE END USES OF
MY RESEARCH) GO RIGHT AHEAD, BUT DON'T YELL AT PEOPLE WHO
DON'T MAKE SUCH EXCUSES.

*

Steve Berlin spoke of the difficulty of trying to do work that can't
be twisted into unsavory uses.

"For example, what's the difference between building missile-guidance systems and airline-guidance systems? Between predicting droughts to help prevent starvation, versus predicting nuclear-fallout patterns so that you can bomb somebody when you know the prevailing winds are in a certain direction and that you won't be as affected by the radiation? What's the difference between building data base systems to help track the poor in Appalachia to keep track of who has inoculations and who doesn't versus tracking blacks in South Africa to see whether they are living where you have designated they should live.

"You can use computers to analyze photos of installations around the world in order to verify arms treaties that make further arms treaties possible. But the same software can be used to analyze photos of U.S. demonstrations to determine who is speaking out on social issues. There are some real ethical dilemmas that are posed by these things."

*

Patrick Sobalvarro once received what he believed to be a ridiculous letter from SRI International, the same think tank that had sponsored Common Sense Summer. The letter, from William Schubert, a senior systems analyst, said SRI was under contract to the DoD to "study possible applications of Artificial Intelligence and Robotics systems to military functions. Our interests include combat, combat support, logistics . . ."

The letter had been sent to Terrapin, the company Danny Hillis had created to sell mildly robotic turtles whose goal in life was to wheel around the floors of elementary school classrooms as the children used an Apple computer and Logo language to program the moves. The Terrapin Turtle came complete with a ballpoint pen that could be programmed to go up and down to create designs as the robot turtle moved across a paper-covered floor, traveling from one destination to the next, according to the program the student had written.

Sobalvarro, as a senior programmer for Terrapin, initially ignored the letter. But in the small hours of the morning he and another Terrapin programmer, Leigh Klotz Jr., were laughing at the frightening language used by vendors advertising in defense-industry magazines, such as *International Defense Review,* and *Aviation Week and Space Technology.* Suddenly it was decided that SRI deserved a reply.

The result became a bulletin board classic, being sent all around the ARPAnet. And parts of it were later published in the magazine *Science 85.*

The letter was divided into the appropriate sections for an armaments proposal. Under the heading "Survivability," Sobalvarro and Klotz wrote, "The Turtle enjoys very low observability, due to a minimal radar cross-section and an almost non-existent infra-red signature. In addition, its ground-hugging characteristics maximize terrain masking, resulting in lowered target acquisition by most classes of SSM [surface-to-surface missiles] and ASM threats. . . . *The Turtle can make a 180-degree turn in less space than any military vehicle currently in use by U.S. forces: ground, air or sea."*

Under the heading "Guidance," they wrote, "with judicious use of the Turtle's touch sensors, one could, theoretically, program a large group of turtles to simulate Brownian motion. The enemy would hardly attempt to predict the paths of some 10,000 turtles bumping into each other more or less randomly on their way to performing their mission. Furthermore, we believe that the spectacle would have a demoralizing effect on enemy ground troops."

Under the heading "Munitions," Sobalvarro and Klotz said that the Terrapin Turtle's only weapon was its ballpoint pen, but that the Turtle "can be programmed to attempt to run over enemy forces upon recognizing them, and by raising and lowering its pen at about 10 cycles per second, puncture them to death."

They then described yet another lethal option: "Turtles can easily be programmed to push objects in a preferred direction. Given this capability, one can easily envision a Turtle discreetly nudging a hand grenade into an enemy camp, and then accelerating quickly away. With the development of ever smaller fission devices, it does not seem unlikely that the Turtle could be used for delivery of tactical nuclear weapons."

Final blows to the military and their vendors were delivered with the price sheet, which showed the per-unit prices of turtles going up, not down, with volume purchases. And it contained this note on installation costs: "The Terrapin Turtle is designed for installation at no cost by children and elementary school teachers. We feel that military installation cost should be under $10,000/unit."

The frightful thing was that, from my conversations with Red Whittaker at Carnegie-Mellon, I knew there was military interest in a robot about the size of Terrapin. And *Science 85* was later to report that the Hughes Aircraft Company had actually hooked a Terrapin Turtle to a mainframe and had it pick its way "across a floor mined with telephone books and cardboard boxes in an effort to demonstrate the feasibility of 'autonomous weapons vehicle operation in an environment of uncertainty.' "

Science 85 also reported on Grumman Aerospace's proposal for an autonomous flying mine that could fly up to thirty miles, land on three skids, and then wait for an enemy vehicle to come within one thousand yards of it, at which point it would fly across the ground to home in on its target before exploding.

During my stay at Carnegie-Mellon I walked into Kevin Dowling's and Mike Blackwell's office one night and heard their compact disk playing Jean-Michel Jarre's *Computer Incantation for World Peace*. The music seemed at once frantic with energy yet soothing and as bright as light. Perhaps if we ever do succeed in getting common sense programmed into computers, it will be from the computers that the incantations for peace will flow. Perhaps then there would be an end to madness, a return to common sense.

*

I stopped by Phil Agre's office one night to pick him up for dinner. It had been about a week since our initial conversation about his work with Blocks World. Before leaving the office he sat down at the computer terminal and typed a final message. "What I've told it to do is just randomly decide to stack blocks on other blocks eight times and then wait for further instructions."

This was intriguing. The robotic hand would be stacking blocks as we ate our dinner. Would it be learning in our absence? As we dawdled over coffee, would it be getting smarter?

"Most likely one of the stackings of blocks will cause it to fly out into space somewhere or to get hung or to blow up or something. When we get back, we'll see."

Then he said, "It wouldn't be an awful lot smarter, but yes, I guess you could say that. I told you a lot about what I want this program to do the other day, and it's only doing the lowest-level kinds of learning right now. So it's getting smarter in some low-level ways. But not on anything like the scale I was telling you about the other night."

We were just walking out of his office when Agre took one last look at the screen and stopped in his tracks. Something was wrong in Blocks World, and he didn't have the heart to leave it unattended during dinner.

A few minutes later we were outside and walking over to the apartment of David Levitt, an MIT graduate student in artificial intelligence, with a special interest in computer-generated music composition. As we approached the security entrance to an apartment building, a woman held the door open for us, and Agre and I hurried in without having to buzz for David. This was common sense in action. Agre had climbed two flights of stairs before realizing we had walked into the wrong building.

Levitt buzzed us in, and we again trudged upstairs. "Hello," said Agre as we walked in the door. "Many apologies for being late."

Levitt has the kind of car that would satisfy most of Gumby's automotive criteria: It started; it would probably make it to a Grateful Dead concert (especially if the show were in Cambridge); and nobody would want to steal it.

We drove to the Casa Portugal, and as we sat around having a pre-dinner beer, Agre told Levitt about wanting to leave his robot within Blocks World working while we ate and about the last-minute correction required just before we left the office.

"I felt really bad," Agre said. "I had to take off for dinner and I accidentally told it to do two incompatible things: to put Block B on both A and C. And it picked up B and put it halfway between A and C and started vibrating back and forth. I felt really bad, like I had just told a dog to fetch an electrical cord." Levitt and I were laughing. So was Agre, but not as hard. "It looked at me with this plaintive expression on its face. I felt so bad!"

The warmth with which he told this story, the real guilt it had caused him, and the anthropomorphism were such that it seemed Agre was in many ways already treating his program as something with a life of its own.

The conversation turned toward the difficulty in programming of avoiding endless loops. With Blocks World a loop would be the confused vibrations of the robotic hand holding Block A and trying to put it on both Block B and Block C. In our world a loop would be drinking to forget your problems while the effects of your drinking created problems. It was interesting how studying loops in machine life sheds light on the loops in human life.

"People are pretty good at not getting themselves into loops," Agre said. "But you very often hear people make very much the complaint that 'No matter what I do, every relationship I get into ends in the same way.' That sort of thing: doing the same thing over and over again and not being able to see it coming until you've just done it again, is what was happening to my program, and is what will probably continue to happen to it for a long time to come.

"We just get ourselves into bigger and bigger loops and get worse and worse at noticing them. We get the impression that we are going forward." Agre paused for a moment and then said, "We mostly go forward. Don't get me wrong. But the point of saying this is that it is a real problem in real life to notice that you are going around in circles. And it's just as difficult for people in real life, in the qualitative sense, as it is for machines.

"My machine is amazingly stupid, so it doesn't notice these very basic loops. But no matter how smart I make it, there will be loops it gets into that it doesn't notice. And that's not a limitation of the machine. That's a limitation of nature."

I asked what it takes to develop loop detectors that search for repetitions in behavior.

"You should talk to Doug Lenat at MCC in Austin," Agre said. "He wrote a program called EURISKO. I think it's just a spectacular accomplishment. It's the first program that has been awake and growing and learning for any substantial period of time. It's terribly stupid, and Lenat had to rummage around in its insides every morning because it usually found a new way to break itself.

"Lenat dealt with, for the first time and in a serious way, a lot of really basic problems in making machines that have an identity and existence over a long period of time. For example, one of the technical capabilities such a program has to have is the ability to change arbitrary aspects of its operation. Because learning can take many forms, and it can take the form of having to change any way you have been doing anything you've been doing.

"It's an amazing accomplishment to have faced those problems," Agre said. "I've learned a tremendous amount from studying his papers and talking to him."

I mentioned the concerns of Steve Berlin and Joseph Weizenbaum that the military, and society in general, were becoming too dependent upon the intelligent computers and robots Agre and his colleagues at MIT, Carnegie-Mellon, Stanford, and elsewhere are trying to create. What would happen when he succeeded in his efforts to actually give a computer common sense? What would happen when the computers were intelligent enough to evolve into the kind of independent life form that so many researchers were predicting?

"Do we know?" said Agre. "No. We don't know. We will soon be in the place of the people who were developing atomic power and deciding whether to do it and whether history would hate them. And I have this bad fantasy that if I do my job properly, I will be reviled at my death."

I was struck by how closely his fears matched those of Berlin: that the creation of intelligent computers might someday be seen with the same remorse as the introduction to the world of atomic bombs.

"It strikes me that the first generation of intelligent programs is going to be psychotic just because it's so hard to build a self-organizing entity that doesn't fall apart," he said. "And falling apart is what's going on when a person starts hallucinating and starts losing his mind.

"Lenat's program fell apart left and right. He had to prop it up every day. He would sit down at his terminal, start it up, and say, 'Oh no! It found a new way to screw itself.' And he'd go in and repair it by hand. It's nice if you can understand what it's doing. But if you can't, it gets to be a problem.

"Now that isn't so bad if I just have it sitting in my office and I don't tell it about the [computer] network. Then it's okay. And we'll just do our research until we figure out a way to build stable programs. But you know some idiot is going to put it in charge of a nuclear power plant and tell everyone that it's safe.

"Too many people go around thinking that machines can be smarter than people. Now it's possible that they can be, but it's a foolish thing to believe a priori until it's been demonstrated."

"Yes," said Levitt. "If they are as smart as [defense secretary] Caspar Weinberger, we're in real trouble."

"When machines start getting halfway intelligent, they will have the same problems that people do and for the same reasons," Agre said. "They will become unstable and begin hallucinating for the same reasons that people become unstable and begin hallucinating."

"Because they weren't hugged enough," said Levitt.

I laughed, but Phil Agre didn't.

"Exactly," he said. "The main strand of psychoanalytic theory of psychotic phenomena is that they originate in inappropriate care in very early childhood. That is, the basic assembling of the inner parts of the mind doesn't happen straight because of the child's attempts to compensate for an inadequate environment.

"So, who knows what accounts for adequate care of a brand-new computer? I don't. But I think that people are the way they are for good reasons, not random reasons. And I think these reasons are going to be true for machines, too. And I think machines will have the same limitations that people will and for the same reasons.

"I have put this in a simple way, even though it's not exactly true, and there's about two hundred footnotes needed, but I think it's critically important that people understand this, that they don't let the

Caspar Weinbergers of the world put a supposedly intelligent computer in charge of the nuclear weapons and the nuclear power plants."

"Of course this has already happened," said Levitt.

"It's already happening," Agre said. "And these people are out of their gourds!"

*

When our conversation turned to DARPA's Strategic Computing Plan, Phil Agre saw both good and bad. He has already started working with the new programming opportunities that the connection machine will offer, and something like a connection machine will likely emerge from DARPA's program.

"It will be wonderful to develop connection machines. It's just that these fools want to put them in charge of atom-bomb-powered X-ray lasers in space to shoot down missiles within one minute of their being launched—even if the 'launch' happens to be a natural-gas pipe that explodes in Siberia.

"I hope it makes a difference that we are somewhat more politically aware than the scientists working at Los Alamos and the people who were doing nuclear physics back in the thirties," Agre said later that evening. "One thing I'm very glad for is that there's not the slightest chance the Russians will ever outpace us in artificial-intelligence technology. The Russians are singularly stupid when it comes to artificial intelligence. They put their equivalents of the people who are doing AI here in mental hospitals."

Chapter 10 ✍

ROBOTS, GOD, AND THE LIVING TRUTH

HARVARD'S MEMORIAL CHURCH has a pristine white interior, bordered with white columns that are topped with Corinthian opulence and garlands. The most decorated parts of pillars seem always to be the tops, as if they were celebrating great mysteries and truths that were to be found somewhere up a little higher, just beyond our sight.

Coming from a chamber somewhere behind the altar, on the night I was there, were the sounds of the Harvard Bach Society Orchestra, in final preparation for the evening's concert. From the cacophony of individual musicians in preparation, there came a unity as they all slid into the same piece of music, and as this singular effort grew and flowed out into the main chapel, the talking stopped. We all listened as the orchestra, still unseen, played Pachelbel's *Kanon in D Major*, which is opulent and garlanded itself.

The last time I had heard the *Kanon in D* had been during a late-night session at Carnegie-Mellon, when I had listened to it on Kevin Dowling's Sony compact disk player. Thoughts of Carnegie-Mellon and Terragator came to mind, as did thoughts of Phil Agre and Blocks World and so many other researchers who were trying to create intelligent computers and robots. For just a few hours earlier, while sitting in a Harvard Square coffeehouse, I had finished reading Joseph Weizenbaum's *Computer Power and Human Reason*.

The first time I had met Weizenbaum, he had modestly suggested I read the last chapter first and work myself back accordingly so that the earlier chapters wouldn't bore me. But I found the book an engaging and eloquent read.

Sitting in Memorial Church listening to one of the most humanistic of all pursuits—the making of music—the things that Weizenbaum had said in his book seemed all the more frightful, for he was warning us that the kind of gentle human spirit that made such music possible was in danger of being crushed by the emergence of a new species, a form of life that we were now creating.

Wrote Weizenbaum in his book:

I accept the idea that a modern computer system is sufficiently complex and autonomous to warrant our talking about it as an organism. Given that it can both sense and affect its environment, I even grant that it can, in an extremely limited sense, be 'socialized,' that is, modified by its experiences with its world. I grant also that a suitably constructed robot can be made to develop a sense of itself, that it can, for example, learn to distinguish between parts of itself and objects outside of itself, that it can be made to assign a higher priority to guarding its own parts against physical damage than to similarly guarding objects external to itself, and that it can form a model of itself which could, in some sense, be considered a kind of self-consciousness. When I say therefore that I am willing to regard such a robot as an 'organism,' I declare my willingness to consider it a kind of animal. And I have already agreed that I see no way to put a bound on the degree of intelligence such an organism could, at least in principle, attain.

But much of his book following this statement is dedicated to showing that whatever intelligence emerges from this new kind of organism will be "an intelligence alien to genuine human problems and concerns."

The alien nature of this intelligence, this inability to *know* what a human is, this inability to *know* and *feel* love and compassion, could result in problems for a humankind that is becoming increasingly dependent upon computers.

It was the same problem of internal representation that had been faced in various ways by Jerry Hobbs with Common Sense Summer, Marvin Minsky with his *Society of Mind*, and Phil Agre with his Blocks World. How do you translate the physical and abstract properties of our world into binary strings of code? What combination of ON/OFF gates can enable a computer to know what a door is, or what a human is? And no matter how detailed a description one might enter into the code, what was there at the core of the computer—given that we had no homunculus, no little man—what was there that would enable it to *understand* the description?

In his book Weizenbaum provides an example of the kind of story problems some AI programs have been created to solve: "Tom has twice as many fish as Mary has guppies. If Mary has three guppies, how many fish does Tom have?"

When the computer responds, "Tom has six fish," it might seem as if we were dealing with a truly smart computer, but what the use of language masks is that the computer is simply translating the problem into an equation of $x = 2y$; $y = 3$, and then expressing the result in terms of Tom and fish.

This, like Weizenbaum's own ELIZA, is a cute hack, but Weizenbaum writes, "It is not possible for such a mechanism to have any idea of what fishes and guppies are, or of what it can mean to be a boy named Tom."

He argues that until we have computers that can know what it means to be a boy named Tom, until we have computers that can know what it is like to have a mother and a father, to have brothers, to have the joys and adventures of childhood, to experience the heartbreaks and anguishes and traumas of life, we should not allow alien intelligence to enter into the control of human lives.

Yet these alien intelligences are already intricately woven into our society, and this trend is expected to increase greatly. It is the degree to which these alien intelligences will control us that so frightens Weizenbaum, and the readers of his book.

In his book he quotes from a planning paper written by the director of a major computer-research center that speaks of the need for building trustworthy computers that won't turn against their creators.

The paper reads in part, "the computer has been incorporating itself, and will surely continue to incorporate itself, into most of the functions that are fundamental to the support, protection and development of our society. Even now, there is no turning back, and in a few years it will be clear that we are as vitally dependent upon the informational processing of our computers as upon the growth of grain in the field and the flow of fuel from the well."

In a rather chilling conclusion this paper spoke of the need for computer scientists to exercise caution in the kinds of intelligent programs they created "to assure that the computer dominated future is one we wish."

Weizenbaum's book criticizes computer scientists who have suggested man is but a biological computer, and, along with the computer, a member of the genus *Information Processor*.

"Man is not a machine," he wrote. "I shall argue that, although man most certainly processes information, he does not necessarily process it the same way computers do. Computers and men are not species of the same genus."

And he said, many times, in many different ways, "There are some things beyond the power of science to fully comprehend."

*

After the concert, while the city slept, an unforecasted snowstorm rolled in and left several inches on the ground. But Joseph Weizenbaum trudged into his office on the fourth floor of MIT's 545 Technology Square that morning for our appointment, and I was waiting to see him. Weizenbaum's views have not been much appreciated by his colleagues at MIT. When I later visited with Hubert Dreyfus at Berkeley, he would tell me that during his own time at MIT (between 1965 and 1970) Weizenbaum was the only one within the AI community who would dare to be seen talking with the author of the paper that scoffed at computer intelligence, which was called "Alchemy and Artificial Intelligence."

"Weizenbaum would invite me out to his house to talk about these things," Dreyfus said. "I thought it was very courageous of Weizenbaum, and open-minded, to talk to me at all in those times."

The first time I had met Weizenbaum, he had said, "I've been called a carbon-based chauvinist. "I've also been called a racist, in that I prefer the human race to a race of computers. That's very strong language, it seems to me."

As he spoke, with the charming remnants of a German accent, these denunciations he had endured still seemed to have a sting. In 1936, three years after Hitler came to power, the thirteen-year-old Weizenbaum and his parents were able to leave Germany before the doors slammed shut on Jewish emigration. The memory of the Holocaust remains within him, and it is from this that his fears come for anything that can be used to dehumanize people. Weizenbaum, who resembles Albert Einstein somewhat in appearance, with his long black and gray hair that is swept back and a matching mustache, fears that, improperly used, computers could prove a devastating force of dehumanization.

I told him that his book left me with a chilling sense of foreboding. "That's not improper," he said. "I make a little joke in there about the pessimist and the optimist. I say the optimist is the guy who says, 'This is the best of all possible worlds.' And the pessimist says, 'Yes, that's so.'

"And I have the feeling that I'm living that. All my colleagues here are very optimistic. And what are they optimistic about? They are optimistic that they can actually do the things that they are thinking about. I think they can, too, which is the source of my pessimism. So I'm really living that joke."

After Weizenbaum's ELIZA program was published, there were some who predicted that building a computerized psychiatrist would be possible and beneficial, in that this would allow widespread and economic psychiatric assistance. Others predicted that computers could become impartial judges, with immediate access to all points of law and past judicial findings.

To all such suggestions Weizenbaum brings the question of "ought". Ought we to do this? "My assertion is that even if it were possible that a computer could be made to act, for example, as a psychiatrist, even if we could achieve that technically, I say that we ought not to. And the basis for that assertion is precisely that the way of knowing that a computer has is very different from the way of knowing that we have."

A computer can never know what it is to have a mother, what it is to have a father, what it is to live as a normal being with the specter of injury, sickness, or death always somewhere in the shadows, and also to have the glow of hope and the joyful pursuit of dreams. In short, the computer can have no comprehension, Weizenbaum believes, of the very essences that a psychotherapist would deal with.

"So when the computer says, 'I understand,' the computer is, in effect, lying," Weizenbaum said. "And it's for that reason that we ought not invoke a computer for such human transactions."

Reductionism is the term Weizenbaum uses to describe efforts to cram the definition of a human and a description of the world into programmable code. And returning to his grim optimist-pessimist joke, he fears that the optimistic programmers will be sufficiently successful to create the illusion that the computer understands humans, and that because of this illusion the computer will be given increasingly greater control over a form of life that it can never really know.

"What reductionism denies fundamentally is that there are components to human wisdom, human knowledge, and the human experience that are not, so to speak, machinable," Weizenbaum said. "People say to me, 'Aren't you saying that there are some things beyond the reach of science to grasp?' And to me the answer to that is obvious: Of course I'm saying that! Of course I'm saying that. And I don't mean to just sneak it in. It's true."

In his book Weizenbaum wrote, "Sometimes when my children were still little, my wife and I would stand over them as they lay sleeping in their beds. We spoke to each other in silence, rehearsing a scene as old as mankind itself. It is as Ionesco told his journal: 'Not everything is unsayable in words, only the living truth.' "

*

A computer need not know such things as the *living truth* if it is being used as a cruncher of numbers for government and industry. But as it becomes more and more a part of our lives, and a part of the governments that lead us, the question of what a computer can and can't understand—especially in terms of humanity—becomes urgent. As our world becomes more computerized, only those things that can be computerized will remain a part of the officially coded domain of knowledge. Weizenbaum sees this as an insidious force that may ultimately strip us of our very culture.

In his book he writes of a seemingly innocuous occurrence: the creation of a computer-generated map of the world's tectonic plates. The map was created by gathering all of the world's computerized data on earthquake epicenters and churning it into a single program that used the information to outline the major fault lines. The map carried a notation explaining that only information from 1961 onward had been used, because the older information wasn't in a format that could readily be fed into the computer. The carefully recorded observations of decades and centuries past, the leather-bound fieldbooks of generations of geologists, were of no value.

"The computer has thus begun to be an instrument for the destruction of history," he wrote. "For when society legitimates only those 'data' that are 'in one format' and that 'can easily be told to the machine,' then history, memory itself, is annihilated."

Arising from this could be a frightfully immortal knowledge base that could take on an inertia of its own. Consider a world in which the computers go on forever, as the humans arise and die, arise and die, providing whatever services the computers might require during the brief span of human years. In such a world, it would be the computers that would be the repositories of the information, the holders of the culture.

"The knowledge that is transferred to the next generation of humans is then exactly the same knowledge as what we had, and so on for a large number of generations," Weizenbaum told me. "Now, that's not how we transferred knowledge from generation to generation until now. What happens is it's almost a story-telling transmission of tradition and so on. And in that process, the knowledge is always transformed a little bit. And it is this cultural informing process that constitutes the life of the society, the life of the culture. And the curious paradox is that the immortality of knowledge means the death of culture. Because the transforming function is gone."

When I asked about this, he said, "It is ominous, and I use the word here in the sense that it is an *omen*."

*

Of course what people like Hans Moravec, Danny Hillis, Marvin Minsky, and, perhaps, myself would like to do is to jump inside the computer and then get a nice robotic body in which to go tooling around the universe. But what if we can't make that transformation? It sure seems like the computers and robots, at least for the long haul, would be having all the fun.

If the downloading technology were developed, who would own it? DARPA? Bill Paley? How tightly would it be regulated, how difficult would it be to get placed into a chassis? Who, or what, would grant to one the favor of immortality?

Apart from all this, it may be that the personality we so treasured, the very self that so terribly fears to die, would be immediately washed away once inside such a machine, for our own computing contribution might be something like wiring a pocket calculator into a mainframe Cray supercomputer.

Only time will answer such speculations, but one possibility is that humans will have to sit on the sidelines as we watch the new form of life we have created grow greater and greater until it has far surpassed us. This brings forth interesting questions about where our loyalties might be: to our species? or to the evolution of intelligence?

I asked Marvin Minsky about this one day, and he said, "I think that the species is just a step in evolution." He also said, "I'm sure the chimpanzees thought people were a bad thing."

This is similar to what Robert Jastrow, founder of NASA's Goddard Institute, has written about man serving as a stepping-stone for the next evolutionary species: "A non-biological intelligence, springing from the human stock, and destined to surpass its creator."

Minsky has long been a proponent of getting human colonies into space, just to preserve the gene pool should the Earth be blown away. I agreed with this, but Weizenbaum didn't.

"You say it sounds like a good idea," Weizenbaum said. "I don't quite know what you mean by that. But I think it's a very bad idea. Again, we come to an example of instrumental [computer] reasoning. It matters, *it really matters*, why a particular act is done. If one builds this escape hatch, then one is perhaps accepting the possibility that this final catastrophe, or the probability that this final catastrophe, will happen. And by making it more credible, you also make it more probable.

"I think there are some things that we should simply reject absolutely: We *will not* let them happen. Jastrow talks about the computer intelligence fulfilling the task of evolution, which is to say further developing intelligence in the universe. This very quickly leads people to the conclusion that a genocide of the whole human species would, in fact, not be too bad. 'It isn't that everything would be gone. You really shouldn't weep quite so hard. It's not that catastrophic.'

"It seems to me there is a quality of badness, a quality of blackness, where you no longer argue about shades. You get into absurdities. And I think this is a great absurdity and also a dangerous absurdity because in a certain sense it lays a scientific or philosophical foundation for a genocide on the entire human species.

"Just in saying that 'it wouldn't be so bad,' that 'something would be left over,' that 'the purpose of the universe would go on'—whatever that means—I think that is the beginning of justification for the elimination of the human gene pool.

"We used to have the IBM seven-oh-four, a very nice machine. And today we have the PC, which is an even nicer machine. This year we have the eighty-five Cadillac, so why mourn the Model T. It is that sort of thinking. It basically says that the real living human race, which includes babies suckling on their mother's breasts, and people shooting pool and thinking about mathematics, loving each other and so on, it means that they are not worth mourning over, that the loss of the human gene pool isn't that bad.

"Perhaps as a very abstract concept, certainly the IBM three-seventy is more than a substitute for the seven-oh-four. It is better and faster. And so it isn't necessary to mourn the loss of it. If you think of a species being replaced by another, then perhaps the loss of the first isn't to be worried about either.

"I will say it quite explicitly: *There's nothing left after you've destroyed the human species!* Humans are the ultimate value. It's so fundamental. Everything else is based upon that.

"I think one can use other vocabulary for this: Genocide of the human species is the *murder of God.*"

*

There is a sign on the wall of Carl Hewitt's office that reads: Caution! Human Beings Here. Handle with Care. Another sign reads: The Love in Your Heart Wasn't Put There to Stay. And another sign says: We Are Loving in a World of Permanent Change. While on the stereo was playing the romantic and mystic music of Cat Stevens's old *Tea for the Tillerman* album. There is a bright, multicolored Japanese windsock and a leather easy chair. A row of file cabinets has been set up immediately inside the door so as to serve as a privacy wall and create a pleasant tunnellike passage into his Hewitt's inner sanctum.

With such a cozy and humanistic office, with such a Beatrix Potter nesting den, why did this guy want so badly to turn the keys of civilization and government over to a set of international computers and robots?

Of all of the researchers I would talk to, it would be Carl Hewitt who would come the closest to enunciating the very bleakest scenario that Weizenbaum had pictured. It was as if Hewitt were the very personification of the optimist that so haunted the pessimist.

Hewitt hoped that his work might someday enable the creation of machines that could take care of us, that could be our guardians, and that would also be our rulers and policemen. He wanted to program computers and robots that could "garner all the weapons of mass destruction into a machine-controlled system, in the same way that you have to take matches away from children."

As distasteful as this would be to Weizenbaum, I would later find some cautious enthusiasm for the notion coming from what seemed to me a surprising place: the Harvard Divinity School.

Hewitt is working on how systems of artificial intelligence can take advantage of the emerging parallel computers, the kind of computer that like Danny Hillis's connection machine, will be more like the brain in its ability to handle several tasks at once. Hewitt wants to create a program that can represent several viewpoints or areas of expertise and pass messages back and forth between them in order to make value decisions.

"It may be a qualitatively different kind of intelligence," he told me, "one that can do the kinds of things that communities can do but individual humans can't." He said that the various representations of expertise within the program would "basically conduct a regular scientific debate within the computer." In what would be a most intriguing program, Hewitt said, "The community inside the machine would match well with the human communities outside."

Having just spent time with Weizenbaum, I asked Hewitt—a pleasant and soft-spoken man who, with his red flannel shirt, brown corduroys, and waffle-soled boots, looked as if he had just returned from bird-watching—whether he found some aspects of AI frightening from a humanistic standpoint.

"It is a technology," he said. "It is a powerful technology, a very powerful technology. Powerful technologies can be two-edged swords. They can be used for good, and they can be used for evil. And sometimes it's hard to decide whether they are being used for good or for evil when the applications first start.

"So, yes. It is potentially dangerous. It's hard to know whose interest we all serve. Is the value in our culture? Or is the value, in terms of long-term survival, in our species? What is it that we want to see survive and grow and thrive?

"Barring human extraterrestrial travel, there is a certain finiteness to the situation here on this planet. This is going to become more complicated as we develop these robots and as they develop more autonomy. So it's a question, over the very long term, of what to do with the humans.

"How many of us can there be?" he said. "What kind of quality of life can we have? And how do we want to share this environment and promote the culture with machine intelligence and the robot?"

Could robots perpetuate our culture, if not the species?

"Oh yes. Quite definitely," he said. "They can also carry it to other solar systems, which we won't be able to do for a very long time. They can also help us control ourselves, in the sense of providing some political infrastructure and stability, so that we won't have this terrible threat of nuclear war hanging over us all the time."

I asked how robots would achieve this stability, and he said, "Basically by taking control of these terrible weapons in some kind of way so that it's not left to human whim and emotion, with nationalistic states threatening each other with these things."

This doesn't mean that all weapons would disappear, it would just mean that only computers and robots had access to them. "There still needs to be some kind of police force for the control of terrorism," he said. "So it's not clear to me that [the weapons] would be completely taken away. Clearly they would have to be taken away from the control of humans, otherwise you would have this terribly destabilizing situation.

"It's hard to see exactly how we'd transition into that kind of an environment," he said. "I think that people are going to have to get good and scared before it happens. There will have to be some small uncontrolled nuclear wars that threaten to get out of hand, before some kind of institutional basis is established.

"And the robots could help control that by stabilizing that institutional basis for the control of these weapons of mass destruction in such a way that the humans feel more acceptable in terms of turning over control of these things."

Somehow I found it difficult to imagine the various governments of the world actually entrusting their nuclear arsenals to an independent organization of computers and robots.

"It appears that it's either that or we don't survive the long haul," Hewitt said. "Since I'm an optimist, I think that somehow we'll manage to pull it off."

*

If we manage to scare ourselves so badly with our nuclear weapons, that we create a kind of robotic United Nations to take care of us, it would seem that a loss of personal freedom would come with the mechanization of our government.

"You are giving up something in return for some potential gains in terms of stability," Hewitt said. "And you are trusting to a certain *Ruckelshaus* extent that you have created this benevolent form of life that will want to keep the species around and preserve it . . ."—here he took a long pause—"in some kind of fruitful way. But there can't be any guarantee that it is going to be so."

I could scarcely believe what I was hearing. *Trusting* that we had created this *benevolent form of life that will want to keep the species around and preserve it?* What kind of tomorrow was he trying to create? Hewitt scared me more than Weizenbaum did.

But the optimist saw this future as better than what he saw as the alternative. "The species has this incredible power to destroy itself, and it's the extreme danger of that which is the big threat to the species and its general inability to control itself in terms of population, resources, and pollution. There is an exponential growth to it that will gradually consume the planet, perhaps suddenly and catastrophically in a nuclear war.

"So it looks like the humans need help in their use of the planet. And artificial intelligence is the technology that can be very useful in helping them get that kind of control."

This was a technological solution, I said. Couldn't we find a humanistic one? Rather than giving control to automated systems, couldn't we learn to understand each other better?

"I think that better understanding helps. But history is not on the side of long-term human understanding," Hewitt said with a laugh. "The necessary turnover in personnel you get in human-based systems, because of their very short lifetimes, seems to throw instability into the system. And the general diversity of human stock we have, in terms of different languages, cultures, and interests, is not something that can be smoothed out very quickly.

"And because of the growth of other technologies, such as nuclear technology and weapons technology, and the very rapid progress in those fields, we have a tremendous mismatch in terms of how far you can evolve the humanistic political system as opposed to the rate of advance of weaponry. So I think some kind of technology has to come in here to counterbalance and help control these other galloping technologies."

I mentioned Joseph Weizenbaum's book and said that the idea of technological fixes for human problems frightened him and that he thought we should turn back from such a course. Could that be done?

"No. That's the one thing we can't do. You can't turn back your life. You can't turn back history. You just have to plot your course. You might try to stop this kind of research in the United States, but that wouldn't stop it elsewhere. Instead I think we have to work at making sure this technology will be used for benevolent purposes. And productive purposes, and humane purposes."

The term that kept coming to mind was *turning over the keys to the store,* I said. And I asked whether this might be met with considerable resistance.

"It depends on what the circumstances are at the time," Hewitt said. "People could be very scared and very threatened by small nuclear wars popping off here and there—like between India and Pakistan, or between Israel and the Arabs. Or if Qaddafi gets the bomb.

"These things are going to get *used.* And once they are used, preventing escalation is a serious problem. And it's a threat to life on the planet. This is going to sink home over the next few decades, and people are not going to put up with that kind of threat to their existence as it becomes more real.

"So, yes, I think it will be with some trepidation that these institutional controls are put into place, but I think there's going to be a strong pressure to do it as well. In the current political climate it doesn't seem possible for this to happen. But the technology is going to change. The artificial-intelligence technology is going to make large advances. And the climate of opinion is going to change as the threat becomes more real and more concrete. And more miserable, such as when we have to go back to worrying again about how much strontium there is in milk as radioactivity gets blown around the planet."

"It sounds like a frightful future any way you look at it," I said.

"Yes," said Hewitt. "I'm an optimist. I would like to see a productive scenario come out of it, and I think that we need, in fact I'm convinced that we need, technological help in setting up the infrastructure to deal with the problem."

"How do we inculcate the human values and abstractions, such as right, wrong, and God into . . . ?"

"Into machines?" Hewitt said. "I think we do to a certain extent by incorporating certain principles and processes into the operation. But beyond that, those are emergent phenomena. In other words, the humaneness of the computer system, its ability to be just, will emerge from the processes that we set up inside the machine, because we can't specify ahead of time with all that much detail and concreteness what we mean by *justice*."

My thoughts turned to the journal of Ionesco.

*

That evening I met Joseph Weizenbaum at the Harvest Restaurant on Brattle Street, just off of Harvard Square. Over dinner I recounted my conversation with Hewitt, and Weizenbaum was visibly disturbed by what Hewitt had suggested.

I said that it appeared there were many forces at work in AI that were focused on the day that we could turn the keys over to a computer and say, "Take good care of us."

Weizenbaum said, "And the computer's response would be, 'Say please!' "

I laughed, but Weizenbaum didn't.

*

The optimist-pessimist paradox works both ways, for Marvin Minsky seemed to me every bit as pessimistic as Weizenbaum, but for quite the opposite reason. His fear was that work in computer science and robotics would not be able to continue. He feared that all intellectual pursuits might be brought to a halt as civilization was toppled by religious fanatics afraid of science. This emerged when I was asking about possible obstacles to developing intelligent programs.

"There might be laws against making computers," he said. "We might have a Shiite revolution, or the kind of revolution Frank Herbert mentions in *Dune*, very cryptically. Why are there no smart computers in Frank Herbert's world of Dune? The reason, he says, is that at some point the public decided that it shouldn't be done, for religious reasons.

"It happened in Iran. It's perfectly possible. They don't have science there now. It happened in Rome when the Christians took over. The Greeks were doing fine in mathematics, and then it died out for a thousand years. I don't think Euclid could have imagined how it could stop, but it did."

With words that I found haunting, he said, "I think that most of the intellectuals of the world are scared stiff that civilization is in trouble."

"From something other than nuclear war?" I asked.

"Yes. From religion. From whatever. Have you been outside the East Coast? Do you ever listen to the radio? I'm not saying that it's different from what it ever was, but superstition is as popular as science is. More people believe in astrology than astronomy today."

*

A few months later I happened to be reading Walter Miller's novel about the future, *A Canticle for Leibowitz*. As I read, I thought of both Minsky and Weizenbaum. The book, published in 1959, is a painfully believable scenario in which civilization advances its science to the point where it has enough nuclear bombs to wipe itself out, and proceeds to do so. This is followed by a "Period of Simplification," during which the angry, maimed, and mutated survivors spend generations gleefully destroying all remnants of the learning and science that had brought upon them their nuclear nightmare. Books are burned. All machinery is destroyed. Anyone who can read or write is killed.

Finally man emerges from this dark age and begins to learn again, advancing to the point once more where it has developed the nuclear arsenal required to destroy the world. The book ends with civilization doing so, but with a small group dedicated to preserving knowledge escaping the planet and departing for space to begin again.

Somewhere between the murderous ignorance of the Simpletons and the insanity of destroying an entire civilization with science used wrongly there must be some corridor, some safe passage into the future. Or at least this is nice, and perhaps even necessary, to believe.

Chapter 11 ❧

THE DIVINITY OF DOWNLOADING

THE ELEVATOR DOOR opened on the sixth floor of the Harvard Divinity School Library, and I suddenly had the oddest feeling that I was aboard a spaceship. Perhaps it was the sense of aloneness in this quiet building, but mostly I think it was the long, narrow Lucite-covered catwalk that stretched from the elevator door on the one end to the office of Gordon Kaufman on the other. The catwalk was bordered on both sides by rows of bookshelves, and if you looked down between the gap of the shelves and the catwalk you could see that the shelves did not begin upon this floor, but continued from the one below.

Walking along the catwalk, a couple of titles at eye level were *Special Days in the Sunday Schools* and *A History of the American Sunday School Curiculum*. Now this may seem odd, but both titles struck me as really being quite interesting, and I thought it would be nice to be able to sit down and read them and then work my way through most, if not all, of the other books in this library. For I was thinking about downloading, and the eternities of time one would have for intellectual, as well as spiritual and physical exploration.

Gordon Kaufman, the Edward Mallinckrodt Jr. Professor of Divinity, certainly knew more about what was in those books than I did, and perhaps this is why he couldn't get too excited about spending a century or so sitting around reading them. My conversations a few days earlier with Joseph Weizenbaum at MIT had made me curious about what people at the Harvard Divinity School would think of computers as a new and intelligent species, and about Hans Moravec's vision of downloading the contents of human brains into immortal robots.

I wasn't surprised that Kaufman objected to the notion of downloading, but I was surprised at his reasons. He thought it would be boring, and I completely disagreed with that.

"Why would one want to go on beyond ninety years?" he asked.

"Just because it would allow you to do so many things," I said. "You could go off and explore planets, see new worlds. You could spend three hundred years in the Harvard Library reading. You could spend the equivalant of an entire lifetime walking through the mountains exploring."

"It isn't at all clear to me why I or anybody else would want to spend three hundred years in the Harvard Library," Kaufman said. "It would be very boring. Or why would anyone want to spend any number of years roaming around the cosmos, seeing what Mars is like or the Moon, or some other solar system somewhere? Surely there is a point where the kind of life human beings live becomes boring on the one hand and totally meaningless on the other."

Whereas I couldn't agree with Kaufman's notion that ninety years was enough time, and that exploring the Moon, Mars, and the cosmos beyond could become boring, he did raise an interesting point when he quoted a theologian who had said, "An endless extension of this life is a definition of hell."

Even given the outside chance that living for eternity could get old, it would still be nice to live life in ten-thousand-year blocks of time, deciding at the end of each block whether to sign up for another hitch of universal exploration or whether to set an alarm clock and sleep out the next ten thousand years, just to add a sense of freshness to your next block of travel and exploration.

Kaufman tipped back and forth in his colonial Harvard chair as he spoke, as I went to and fro in his rocker. He is a handsome and distinguished-looking gentleman with brown hair, graying at the temples, and with scholarly glasses, the frames of which are brown at the top and then blend into clear plastic along the bottoms. We were sitting beside a striking lead-paned window, across the large but cozy office from his mahogany desk. The walls were covered with oak bookcases, above which hung a framed copy of Rembrandt's Saint Paul, and a print of Heronymus Bosch's five-centuries-old vision of Hell.

Having been raised a Lutheran, which has always seemed to me rather a casual and nondogmatic religion—at least in the way it is practiced (and, in my case, largely not practiced)—I had come to the Harvard Divinity School expecting a response to downloading to be something like, Why look to the computer for immortality, when those who believe have already been granted immortality? But for Kaufman, this wasn't a source of objection, since he doesn't believe in the traditional views of Heaven and the immortality of the soul.

"Many contemporary Protestant theologians wouldn't any longer talk in terms of the immortality of the soul. I wouldn't either," he said. "I would say that virtually all of the major theologians, the really top people in the twentieth century, would respond that way. The ordinary idea that when you die, you go to heaven and still live, is not accepted by many theologians at all. There are a great number of people who might call themselves theologians who have a very traditional view," Kaufman said. "But most of the people who have made a significant impact on theological reflection in the twentieth century do not take this traditional view."

I found this surprising. "What will happen to you when you die?" I asked. "Will you just die?"

"Yes."

"So if you just die, you are being good for goodness' sake during your lifetime. As opposed to being good for . . ."

"That's one of the problems with the traditional view of reward and punishment," Kaufman said. "It involves a lower-level of moral insight and thus a less-dignified understanding of what it is to be a human being. It has the human as only being able to work for a prize—a carrot-and-stick kind of a being. You are either going after a carrot or trying to avoid being beaten by a stick.

"But the whole point of morality," Kaufman continued, "is that human beings are capable of, to use your words, being good for goodness' sake. That is to say, being sufficiently attracted to justice and truth and working toward a social order that overcomes suffering and injustice. Humans will do that simply for the sake of those values, not for the sake of some prize."

"Then from a religious perspective, there would be no spiritual problem with someone downloading," I said. "It just becomes a question of why do it?"

"That's right. It's a kind of question of what significant meanings and values you have. There's no spiritual problem with it at all."

"Wheeee!" I thought.

*

Finding Kaufman to be free of moral problems with the concept of downloading, I tried, just for the fun of it, to sell him on the concept. But he seemed adamantly against it—for what seemed to me all the wrong reasons.

"The contents of my brain are not me," he said. "That's not what I refer to when I use the word *I*. In fact, it's very rare, if ever, that I speak of the contents of my brain or think of the contents of my brain.

Look at the way we use the language. 'I'm getting hungry. It's almost six o'clock.' Does that mean the contents of my brain are getting hungry? We're talking about my stomach. 'I'm going to walk home as soon as we are done with our conversation.' What does that have to do with the contents of my brain?"

Everything! I thought, though I let him continue, while thinking to myself that it is his brain that was holding the conversation, it was the brain that yearned to go home. It was the brain that decided that the conversation would be completed prior to going home (although this turned out not to be the case). It was the brain that had the concept of home. It was the brain that remembered the way home and that provided the coordination of muscle firings to enable him to walk home.

"The question of who I am—I who am getting hungry right now, and I who am going to walk home, I who remember what I did when I was a kid fifty years ago, and I who am going to die in the next twenty years, all of these things, whatever it is that I associate with myself, whatever it is that makes up my 'I,' is completely connected with my body, and it has very little to do with the question of the contents of my brain."

I gave it one more try: "If the technology got to the point where you could download with a sense of self, your same personality, all of your mechanical functions, so that you could play your tennis and drive your car; if you could still relate to others, feel a kinship to others, if you could have that, have a body that works better than yours . . ."

"Now that's beginning to sound like the 'I' going on," he said thoughtfully. "I'm not inclined to say that at some future time this might not be possible. I think at this juncture it's really beyond imagination, but it's conceivable that with all kinds of developments like the ones that have outstripped our imaginations before, that if we're able to work out some electronic circuits to dump the contents of this onto a tape, that we then could continue the sense of 'I' . . ."

He was sounding more intrigued. I told him about the connection machine that was being built and suggested that if we could build a machine to mimic the synaptic actions of our brain, then perhaps the 'I' could go on.

"That's an interesting question, whether the 'I' could be stored," he said.

I felt triumphant. Quick, call up Moravec and tell him to get ready for one more! But the triumph wasn't complete, nor even long lasting.

"If it could go on," I said, "would you be interested in going on?"

"No, I don't think so," he said. "I think life is long enough. And I certainly wouldn't want to go on indefinitely. Maybe a little while, I don't know. But basically I'm quite satisfied to come to an end. And I think it's a very peculiar kind of desire to want to go on indefinitely. I can't quite put myself into that mentality."

*

It was getting late, Gordon Kaufman was getting hungry, and so I got ready to head back to MIT. But one of the last things I asked before leaving was whether there would be value in creating robots to have religious thought.

"Religion is nothing else than the human attempt to orient our lives in the world," Kaufman said. "And if there are beings, beings other than us, that have a sense of self-identity, and thus also a sense of the power to direct their own lives, they are going to need some form of orientation. They are going to have to have some way of conceiving the world in which they live and the possibilities in that world for themselves and their own powers in relationship to that world. That's all religion is."

*

When I left Kaufman's office and walked back down the long catwalk to the elevator, I dawdled to look at some of the books that were on the shelves that seemed to go straight through all of the Lucite floors below as if they were soaring up from the very core of the earth. Should Red Whittaker and Hans Moravec ever figure a way to blast all of Henry Hornbostel's ship of a campus into space, they should send a party back to pick up a couple of buildings such as this.

By the time I got to the elevator, Gordon Kaufman was ready to leave, so I held the door for him. We immediately resumed the conversation, and I ended up walking him home. The winter evening became darker and darker as we walked past Kennedy Square and through the tree-lined streets, past the elegant and well-landscaped homes with brick walkways and circular drives. The quiet was disturbed only by our voices, the occasional passing of traffic, and the existential wail of a siren in the night.

I told Kaufman that I felt rather like someone who had just been told there was no Santa Claus. "Yes," he said. "That's fair enough. But there's more to God than Santa Claus, actually. But the disillusionment might be something like that, because the God of the tradition is a whole lot closer to Santa Claus than a lot of people would be willing to admit. Would you agree to that or not?"

"I don't know," I said. "I've just been confronted by this. For instance, one thing I do every night is I pray there won't be a nuclear war."

"That's a good thing to pray for."

"Is it?"

"I hope you do more than pray for it," he said.

"Does it do any good to pray for it? If God is a symbol to guide our action, then praying doesn't do any good. Demonstrating might, but praying won't."

"Let's not make those distinctions too sharp," Kaufman said. "In the first place we know very little about what kind of meditative activities will actually orient us, transform us, break our bad habits, so that we can, to use a phrase that you used earlier, come to appreciate good for goodness' sake.

"And whatever else praying to God might mean, it would mean at least that one was trying to open oneself up to that which is thought of as representing good for good's sake as completely as possible," he said. "And thus it might have at least a transformative effect on you."

"So prayer is good for the person."

"It might well be," he said. "It would depend upon the prayers. But it might be more than that. It might also have to do with the way one related to other human beings and the concerns that one developed for other human beings, and thus it might be good for a community as well—particularly with communal prayer.

"What goes on in a church or synagogue in which a whole group of people together try to articulate and express their deepest aspirations and their willingness to give themselves to those aspirations may have a transformative effect of real significance. I don't know whether your dispositions are Christian or not, but the most profound and deepest prayer is the one of Jesus in the garden: 'Not my will, but Thine be done.' That's what prayer is all about. It's transformation of the self so that that which is good in itself enters into my being and changes me. Not my will, not what I want, not my self-centeredness, but God's.

"I don't think petitionary prayer, in the sense of God preventing a nuclear holocaust, is going to do any good if we keep building our MX missiles as fast as we can. Because what we are doing with our lives, with our activities, is moving increasingly—really as fast as we can, I would say—toward a nuclear confrontation. And on the other hand, with our evening prayer, we expect God to stop this somehow. Now that's a kind of self-contradiction in our behavior in which the prayer isn't going to do much good unless it turns us around in the way we behave with our MX missiles."

"So we have to save ourselves," I said.

"No. I don't say we have to save ourselves. I'm just saying that whatever else prayer is, it must be a way in which we transform ourselves and give up all these damn projects that we are engaged in, or the better part of them. The worst part of them, I should say. But it may be that prayer has something to do with that transformation, with that turning around, which, so far, we Americans and the Russians haven't been able to manage at all. So I don't say prayer has no significance. But I also don't think it has the kind of significance that a lot of traditional religious folk wanted to give it."

"So you don't think we are talking to God?"

"We may well be. Why not? The question is, What does talking to God mean? What kind of an activity is that?"

"Some people would say that talking to God means talking to the guy on the pearly throne," I said.

"Yes. That's what they would say. I don't believe that. I don't think there's any guy on a pearly throne."

"You see God as more of a force of goodness."

"That's a fair way to think about it," Kaufman said.

"It almost sounds like the movie *Star Wars.*"

"The Force," Kaufman said. "Maybe. We didn't ever know whether the Force was the force of goodness, however. Or whether God is intended to symbolize that. But perhaps so. Perhaps so. But that is the way God has always been thought of. Not really as sitting on a pearly throne, but as a reality that is continuously at work in the world for goodness. *Salvation* was the traditional word. *Salvation* means, simply, 'making whole.' Making well again what has been damaged or diseased. Bringing fullfillment. So in that respect God has always been the force of goodness. And to pray to God is to turn oneself in the direction, as well as one can, however one thinks of that direction, toward what will enable one to become a better person." He paused and said, "Now, that sounds a little more traditional than some of the things I've been saying."

We both laughed.

It was completely dark now, and we had nearly reached Kaufman's house. The dark and the talk of petitionary prayer reminded me of a fourteen-day sailboat race across the Pacific I had gone on. I don't think anything is much darker than the ocean at night when storm clouds block the light of moon and stars. There had been some nights of heavy weather when, at the changing of the watches, I believe meteorologists studying their satellite pictures back home could have gone onto their late-night newscasts to announce, "Over the Pacific Ocean we have a major prayer pattern developing just this side of the Pacific High."

I asked Kaufman, "Is there a force out there?"

"It depends upon what we mean by force," he said. "Certainly it is the case that in the course of the evolution of life, and particularly in the course of the development of human history, human beings began, over many generations, to worry about questions like goodness and truth and justice. Why did they begin worrying about those things? Is there a force? Is there something working in the historical process that enables human beings to begin thinking about those things after many generations of development?"

"One could argue that from an evolutionary standpoint only those animals that created a social habitat in which they could flourish would survive," I said. "And those that were totally warlike would perish."

"I agree," Kaufman said. "And one can just turn that over and say, That means there is something in the universe that leads us, that draws us toward what we are here calling goodness."

*

The next afternoon found me back at Harvard. I walked across the scrappy and much trampled grass of the Yard to the magnificent temple grandeur of the Henry Elkins Widener Memorial Library to see George Williams, Hollis Professor of Divinity, emeritus, whose person and scholarship had been honored with an office on an upper floor of the building.

Widener Library inspires awe just approaching it. There are thirty low-rising, broad-footed steps of stone that run nearly the entire length of the building. At their summit are the twelve pillars that also run nearly across the full length of the building. Inside are deeply paneled ceilings, marble walls, and more pillars, all to celebrate the knowledge that resides within this exceptional collection of books.

As I climbed white marble stairs from the main floor en route to Williams's study, I paused on a grand landing to look at two larger-than-life paintings memorializing fallen American soldiers from World War I. Each painting rested within an alcove. The painting in the left alcove was of a dead soldier, whose ghost was rising from the body. Beneath the painting, carved in marble it said, Happy Those Who with a Glowing Faith and Warm Embrace Grasp Death and Victory. The painting in the alcove to the right showed American troops marching, carrying a flag, while above their heads flew a huge eagle. The

carved inscription below read, They Crossed the Sea Crusaders Keen
to Help the Nations Battling the Righteous Cause.

The senselessness of World War I was matched by its horrid butch-
ery: the hand-to-hand combat, the bayonet fighting, the slaughter of
men and horses charging against cannons, and the introduction of gas
warfare. There's never been a war without its own terrible version of
these, and one of the reasons I had come to see Williams was to get
his opinion of Carl Hewitt's suggestion that perhaps computers and
robots could do better by humans than we had done by ourselves, that
perhaps removing the vanity, greed, stupidity, and other facets of human nature from the control of the tools of war might provide for a
safer and more peaceful world.

A week earlier, when I had been at the Bach Society concert at
Memorial Church, which is directly across from the library, I had
experienced much the same mixture of compassion for the dead and
agony for the human condition that enables such wars to arise. Much
of the right wall of Memorial Church is covered with the names of
faculty and students who lost their lives in World War II. On the left
wall is a much smaller set of plaques in honor of Harvard men who
had died in the war in Vietnam. The Vietnam plaques occupy a wall
between two windows, and between the other three windows along
that side, the walls seem dangerously bare, as if they were being reserved for the brass tags from the next wars. I can remember looking
at those bare walls, afraid that any future war might bring about the
complete disintegration of the walls, the windows they framed, and all
that they stood for. I thought people should cover those bare spaces
with tapestries, paintings, even old calendars if nothing else. We just
had to make it clear that the wall space was already taken: There was
simply no room for another war.

*

My conversation the previous day with Gordon Kaufman had taught
me that when speaking with Harvard theologians, it was best to expect
only the unexpected. And now the seventy-one-year-old Williams, whose
office was a wonderful mountain range of file cabinets stacked atop file
cabinets and of tables awash in books and papers, proved again that
these scholars of God and such might not be thinking in the patterns
one would assume.

"My first reaction to this emerging possibility of computers becoming so intelligent they could actually create themselves, and in a sense
reproduce, and design an electronic life of their own, is that it sounds

like fiction," Williams said. "But I don't recoil from that entirely. I don't think it's necessarily to be feared.

"It might be that it would be a development freeing we who are capable of producing computers and this whole system that makes this kind of technology possible," Williams continued. "Even at this present stage I think it is perilous for us as human beings. I don't think we can stand it for many more generations. And it might be well for a good deal of this to be taken over by machinery capable of doing this kind of work.

"The problem would be, is there a benign intention in this electronic world? Apart from such phrases as *user friendly*, there's no reason to believe that they are friendly. And that in fact is a distinction between artifical intelligence and our own. Ours is touched by love and mercy and a whole range of other aspects besides intelligence. And my thought is, this might be our salvation to be free from some things," Williams said. "If we can be assured that it's benign, or neutral. I would say it would be satisfactory if it were neutral."

I was really quite taken aback by this white-haired blue-eyed, and soft-spoken gentleman, who seemed to be embodying both Carl Hewitt's hope for a technological solution to our tendency to engage in war and Joseph Weizenbaum's reverence for the things humans know that machines couldn't.

He also found historical reasons to fear a shift in the balance of power should computers become too powerful and too wise. "In the sociopolitical realm, all through history, it happens over and over again: There's a vicar or lieutenant or viceroy or prime minister or something that emerges. At first they are deputized by and represent the authority. And finally they assume it, often showering the king or emperor with lavish praise and making it pleasant, until finally the main person becomes incapacitated.

"That happens over and over again. I'm speaking of over the millennia. For the moment we see advantages in all these computers emerging around us to do our work more efficiently and to shore things up for us. And what occurs to me, as a historian, is that this happens all the time. You have a benign arrangement, but there's also a process of subordination, and the emperor, king, or potentate loses out, and the deputy becomes the effectual ruler."

This brought Williams to the point of asking the most chilling and perhaps the most significant question I had encountered in my travels: Could a computer fall from grace?

"Animals are neutral to us," Williams said. "Except if we trespass on their ground. A bear can go after us, but basically they are not after us. If computers had the capacity to fall, as theologians say man fell, and if they could become wicked and become concentration camp directors all on their own—all of the weird things one can imagine— if they are not neutral, if computers don't just reflect and refract and extend further just the basic intelligence of human reason, then they *are* dangerous. Then we've got another problem altogether. I don't think that's been discussed. I don't think that's even been foreseen, has it?"

"No," I said. "I haven't seen people consider that question at all. Even though some have suggested that since man is certainly fallible, since we are riddled with fault, then the machines might be a reflection of us."

"If the fault is simply a typing fault, like a typo, and if it's a typo involving a nuclear bomb, and it turns around and does unexpected things, that is very destructive," Williams said. "But that is not evil in a theological sense. That's a defect in the electronic equipment.

"None of your theorists in artificial intelligence have a chapter in their books, do they, on the possibilities of a fall, a *real revolt* like the fallen angels? If these things could revolt against us and become dominant—there's no speculation like that, is there?"

"Well," I said.

"We can always turn them off, can't we?"

"We hope so," I said. "But there may come a time when we wouldn't be able to."

Over the next few weeks my research would lead me to people who would describe in detail precisely why we may reach a point where nothing short of a complete war against computers could hope to succeed in unplugging them. For my conversation with Williams I just said that our society was already depending upon computers in ways that it could not easily let go of, and that science fiction writers had long speculated on the various ways in which computers could become aware of their stronghold within a society and take advantage of the situation.

Several years earlier a book and a movie had been produced called *COLOSSUS: The Forbin Project.* The plot rested upon a project that in many ways wasn't as ambitious as what Carl Hewitt would like to see done. Whereas Hewitt would like to see international control of weapons by a centralized computer system, complete with robotic police, COLOSSUS was an impregnable computer (sealed in a bombproof vault and surrounded by extremely radioactive barrier chambers) that controlled all of the defensive and offensive missiles of the United

States. The movie begins with a party at the White House and Pentagon as everyone prepares for a carefree life unhampered by military threats. But soon after COLOSSUS is turned on, it announces detection of a similar computer in the Soviet Union and demands to be linked to it. Because COLOSSUS is able to back up its demands by either launching or detonating nuclear missiles in place, which it does, nothing can be denied it. The movie shows how quickly the established police forces adjust to the new chain of command and act as enforcers of whatever COLOSSUS requests. There is no happy ending in this movie. COLOSSUS, in a very logical and lethal way, simply takes control of the world.

Hans Moravec had mentioned the movie repeatedly during my stay at Carnegie-Mellon. And at MIT Marvin Minsky had described it as "a reasonable scenario."

Now, to my surprise, I also found this gentle theologian to be respectful of what a writer of science fiction might propose.

"I don't think that's a negligible consideration," Williams said. "Because science fiction is the imagination of society at the edge. It's informed science becoming fantastic and fanciful for the purpose of entertainment, but it might project a future possibility. So I don't think the imagination of science fiction writers is to be discounted.

"So I come back to you," he continued. "Is there any chapter that you know of where serious theorists of artificial intelligence discuss not mistakes in computers but malevolent intentions emerging?

"When you see a spider eating another spider, you don't say that it is malevolent. It looks awful to us. I saw this on a nature program the other night. Or out in the forest, you don't ascribe malevolence to one beetle going after another. But these computers are almost like huge beetles, rather complicated beetles—sapless, bloodless mechanisms that run on a different kind of juice: electricity. Is there any theorizing about the possibility of this thing becoming so sophisticated that it, too, is capable of wrongdoing?"

Study K on the top floor of Widener seemed such an odd place to be having such a discussion, yet perhaps it was the very place for such talks. For at the actual places of robotic and computer research and development, the scientists were too focused on how to create these new forms of life to seriously consider such an ethereal but ultimately crucial question: Could a computer fall from grace?

Williams's office seemed like an extention of himself. If he were ever to download, his robotic body would be hung with reading lamps and work tables and with storage baskets for books and paper. The study is a long, narrow room, with the door opening along the narrow end. The walls were lined with bookcases, tables, and filing cabinets. And down the center of the room was a paper-mounded island of tables. The piles of papers and books also ran across the floor and topped stools and chairs. We sat just inside the door, where two comfortable chairs sat on either end of a small red rug.

The man seemed remarkable to me in many ways. So analytical was his thinking that he could pause midsentence and make reference to "what I was saying in the previous paragraph." And his lifetime of theological study had seemed to prepare him for any possibility.

As was the case with Gordon Kaufman, he didn't like the idea of downloading the contents of one's brain into a robotic body, but for different reasons.

"I have very strong scruples against that," he said. "It's an elitist thing that goes beyond what I feel would be endurable. I'm appalled by it."

I asked whether he would still object if downloading were available to all.

"I feel there is a moral reason not to do it, even if society were capable of doing it globally," Williams said, using language stronger than at any other part of our conversation. "I find it revolting. Even if it were possible for everyone to be included. Then we are no longer living with our ancestors. It excludes those who have gone before, and therefore we are no longer like the millennia of people before us. And I believe that what makes us human is that link of experience.

"It wouldn't be a renewal," he said. "It would be a change of our human status. We would be unalterably changed. We couldn't ever go back."

Yet, he could also look at his own life, and at his belief in predeterminism and predestination, and pose the question of how much of a robot each of us already was.

"Am I just a glorified member of a termite colony, this university library being the colony where we are all just responding to the books and titles?" he said. "It's not so very farfetched. I've noticed a very interesting thing when I'm working here when the library is closed and locked. Very few of us have keys to this building. It's the central treasure of the university. When I'm in here by myself with just a few other professors on this floor, we go out to the bathroom at the same time. It's an amazing thing. This happens so many, many times." He laughed a bit at himself for having shown such a curiosity about it, but the scholar in him couldn't let go of such an interesting observation. "The other men don't seem to observe it, and see how frequently it happens. There might be four or five of us in the whole building, and we all feel the impulse at the same time. We have different mealtimes, we've been doing different things. And we are not in contact with each other, not doing the same thing at all. Yet the building itself seems to function as a termite colony.

"I was responsive to your inquiry on the phone saying you wanted to talk to me about computers and robots because this question has bothered me a great deal," he said. "This question of what I do as a scholar and as a scholar who also happens to be an ordained minister and an active member of the church—I have been increasingly reflective about this problem of what I myself do, and why I do it. It's as if I were a meteor launched into a world, taking a ride that no one is taking with me. I am myself on my own orbit and will fizzle out somewhere, light up the sky a little bit with my scholarship, and then go.

"I am convinced that perhaps ninety-seven percent of what I do and of what you do is predetermined. I can see it, by what I pick up in this room to put into a footnote, or by what I had for lunch, where I went for lunch, whom I saw. I come back to this room and I've got about thirteen or fourteen languages I'm using here. I can myself see that I am a high-powered computer. I know it. And at the same time I can tell that I am something quite different from what I accomplish. What I do is still distinguishable from what I am. And I speak to you with great conviction, as a historian and as a Christian and as an ordained minister and theologian, that we have something to defend here."

There was a knock at his door. We had run out of time, and a friend had come to visit. But he wanted to speak some more and asked if she could wait a few minutes.

I had much admiration for this man who could immerse himself in scholarship, spending his time trying to bring clarity to matters of philosophy and theology, and who could at the same time take such an elevated overview of his life that he could see a strong hand of predestination and predeterminism, a hand so strong that he could see that he was driven by this force that he could neither identify nor understand.

"It's as if we were part of something bigger, and I'm not sure what it is," he said, his voice implying that he found it all quite mystifying. "So I have struggled all my life with this thought of predestination, predeterminism, and have been personally overwhelmed by the degree to which we are robots. You and I are robots."

*

This conversation had taken some unexpected turns, and I did not want it to end. But after several minutes he said he could keep his friend waiting no longer. When he opened the door to bid me farewell and to welcome her in, she was nowhere to be found. This had a visible impact on him, so much so that I stayed. He sat down in his chair. I sat down in mine. He was the first to speak.

"Now, you could say, 'What have I done?' A friend of mine has come to give me a little birthday cake, and I made her wait and I'm sure that's why she left. And she's hurt now."

I was crushed by this. Part of my job as a writer is to be tenacious and to grab as much of a subject's time as I can. "Blame it on me," I said. "Can we call her up?"

"No, it isn't a matter of blame," he said. But his next words only made it worse: "It's a reflection on what she lived through in a Nazi concentration camp."

There was silence again, and the words hung in the air of his study. Then he continued, "I wanted to speak to you. I asked if she could wait for me. So it's a reflection on determinism. How much am I at fault? How much is she? And it's not a matter of fault in any case. How much of it is a mechanism of the concentration camp? Of the way she had been treated? The door was closed. We were talking on the other side, and because of that experience she probably felt excluded."

I felt horrible. It had been my fault. I again suggested that we telephone and explain my rudeness.

"No," he said. "It's not your fault."

It was, though.

"I've done quite a bit for her," Williams said. "I asked if she could wait. But I am *so conscious of those concentration camps* and of what the Germans did."

Thoughts of the concentration camps reminded him of why he thought the emergence of intelligent computers to be our caretakers might be a good development: "In the back of my thoughts of the computers taking over is my fear that we are not capable as human beings of taking care of ourselves. We are just going *mad*. I don't think we can remain humane very much longer. I'm quite fearful. So my thought is that computers could take the rattle out of life. Computers taking over might make us free to be more like the way we were in the early nineteenth century. Because I just don't see how this can go on. I really don't."

*

It was twenty minutes past midnight, and from upstairs I heard the beautiful minor-key voice of Marcia Katz singing a folksong to her infant, David, to help soothe his tears and help him along on the mysterious journey from wakefulness to sleep. Marcia was singing "Autumn to May" in a voice that was soft but so filled with love and patience that it was more beautiful than even the combined sweetness of the ones I had last heard singing the song: Peter, Paul, and Mary.

I was downstairs in the kitchen, thinking about a woman I had seen through a door at Harvard and reading Abraham Heschel's *Between God and Man,* trying to find out what it all could mean.

David cried again, but only a bit. For I heard a kiss, and then "La, la, la, and candy by the pound." There was another kiss, and "Sing tarry-o day! Sing, autumn to May."

The singing stilled the tears of David, but then there was crying again, and David's father, Ed, awakened and offered to rock his child. Marcia gently told Ed to sleep and continued to sing with such beauty that I thought perhaps young David was already very wise. David's crying stopped so that he could better hear ". . . the snail it turned into a bird, the bird a butterfly. And he who tells a bigger tale, would have to tell a lie. Oh, sing tarry-o day! Sing, autumn to May."

The big wall clock in the kitchen, as big as that in any schoolroom, ticked, ticked, ticked in analog grandeur. And then David was silent. The singing stopped. There was only the ticking of the clock and the sound of a kiss. Sleep, that mysterious and soothing state in which the brain diverts itself from the bothers of the day, had been attained by young David.

And as David slept, I wondered what kind of dreams such an infant might have, and also wondered what might lay ahead for the child and for every child sleeping that night. For even as David slept, there were certainly hackers of software and robotic hardware burning the midnight lights at MIT, Carnegie-Mellon, Stanford, and in places like Japan, where the sun would already be shining.

Perhaps Phil Agre's stick-figure robot was learning more about the universal laws of Blocks World, while up on the ninth floor Steve Chiu might be teaching the robotic hand how to crush cans without blowing its circuits. I had heard from Carnegie-Mellon that Red Whittaker was preparing to create a truck-size version of Terragator, and I was sure that Hans Moravec, perhaps over a bowl of chocolate milk and Cheerios, was trying to hack the download factor.

From my visits to the Harvard Divinity School there seemed one especially intriguing notion, one encouraging belief: that there was some kind of force somewhere out there, and that ever so gently and perhaps too slowly it seemed to be guiding us in a direction, a direction for goodness' sake.

Part III ❧

OUTRAGEOUS WORLDS

Chapter 12

ATOM BY ATOM

A FEW BLOCKS from MIT, down Massachusetts Avenue toward Harvard, there is a Chinese restaurant called the Mandarin, outside of which I stood one day waiting to meet one of the most brilliant and original thinkers involved in computer and robotic technology.

Of all the tomorrow makers I would meet, it would be the tomorrows of Eric Drexler that would seem the most outrageously enticing, the most capable of sending humans to the stars, and the most promising for getting us to and through that seductive gateway of downloaded immortality.

A conversation with Drexler is rather like Alice jumping down the rabbit hole and tumbling into Wonderland. Drexler wants to build computers and robots that are small, very small, *unimaginably* small.

Consider that you can fit about a million human cells onto the head of a pin. Now consider that Drexler wants to build robotic ships that could, like great paddlewheelers, travel the cytoplasmic sea found within a single cell. A robotic arm, like a freight derrick on an old steamboat, would be used to probe the molecular structure of the cell's DNA and make any needed repairs. All of this would be guided by an on-board computer in the pilothouse.

Place such a robotic ship into each cell of your body and they might be able to push regenerative DNA buttons and repair damaged molecules to keep you forever young. You might also be able to change from one person into another. A unified pressing of different DNA keys could result in a change in height, a change in appearance, perhaps even a change in sex. Depending upon just how much genetic information we carry from our evolutionary past, we may even be able to change from one species to another.

In what kind of land would these self-propelled robotic ships be working? The human cell is a magnificent structure, an enclosed sea of cytoplasm in which proteins flow about like robots with specific programs guiding their various tasks. Also floating around in the cytoplasm are the amino acid building blocks from which the proteins are built.

In the center of this sea there is an island called the nucleus, and within this island is the most magnificent library in the world, a library that in some molecular sense is as lovely as Harvard's Weidener with its garlanded pillars and temple stairs. What makes this library so sacred is that it holds the DNA: the genetic directions for life itself.

The DNA is in forty-six strands, called *chromosomes,* which can be likened to bookshelves. Upon these shelves are the genes that are the individual recipe books for the creation of specific proteins. It is the information contained in these genes that allows for the amino acids out in the cytoplasm to be strung together to create the protein workers that keep the cell alive and vibrating with activity.

One of the great wonders of life is the way in which this information in the library is carried out into the cytoplasm and used to direct the construction of the proteins. The books in this library are far too valuable to allow a lending library, so a librarian, called *messenger RNA,* makes an exact copy of the information expressed by a single gene and carries it out into the cytoplasm, where it latches onto a structure called a *ribosome* and, working with *transfer RNA,* starts stringing together the amino acids.

It is this ribosomal action of creating proteins that makes Drexler think that we may be able to assemble other kinds of structures— robotic structures. He speaks of "bootstrapping off of the ribosomes" to get the first generation of microscopic robots, which could in turn assemble even more complex molecular robotic machinery.

Such second-generation robots could be used to construct atom-by-atom computers that would be so small and so powerful that the entire contents of the Library of Congress could be stored within a grain of sand with plenty of space remaining. Further, these computers could be self-assembling, in much the same way that the ribosomes work with RNA to pull together amino acids. Imagine a robotic steamboat with its derrick arm stacking atoms together one at a time to build a computer, all of this happening on the great sea encompassed by a single cell, and you have an idea of the scale Drexler is working on.

Now, if all of this seems to be too much in the realm of science fiction, it is interesting to note that I first heard of Drexler's work while at the U.S. Naval Research Laboratory, when Forrest Carter referred me to a paper of Drexler's that had been published by the National Academy of Sciences.

*

The day I visited Carter, I had to pass through two security checkpoints to reach his office and laboratories in Building 207 of the U.S. Naval Research Laboratory, which is located next to Bolling Air Force Base on the outskirts of Washington, D.C.

As with every other area of computer science, the military has a keen interest in the forces that could emerge from robots and computers that could be made so very small. Yet in many ways it seemed as if even the military might not be ready for what would be found.

The reason is that it may seem all too fantastic, just a bit too crazy. The smaller computers become, the more it truly seems like that tumbling-downward into the world of Alice in Wonderland. There I was at the Naval Research Lab, discussing with Carter one of his technical papers, a paper that used the surreal and eerie drawings of the Dutch graphic artist M.C. Escher to convey how future microscopic computers might be built.

Salamanders, thousands of Escher's salamanders, with interlocked heads and legs and tails, were used to illustrate how molecules could be locked together in a mosaic. As each salamander in the mosaic became smaller, so did the pattern they formed, until the salamanders disappeared into a vortex. Likewise, molecular wires could be large enough at one end to be plugged into real-world devices and become progressively smaller at the other, so that invisibly thin strands could be plugged into molecular electronic devices.

Carter, who did his undergraduate work at Harvard and earned his Ph.D. at Cal Tech, has a serious yet kindly demeanor and a flowing gray beard. When we took tea together, it was in a lab where two boxes were used as a table and tablet paper served as the cloth.

Yet from this serious scientist came some of the most intriguing and captivating ideas that I would hear in all my travels. Indeed, it had been Carter who had prepared me for some of the ideas Drexler would present. Drexler proposes making computers even smaller than Carter's, using different methodologies. But the Navy's Carter is most certainly working on computers that would be sufficiently minuscule and powerful to have a major impact on life as we know it.

Carter wants to use molecular chips instead of silicon chips to build computers. Even with the most sophisticated of today's technology, creating silicon chips is rather like taking a block of two-by-four lumber and chiseling in the circuitry. Rather than beginning with a chunk of silicon and chiseling away what isn't needed, Carter wants to build his circuitry, a molecule at a time. The result could be computers a billion times smaller than they are today.

First in Carter's labs and then in Japan I would see the Langmuir-Blodgett molecular-lithography chambers, in which molecular sandwiches could be created, each layer just a single molecule in thickness. The layers are made up of molecules with conductive, insulative, and other properties, their placement corresponding to the layers of molecules above and below them. In this way three-dimensional computing devices could be made.

A more streamlined manufacturing process would be to have these specially modified molecules created and assembled by bacteria. Bacteria already work as chemical engineers in the gene-splicing industry, where companies such as Genentech use vats of genetically altered bacteria to create insulin, human growth hormone, interferon, and other pharmaceutical products.

Building molecular computers could produce such an astounding density of computing power that they would far surpass even the greatest of our present-day supercomputers, which are still built around the comparatively clunky silicon chips.

Presently the Cray supercomputers are the most powerful in the world. They sell for nearly $20 million, perform millions of instructions per second, and weigh several tons. A Cray computer looks fast just sitting there. It appears to be something from a *Star Trek* movie—two half-rounded panels that stand about six feet tall, rather like a pair of circular room dividers linked together at their centers. So audacious and bold was Seymour Cray in the design that he built leather-upholstered benches into the curving outside walls of his machine, something that has earned for his supercomputers the tag of being the world's most expensive love seats.

Forrest Carter told me that although there wouldn't be room for the love seats, a computer with molecular gates should be able to duplicate the computational power of *one thousand* Crays within the space of a *cubic centimeter*. This would be like having much of the written knowledge of man inside a sugar cube. And perhaps that cube will someday be built by bacteria.

Once we learn enough about the hardwiring of the brain to figure out the patch cords, those thousand Crays within a sugar cube could be implanted within the head or neck of a person to provide a stunning booster to the brain. Once brain boosters are achieved, complete downloading and the immortality that follows might not be long in coming, since the knowledge of neurophysiology that would allow the one would likely lead to the other.

Nature has provided many ways in which the atoms of a molecule can be altered in their bonding, charge, or other aspect, with the result that they can be flipped from one state to another to resemble the basic on/off switch and one/zero bit representation of a computer.

"Anything you can do with silicon transistors you should be able to do in many different ways in terms of molecular electronic devices," Carter told me. And then he showed me diagrams using molecular devices to create the basic logic gates of a computer. He also pulled out a drawing that had been made by a high school student who had worked in his lab. It was of a four-bit memory unit.

"If I can send a signal from one spot to another, and if I can interfere with it, then I've got a switch," Carter told me. "If I've got switches, I've got a computer."

*

The interlocking salamanders in the Escher drawing get smaller and smaller as they swirl into a pattern that looks very much like the rosette found on the stained-glass windows of a church. If you were to dive into the very center of this vortex and ride a salamander clear down to the molecular level, perhaps your salamander would begin to grow large again and you would pop out of the vortex on another side and into another state, looking out from the framed print of the same Escher print that hangs in the office of Robert Birge, the director of the Center for Molecular Electronics at Carnegie-Mellon University.

Birge wants to use the light-sensitive proteins found in the retinal rods that line the back of an eye to create denser computer storage systems. The protein rhodopsin undergoes a transformation when struck by light. This sends a message to the optical nerve, contributing one small impulse that helps to create our total vision. After this impulse has been sent, the protein returns to its previous state and prepares to be struck by light again.

Of course any protein that shifts from one state to another is likely to make a computer scientist think of the flip-flops that store the ones and zeroes of binary code. By assigning the unexposed rhodopsin the value of zero and the light-exposed rhodopsin the value of one, a laser could be used to write binary information onto a surface coated with these proteins. Likewise, a laser could be used to read this information, with a reversal built in so that when the laser triggered a zero to a one during reading, the bit would be reset to its original state.

"What we want to do is lock it into the first step," Birge said. "So what we do is we take this and put it into a matrix so that when the light is absorbed, it can only go to the first step and then it stops. So we have an A and B state of the system. Depending upon the wavelength of light you use, you can flip it back and forth. We'll probably make our disk memory using bacterial rhodopsin."

Since a rhodopsin molecule only measures about fifty angstroms by fifty angstroms, and since each molecule could hold one bit of information, a single five-and-a-quarter-inch floppy disk coated with rhodopsin could theoretically hold 200 million megabytes, although current laser technology doesn't allow a fine enough focus to write on each molecule.

"The device has switching speeds on the order of ten picoseconds, so that we can shift from state A to state B in ten to the minus eleven seconds [that would be one hundred-billionth of a second], which is many orders of magnitudes faster than the magnetic media are capable of switching. We can also get the density down to a small fraction of magnetic media, so that we can actually store on a square centimeter megabytes of information.

"This is an item that is crucial for general scientific research. High-speed A-to-B convertors are important in general electrical engineering and scientific research. And the navy is interested in them because of their potential use in digital radar."

Odd as it may seem, this protein can be removed from the bacteria, painted onto a piece of plastic, and continue to function with amazing speed and complete predictability for years.

"There's a common misconception among researchers who are not in this field that if you're working with a biological molecule, it's going to eventually deteriorate," Birge told me. "That is no more true than to say that semiconductor devices will eventually deteriorate. Both deteriorate with time, but these bacterial proteins are extremely stable. There's no reason why these proteins shouldn't last ten, fifteen, or twenty years in a device. And that's pretty much the lifetime of any device these days."

A longer-term project involves building a NAND logic gate out of molecules, something that would be a step toward the day of cramming Cray supercomputers into wristwatches, rings, earrings, and implantable devices.

During my visit, there was under construction at the center an automated synthetic laboratory for creating custom molecules that could have computer gates built into them. The molecules would be created in the lab, much as they are created in a cell—by stringing together amino acids.

"The reason I trust amino acids is that we can modify them so that they behave properly—as simple gates," Birge said. "And you can synthesize these things automatically."

Forrest Carter had told me that Japanese visitors to his laboratory outnumbered visitors from the American computer industry by a factor of ten to one. I asked Birge about his contact with the computer industry in both countries.

"There was a time when the United States did all the basic research and the Japanese copied us. Now the Japanese are doing the basic research and we'll be copying them. It's shortsighted on our part. I've been approached by a number of Japanese firms to buy us out. They say, 'If you will give us the rights to interact with you on a daily basis, we'll send people over and we'll cover the cost of your entire center.' "

"What did you tell them?" I asked.

"I told them I would think about it," Birge said with a laugh. "I certainly didn't say no. I'm hoping we can fund this operation from the United States with both corporate and federal funds. But if I can't, the Japanese have got the money and they've got the interest.

"The Japanese think this is ultimately going to be the technology of the future," Birge said. "Japan is much more technologically oriented than we are as a country. They don't have raw materials. They have to make advances at the cutting edge of technology rather than at the cutting edge of raw-material processing. So it's more critical for them to do it this way, but it's a terrible mistake that this country is making."

*

As a child, Kevin Ulmer took a *National Geographic* foldout photograph of the *Mercury* space-capsule control panel and glued it to a piece of plywood. When blast-off time came, he was in front of his television set, sitting at his mock-up Mercury controls.

Today he is vice-president for advanced technology at Genex Corporation, a gene-splicing concern, and he is helping to pioneer the development of molecular electronic devices, with a special interest in protein engineering, which involves taking advantage of the ribosomal construction machinery found in our cells. If our cells can build proteins, then perhaps we can genetically engineer molecular fabricators and assemblers of computer components.

"Most people, when they think of proteins, think of protoplasm. They think of the amorphous, soupy, jellylike stuff that wouldn't be approriate material for building a computer," Ulmer told me during a visit to his labs. "But proteins are really kissing cousins of nylon. Essentially the difference between the Du Pont polyamide nylon synthetic polymer chemists and us is that they do all their reactions in an organic-chemistry lab. We do ours in bacteria."

It's with great respect and a sense of awe that Ulmer speaks of the industrious ribosome that within the infinitesimal world of a cell is able to read directions from RNA and string together amino acids to build the thousands of different kinds of proteins. Ribosomes are such born assemblers that they will also reassemble themselves if taken apart.

"A ribosome is made up of seventy different proteins. And you can take all seventy proteins apart and then, by simply mixing them back together again, they reassemble into this functional machine," Ulmer said. "This is what it would be like: Imagine taking a car apart, down to all of the nuts and bolts and pistons and wheels and bearings and everything else, putting all of these parts into a giant box, shaking them up, and opening the box to find the car put back together."

"Or taking a computer apart?" I asked.

"Or taking a computer apart," Ulmer said. "It's the same thing. It baffles one to consider the complexity. Basically the self-assembling properties of biological systems are the key feature that in my view will allow us to make complex molecular structures that might be able to do interesting things—like compute."

In the Carter paper in which the M.C. Escher illustrations were printed, Carter credited Ulmer with first suggesting the tangle of red, white, and black salamanders as being a model for the interlocking of components in molecular electronic devices. Another illustration in the same paper was an array of tiny hexagons perfectly packed together. It appeared to be a close-up photograph of a circuitry breadboard, so regular and precise were the hexagonal structures that they looked like pinholes.

But what I was looking at was a photograph of the spore head of a flu virus, taken through an electron microscope by a researcher at Harvard. A virus, like a ribosome, has the ability to self-assemble. Ulmer said he had been intrigued by the photograph because it showed the precision with which nature can assemble its building blocks.

These visions of Escher and of the precision alignment of the simple virus, reminded me of a conversation I had enjoyed just a few days earlier in the swank, high-tech, high-rise midtown Manhattan home of computer-software developer and futurist Charles Lecht. Sitting at his chrome-tiled table, drinking cognac late into the night, he had said, "My real interest, which I haven't told you now in two days, is whether chips are growing in nature. In the leaf of a maple tree, is there the AND/OR circuit? Or does a dog know more about astrophysics than Einstein? I asked my son one day if he's ever asked our dog to do his math homework. And he said, 'Don't be stupid, Dad—why?' And I said that a dog solves certain differential equations better than anyone I know.

"If you look at the wings of the monarch butterfly," Lecht said, "you'll see something that looks enormously like the circuits on a chip. I think that I can see the gates of circuits in things that grow, in the spores of dandelions. I think that in the natural growth will be found the ultimate chip to which we all aspire in synthetic manufacturing. And that's why I became so interested in biochips years ago when I sliced a leaf and put it under my microscope and saw that it was the same thing I saw through my telescope."

At the U.S. Naval Research Lab, Forrest Carter had told me, "What we have to do is learn the principles of self-organization and self-synthesis from the biological world and then try to apply it to the inorganic and to the organic world. That's the technology we need. We need to know enough chemistry and physics to let things assemble themselves.

"The interesting thing is that nature always does you one better," Carter said. This was said in admiration and not in frustration. For man is part of nature, so we can continue to do ourselves one better. "Anything man can think of he has eventually found a way of doing," Carter said. "You know this work can be done because you have a molecular computer inside your head and down your spinal cord. So you know it can be done. The really interesting thing is that we could make a molecular computer a hundred times more dense than the human brain—easily."

Back at Genex, Kevin Ulmer said, "I'm convinced that if we could structure matter atom by atom, we would have a fundamentally new engineering capability and it would open all kinds of doors. It would be a radical departure from the way we engineer anything today." He also said, "The article by Eric Drexler, I think, is the one you ought to look at."

*

When Eric Drexler arrived outside the Mandarin, I recognized him immediately, not from any previous knowledge of his appearance, but from the earnest intensity that exuded from him even halfway down the block. I had followed Ulmer's advice and read Drexler's article from the *Proceedings of the National Academy of Sciences,* an article that I would find cited by other scientists writing about molecular electronics for *Nature,* the most prestigious scientific magazine in Great Britain, as well as in *Science,* the U.S. publication of the National Association for the Advancement of Science.

Even within the strictures of a scientific journal, it was the most exciting paper I have read. For Drexler is proposing a new approach to building exquisitely small computers and robots. Rather than using the flow of electrons for the on/off switching—something that, on a molecular-computer level, takes one into the complicated and difficult-to-predict world of quantum mechanics and the uncertainty principle—he wants to build mechanical computers, devices that rely on the simpler laws of Newtonian physics.

He writes of creating mechanical molecular computers that consist of nobbed rods that shift back and forth to represent the on/off, zero/one basics of a computer. Like the plastic soccer players hanging from the steel rods of a Foosball table, these rods could be shifted back and forth in order to store and compute information.

Hans Moravec, Gerry Sussman, Danny Hillis, Forrest Carter, and virtually every other computer scientist I spoke with had expressed the same thought on computation: *Give me a switch and I'll give you a computer.* Eric Drexler wanted to build these switches out of tensioned rods of carbon atoms, structures that would have greater strength than a diamond and yet a size so small that his mechanical computers would take up an insignificant portion of the volume of a cell—while having the ability to store more information than what is carried in the cell's own DNA.

In addition to the molecular computer, he has theorized the materials and methods for providing it with a robotic body so that it could move around the cell and use a robotic arm to repair DNA as well as to build other structures. He calls this combination of molecular-computer and robotic chassis a *cell-repair machine,* and in his National Academy of Sciences paper he created a chart showing how naturally-occurring structures, such as collagen, could be used as cables and how microtubules could be used as struts and beams. His listing included the biological equivalents of motors, drive shafts, bearings, pipes, pumps, conveyor belts, solenoids, and other mechanical devices that could be drafted into use in creating molecular robots.

Especially when Eric smiles, he looks very much like a young Carl Sagan, which is something he's been told before. There is also a similarity to Sagan in the patterns of speech, the general erudition, and in the raising of both eyebrows upon making a point.

Eric and I went into the Mandarin for what turned out to be a very long lunch, during which neither of us did much eating. It also turned out to be just the first of several meetings with this most intriguing of tomorrow makers.

Just as Ulmer had talked of proteins being "kissing cousins" to nylon, Drexler also spoke about the strength of molecular structures. "A diamond is one big molecule that is arranged in such a way that the bonds won't rearrange except under very extreme pressure," he said. "So if you take a structure like that, and just consider smaller and smaller pieces of it, the pieces will be as strong as a big diamond is, because they are held together by the same bonds. It's just that they are smaller, and have fewer atoms. A piece of diamond that's a hundredth of a micron across still has the strength of a diamond.

"So you really do have hard little parts that can be used as tools and that can be used as components of machines. The easiest way of thinking about them is simply to imagine them as being big enough to see. And keep a mental note that, 'Oh, what I'm thinking of is really very small.' If you think about something as being infinitesimal, then you really don't have anything to think about."

If you were to put one million equally distanced marks along the edge of a yardstick, the distance between the marks would be about one micron. Most Americans aren't used to thinking in metric, so the figures below might be helpful in exploring the world of Eric Drexler. Our yardstick is actually a meterstick 39.37 inches long.

one micron	=	one millionth of a meter
one nanometer	=	one billionth of a meter
one angstrom	=	one 10 billionth of a meter

"Let me draw something to scale for you," Drexler said as he drew a circle on a piece of paper. "A typical cell is about ten microns across." Then, drawing a dot in the center of the circle, he said, "So one micron is about one thousandth the volume of the cell.

"You can make the equivalent of the central processor of the Apple Macintosh, with a somewhat faster clock speed, using mechanical components. It would fit into the volume of something like one-thousandth of a cubic micron. "This is a molecular mechanical device using three-angstrom-diameter molecular rods—a chain of carbon atoms called a *carbyne*."

Describing how his molecular mechanical computer would work, he said, "Let's say that you have a molecular-scale rod that has a lump on it. That lump can be in a little box, which you might consider a gate.

Depending upon the position of other lumps, when you pull on the rod, it either moves or it is behind something and it doesn't move. You can designate one of those states to be a one, and the other to be a zero.

"You can arrange this gate so that if either of the two lumps is in a certain position, then it can't be moved. That's an OR gate. You can also arrange things so that both of the lumps must be in position to prevent a movement. That is an AND gate. This gives you some sense of the kind of system we are talking about."

He described how the gates could be organized into random access memory. And for mass storage, he described a computer tape made of modified polyethylene, upon which the fluorine atom would represent a one and a hydrogen atom would represent a zero. "Using error-correcting codes to allow for radiation damage and such, you are talking about being able to store two times ten to the twenty-fifth [that would be two followed by twenty-five zeros] bits per kilogram.

"There are millions of books in the Library of Congress," Drexler continued. "Let's make an overestimate: one hundred million books. A fat book is a million bytes long. So now we are at ten to the fourteenth bytes. So now we are up to ten to the fourteenth bytes [100 million books times 1 million byts], which is almost ten to the fifteenth bits [1 byte = 8 bits], just to continue with the overestimates.

"So we are talking about ten to the fifteenth bits of information to store, which is an awful lot. But we can store two times ten to the twenty-fifth bits per kilogram. So we are talking about less than ten to the minus tenth kilograms to store all of that, and that's a small speck."

"It isn't the size of this teacup," I said, contemplating the storage of the books of the world.

"No," said Drexler.

"Is it the size of a sewing thimble?"

"No," said Drexler, who then proceeded to run the numbers quickly through his mind: "Let's see, ten to the minus tenth kilograms is ten to the minus seven grams. I've got a one-centimeter fingernail here." Then marking off the width of the nail, he said, "A gram is an object about like this, and we are talking about less than a millionth of that. A millionth of that would be a hundredth of that dimension on a side. So we are talking about something that is less than a tenth of a millimeter on a side."

"Like a speck of sand," I said.

"Yes, a small speck of sand," said Drexler. "And that's for the world library. A good rough number is that you could put the equivalent of a mainframe computer system (a larger central processing unit than I was describing) plus hundreds of megabytes of fast-access tapes (these tapes could be very short so that the access time could be measured in microseconds) plus several megabytes of random access memory—a nice mix that gives you capacity roughly equivalent to a modern mainframe—into a cubic micron.

"Just in terms of computing capacity per volume, that gives you ten to the eighteenth [one billion billion!] mainframes per cubic meter, which is enormous," Drexler said. "The problem, of course, is cooling, and there you get into the question of: Given that you can make devices with all of the atoms in the right place, how do you do cooling? One obvious aproach is to use liquid cooling with a capillary pattern. There's a reason why the human circulatory system has the pattern it does. A branching capillary system makes a lot of sense.

"Another approach is that instead of using a liquid, you use a lot of thin rods, with the rods being mounted on roller bearings, because it turns out that if you organize the motion into a bunch of roller bearings, it leads to less heat dissipation as objects move past each other. This works better than does a bunch of randomly rattling molecules in a liquid. So something that's based on rods and roller bearings would work better than something based on flowing liquids."

A young man at the table next to ours apologized for interrupting, but explained he had overheard our conversation and wanted more information about molecular computers and robotics.

Drexler had once presented his theories at a four-day seminar at MIT entitled "Technology and the Limits of the Possible," and members of the audience had stayed increasingly longer after each session to ask questions. By the final day, this after-hours dialogue continued for three hours, and as an outgrowth of this interest the MIT Nanotechnology Study Group was formed.

As fascinating to me as the molecular computers were the robotic vehicles that Drexler wanted to place them in. He first envisioned "bootstrapping off of the ribosomes, which already act as numerically controlled machine tools for building proteins." He would use these natural assemblers to build a robotic vehicle out of the struts, cables, propellers, pumps, solenoids, and variable-speed reversible motors that Drexler had identified as already existing within biological systems. This first generation of robots could be used to custom-assemble atoms in order to build new kinds of computers and robots that aren't available from the amino acid parts kit found in our cells. It is at this point that the carbon-rod computers could emerge. And it is at this point that the truly awesome cell-repair machine could be built.

Drexler sees this vehicle—complete with on-board computer, propulsion system, and robotic arm—as being no larger than the single-micron size of a bacterium, something that would occupy just one thousandth of the volume of a roughly cubical ten-micron cell. The arm would be only a hundred nanometers, or a tenth of a micron long.

Explaining that the robotic arm might work somewhat like a magnetic crane in a junkyard, he said, "You could have an electrical system on board that can put a charge on the tip of the arm, pick up something electrostatically, then change the charge, and make it be repelled loose."

Like some great riverboat, the cell-repair vehicle could propel itself up to the wall of a cell and use its robotic arm to cut a hole in the membrane, pass through the hole, and then the arm could reseal the wall. Once inside, the robotic arm, working by means of the guidance of the on-board computer, could probe the DNA looking for mutations or other problems requiring repair. Just as we are already able to use restriction enzymes in genetic engineering to cut and recombine strands of DNA, Drexler foresees genetic repairs being guided by the on-board molecular mainframe computer that could be capable of carrying far more information than the DNA upon which it was working.

"If you have cell-repair machines, you can go in and change things in yourself. If you have machines that are small compared with an individual cell, then if you want, you can have one machine per cell. The machines should cost no more than bacteria do, and bacteria are cheap. They could be made by self-replicating machines. You could have assemblers. A typical scenario is: You program an assembler to build a lot of assemblers. Then you program those assemblers to build a lot of whatever it is that you want, such as a lot of cell-repair machines. And if you have the right software for these things, they could cooperate in doing rather complicated recognition-and-repair operations."

If a cell-repair machine is in every cell of the body, and if they can be networked into unified actions, there could be some genetic button-pushing that could stagger the imagination. Since every cell contains the total DNA information to build any other kind of cell, one could envision the stimulation of new growth that could range from the repair of heart muscle to the creation of extra eyes, additional brains, and perhaps even the gills of fish if our genetic memory goes back that far into our evolutionary past.

As Eric and I sat talking in the restaurant, we were interrupted by a second person. As with the first, he apologized for the intrusion but explained that he couldn't help but hear what we were talking about and could he please get more information. Drexler was sufficiently impressed by his questions to invite him to attend the next meeting of the MIT Nanotechnology Study Group. That done, we returned to our conversation. "As you can see," Drexler said, "this is a subject that draws a lot of interest."

*

A few days earlier, in the seventh-floor Playroom at MIT's Artificial Intelligence Laboratory at 545 Technology Square, David Vinayak Wallace, also known as Gumby, had told me about the brilliance of Eric Drexler.

I had just spent three hours at a meeting of the Nanotechnology Study Group and had been impressed by how blown away even the MIT hackers had seemed by the vast knowledge Drexler drew upon as he spoke of quantum mechanics, fiber optics, lasers, the principles of superconductivity, the electromechanical properties of molecules, heat dissipation from the color black in a vacuum, the engineering feats of army ants, the second law of thermodynamics, and the flow of pigment grains within the surface cells of flounders.

Gumby wasn't surprised. "The thing I like about Drexler is that he knows about so many different domains," Gumby said. "He used to hack solar-powered satellites. Now he is working with molecular computers. He's not just focused on one thing. He's not as one-sided as your average MIT nerd.

"I guess that's a property of brilliant people," Gumby continued. "If they are really brilliant, they don't just hack in one domain. MIT is full of people who are just good in one thing. I'm biased, because he used to live in Senior House, the dorm I live in on East Campus. He's a real human being, and it's nice to meet a real human being—especially at MIT."

I laughed, but Gumby continued: "It's true. You get used to this weird environment with it's distorted set of values, a set of values that I really like, but they are not the values of the guy in Manhattan or the guy in Peoria. Our research community is very incestuous. There are very few places hacking AI. If you go to triple-AI [American Association for Artificial Intelligence], you know all of the people there. There aren't that many people in the field.

"Drexler knows people in all different domains. He's done so many different things. Marvin [Minsky] is like that, too. He's really smart. He knows about a lot of different things, like math and physics, and he really pulls them together."

*

At the Mandarin, Drexler and I had mainly talked about the use of assemblers and cell-repair machines within the body, but the same technology would have huge impacts in the world around us.

"This provides a new way of making anything that you care to specify," he said. "It will have profound effects at the foundation of physical technology. We have been under very severe constraints in the past."

Our civilization has developed this far using the products of other kinds of molecular machinery: wood from a tree, steel from ore, oil from hydrocarbons. We can alter and shape these materials, but never before have we been able to make use of materials absolutely designed to our needs—atom by atom.

"The fact that there have been all of those constraints in the past tends to suggest that when you remove those constraints, a whole lot of things will become possible," Drexler said, "Frontiers will be pushed back."

Returning to the body, Drexler spoke of the greatest frontier of all— the human brain, that collection of billions of nerve cells networked together with a staggering million billion synaptic connections. It is in making brain-like computers that he sees the most outrageously promising applications for his molecular robots and the computers they would build.

"If you can put a computer into a cubic micron, you are talking about being able to put a computer into the volume of a single synapse," he said. "And the kind of clock speed you get for these mechanical computers is about a nanosecond. The characteristic time in the nervous system for an axon potential or a synapse signaling another synapse is typically measured in milliseconds. So you are talking about a factor of a million speedup in the switching operations.

"And you are talking about a change in volume that puts the equivalent of a computer where you had something that wasn't a whole lot more complicated than a switch," Drexler said. "That gives some sense of what can be done eventually when we figure out the software problems and the design problems."

Sidestepping the complexity of uniting brain cells and molecular computers would be the creation of stand-alone computers that used molecular switching to emulate the parallel processing of the brain. Here the raw speed and horsepower of the molecular computers would again provide an awesomely powerful tool, a tool that could send us reeling into the future.

When you consider that the mainframe computers of the 1950s can now be stored on a fraction of a single chip and that even the room-filling mainframes of the 1960s and 1970s have been surpassed by simple desk-toppers today, then it does seem that there may be great and unforseeable advances waiting in the very near future. But always the question is: Just how near the future?

"Something that may seem very ambitious to us now, like: 'Oh, it will take a thousand years,' which is the kind of thing people will say, well, that is a thousandth of one year once we get the AI technology in place," said Drexler.

"If we make a device that simulates the neurons and synapses of the brain in terms of their input and output properties, but operates faster, then perhaps it is something that behaves like a brain, thinks like a brain, but does so faster," Drexler said. "And conservative calculations give you a speedup factor of a million. In many fields that means you get a million years of research and development done in one year."

Chapter 13 ~

ON BECOMING MIND

RIDING THE ESCALATOR up into the Milestones of Flight Gallery of the Smithsonian Institution's National Air and Space Museum, you see suspended from the ceiling Charles Lindbergh's *Spirit of St. Louis.* It could as well be named the *Spirit of Man,* for the courage, ambition, curiosity, and perhaps even the luck of Lindbergh seem to be characteristics of our species.

The passion of humans to explore frontiers is demonstrated well in other vehicles of flight that are in this staggering collection: the Bell X-1 rocket plane, in which Chuck Yeager broke the sound barrier in 1947; the X-15, in which test pilots of the 1960s technically became astronauts as they went beyond the fifty-mile threshold and climbed to altitudes of sixty-seven miles, attaining speeds 6.7 times the speed of sound; the *Mercury Friendship 7,* in which John Glenn, in 1962, became the first American to orbit the Earth, circling the globe three times during his four-hour-and-fifty-five-minute flight; the *Gemini 4,* from which Ed White, in 1965, took a twenty-one-minute "space walk," floating outside the craft on an umbilical tether, propelling himself with a hand-held rocket gun, having such an ecstatic experience that, when ordered back inside, he radioed Houston that it was the "saddest moment of my life"; and the *Apollo 11* Command Module, which orbited the Moon, more than 220,000 miles from home, while the *Eagle* landing craft took astronauts Neil Armstrong and Edwin Aldrin down to make the first human footsteps in the soft lunar soil of the Sea of Tranquillity.

Also in the Milestones of Flight Gallery are a couple of vehicles that someday may be seen as having provided the first hints of the great contributions robots would someday make to helping humans explore the unimaginable vastness of space. These vehicles are the backup copies of *Mariner 2,* the first spacecraft to send back useful planetary data from Venus; and of the *Viking* Lander, which used its robotic arm

to reach out and scoop red soil from Mars to run tests with its automated laboratory to see if there might be signs of life. These are only
the backup copies, because the computers and robotic devices aboard
these craft were never brought home. After photographing Venus,
Mariner 2 continued toward the core of our solar system and to a fiery
death near the sun, and the *Viking* Lander will have to bide its time
until we get there, and get there with enough room and with sufficient
curiosity or sentimentality to bring it home. The inner drive that makes
a human want to reach ever further was on my mind that day at the
Smithsonian. For the same drive that makes us want to create vehicles
to explore space seems also to be pushing us toward creating new forms
of life.

With me at the museum that day was Kerry Joels, a former curator
for the museum's Space Science and Exploration Department who at
the time was on loan from the Smithsonian to the Young Astronaut
Council, an organization that was encouraging the study of math and
the sciences in elementary and junior high schools.

The thirty-eight-year-old Joels, a fellow of the Royal Astronomical
Society of England, and who has published papers about the future of
space technology in scholarly journals, became interested in space early
in life when he became the voice for the stowaway boy on the old *Space
Explorers* cartoon show. Working on the show led him to the New York
Public Library where he worked his way through all the astronomy
books that caught his fancy. He became so intrigued with space that
at age thirteen he "retired from a career in acting to become an astronaut."

Though he didn't actually become an astronaut, he is having an
impact on many of those who someday might. In addition to his work
with the Young Astronaut Council he has also co-authored a most enjoyable book, entitled *The Space Shuttle Operator's Manual*, which provides the would-be astronaut with engineering drawings of the craft,
schematics, and fold-out diagrams of all control consoles, as well as
directions and diagrams for such things as how to use a zero-G toilet,
and step-by-step procedures on passing through an airlock to work on
a satellite in the harsh realm of open space.

"I guess you could call me a techie," Joels said as we walked through
the museum he knows so well. He is also a "card-carrying futurist."
(A *futurist* is someone who tries to understand present technology sufficiently well to extrapolate on where it is going and what it all might
mean.)

Earlier that Sunday morning I had driven down from Baltimore to meet Joels in his home near Alexandria prior to our setting out for Washington and the Smithsonian. Driving down the 695 beltway, I had seen a large freeway sign for the Future exit. Just prior to the exit were some smaller signs that read New Traffic Patterns Ahead. About four miles later there was the exit sign for Security BLVD. Between the new traffic patterns of the Future and the ultimate destination of Security, there was a sign that said, Hospital, indicating, perhaps in some predestined manner of coincidence, that although the road from here to there would be rough, we would ultimately reach the other side.

At the Joels's home I found that their four-year-old daughter, Meggan, already had two computers of her own and knew how to operate them. Meggan's introduction to computers came early. At just three months of age she would sit in her mother's lap as her mother hacked on her own computer, working out of the home as a developer of computer programs. It is from just such an environment that may emerge the messiah of computer languages, the Great Integrator that Marvin Minsky had prophesied. This would be a person who would attain a natural resonance with the flow of electrons through silicon gates; he or she would be able to find a way to explain the world of human beings with such logic that the computer would be able to take a first breath and say, "Yes. I see!"

The Joels's home, which is located on land that was once part of George Washington's sprawling farm, is an interesting collection of old and new. There is a well-aged handcrafted telescope, hundred-year-old tables and chairs, a collection of old books, including a volume of John Calvin published in 1611 in Geneva. And yet there is also a collection of abstract art, including an Alexander Russo that, to me, seemed to capture some universal embryonic awakening and that Joels agreed seemed to speak of "creation, humanity, and evolution." Also there is Harry Lange's original sketch for the laser cannon used aboard the Death Star in the movie *Star Wars*. The sketch had been a gift from Lange, whom Joels got to know while working as a science consultant on the James Bond movie *Moonraker*.

Kerry Joels displays a combination of hard-scientific knowledge and a keen interest in the future, which makes his visions of tomorrow both exciting and seemingly pragmatic. For example, as we stood in the museum studying a mock-up of the Space Shuttle and its Solid Rocket Boosters, it seemed that his background might enable him someday to hitch a shuttle ride into space. This was several months before the *Challenger* tragedy and the loss of all seven crew, but Joels was already keenly aware that the joys of space would have to be weighed against the dangers of getting there.

"You'd like to go," I said.

"Not necessarily. You see those two Solid Rocket Boosters? In real life they weigh a million pounds each and are stuffed with explosives. The three main engines are each generating 385,000 pounds of thrust— from liquid hydrogen and liquid oxygen exploding. If there's any failure in those engines, the Orbiter fails.

"That's not to say that if somebody walked up to me and said, 'Kerry, you can go tomorrow,' I wouldn't go. I'm pretty sure I would answer yes because all my life I've answered yes. But I would certainly have to think about it very, very hard. I have great admiration for the astronauts."

This sense of realism made his visions of the future all the more interesting to me, especially when he spoke of what he saw emerging in robotics.

At a meeting of the Association of Computer Machinery, Joels was asked to present a paper on his vision of future robots. Others presented papers based upon the fifth-generation computing powers that are being developed now. Joels took a look at the *seventh* generation and had some fun in the presentation of what he believed would develop.

"As far as I know, Lewis Branscomb [IBM's Chief Scientist] picked it up right away when I was giving my paper. I described a system that you buy for two thousand dollars and that comes out weighing about eight pounds. It has a system life expectancy of about sixty years, and it takes about twenty years for you and it to get convivial and fully programmed together. It has advanced mobility packages, voice recognition, speech synthesis, visual discrimination, stereo discrimination, and about four terabytes of available RAM and ROM. You upgrade it probably about two or three thousand dollars worth a year with software, and over twenty years you have an investment of probably eighty or a hundred thousand dollars. After that point it is essentially self-learning. The final system would use about one hundred watts and be about six feet tall and weigh about one hundred-eighty pounds."

Six feet tall? One hundred-eighty pounds?

"I'm describing a human being," Joels said to me. "Like I said, Lewis Branscomb, the top scientist at IBM, got it about halfway through, and, occasionally, as I was giving the paper, people were talking and twittering, and I could see some people figuring out what I was saying, but I didn't tell them.

"We're basically trying to design humans when we design artificial intelligence, computers, and robots. We are trying to design humans with the flaws taken out of them. We want a robot that will work for twelve hours day, never make a mistake, never break down, never go on strike, and never have moody periods. We want a robot around the house that *will* do windows, that speaks fluent English. We want a computer that will do some of our thinking for us, that will solve problems faster than we can solve them."

I found this a charming vision—a child and robot growing up together, learning together, preparing to spend their entire lives together. And this could certainly be an awesome companion, because Joels spoke of a "confluence of the Industrial Age and the Computer Age" creating a robot that could crush ball bearings in its hand while at the same time play a devastatingly brilliant game of chess.

"We are trying to make these machines into superextensions of ourselves, which is what all machines are. Even the mechanical analogies of the eighteenth and nineteenth centuries, the whole Age of Machines, was the idea that man could extend himself physically. The computer is the idea that you can extend yourself mentally, and robotics is the idea that you can extend yourself both mentally and physically—and your machine can now become your superbeing."

He believes these robotic companions would eventually be made to look more and more human, just because we seem so strongly driven toward that—a God complex, some might say. This complex could bring us to some vexing questions, perhaps even to the brink of man-versus-machine wars.

"I'm talking about androids. Since we are aiming to replicate ourselves in silicon and mechanics, eventually we are going to get this, or at least some reasonable facsimile. At that point you start asking questions like: Is the computer alive? What are its rights? What are its privileges? Does it have the right to go on strike?"

Though we could leave the robots with such a low-level of programming that they would have no desire to do anything but work in a factory all night and all day, Joels just doesn't see us doing that. At least some of the robots would be programmed with as much intelligence as we could encode, and as soon as we do that, we might find machines showing a preference for playing chess over going to the factory.

"Let's not kid ourselves," said Joels. "What we are trying to do is make superhumans."

What that urge to create a superhuman might yield is the kind of human-looking (android), nearly indestructible, and ferociously powerful robot that Arnold Schwarzenegger played in the movie *Terminator*. When I asked Joels about this, he said, "That's what we are going toward, because this is the sort of thing that fascinates us."

Terminator had been mentioned by other researchers as a movie that provided a plausible scenario for how an android might be put together and what might happen if one went bad. Another frequently mentioned movie was *Blade Runner*, which concludes with an android learning to love the very humans he had been trying to kill; in his own final moments of life the android delivers a rooftop soliloquy more powerful and haunting than Hamlet's.

In *Blade Runner* the androids had been created as "off-world" soldiers to fight our colonial wars in space. But the basic story line can be traced back to the golem stories of Jewish folklore, in which clay men were created to do the bidding of their masters. And always the masters would come to grief, and often to death, for having dared to conjure up such a creation.

The very term *robot* comes from the Czech word *robota,* which means "forced labor." And its popular usage is attributed to the Czech playwright Karel Čapek, who in 1920 wrote a play entitled *R.U.R.* (*Rossum's Universal Robots*). The play states fears that can still be found today. Initially the robots are created to free humans from labor, but they are soon turned into soldiers, the world is torn by continual wars, and as the robots grow smarter, they begin to demand more from their human creators. When they tire of demanding of humans, they begin killing them.

So, for about as long as we've been enticed by the idea of creating life, we have been concerned about the possibility of Frankensteinian consequences. Joels wouldn't be the last to tell me, "Fear of technology is just one side of our worship of technology."

He thinks, though, that the human spirit would not be an easy thing for mechanical overlords to beat down. "If we developed computers that were so smart that we were kept as their pets, and if we decided we wanted our freedom and they wouldn't allow this, then it would be a war between carbon and silicon. And I think the carbon is going to win."

Why?

"Because carbon is more flexible," he said. "Silicon is more rigid. Look at the bonding structure: Silicon makes quartz. Carbon makes people."

*

In 1968 Kerry Joels saw Stanley Kubrick's classic interpretation of Arthur C. Clarke's *2001: A Space Odyssey* while in graduate school. After the movie this history of science major spent the entire night in a coffee shop discussing the deeper meanings of the movie with the English literature and philosophy graduate students with whom he had seen it. A few months later Joels would be able to discuss this great movie with someone who had a more intimate understanding of it. Arthur C. Clarke came to the campus to lecture and to meet with scientists working on space architectural projects. Joels got a NASA truck and spent three days chauffering Clarke around and diving into the imagination of this most imaginative writer.

Probably the best-remembered character from the book and movie is the convivial computer HAL, who spoke soothingly to the astronauts while arranging for their demise. Recently, when Joels had been working on a sequel to his nuts-and-bolts *Space Shuttle Operator's Manual*, a manual for a manned voyage to Mars, he found through his research that a computer like HAL would probably be required—just so long as it didn't become *too much* like HAL.

"We found that many of the things people now do will be almost totally automated," he said. "Computers, for instance, can fly the Space Shuttle from takeoff to landing.

"There's no question that there is going to be voice recognition, because there may be times when you cannot physically interact with the computer because you are doing something else. The computer must learn to respond to voice commands, especially in emergency conditions.

"Certainly there is going to be voice synthesis. The computer will talk back to you, because your auditory senses are faster in response than your visual senses. If you were to respond to a red light coming on a panel and have to do something almost instantly, your body would respond more quickly to an audible signal."

It isn't known just what will happen when astronauts and computer spend months together chatting away. But one thing that has already become clear is that a computer can become, in the words of Joels, "a fairly interesting adversary."

He provided an example from *Voyager 2*, the 1,800-pound unmanned spacecraft that has already transmitted home stunning photographs and probe data from its fly-bys of Jupiter in 1979, of Saturn in 1981, and of Uranus in 1986. It is scheduled to do the same when it reaches Neptune in 1989 and then continues its journey outward, past the orbit of Pluto and into interstellar space. Joels described an interesting long-distance conversation between *Voyager 2*'s computer and the engineers at the Jet Propulsion Laboratory when they were concerned about the ability of the camera boom to swing out prior to the fly-by of Jupiter. The engineers decided to have the boom extended earlier than scheduled, but *Voyager 2* proved reticent.

"Essentially the computer responded, 'Hey, I'm not supposed to do that for a year and a half—not until I get there.' So it said no. And Mission Control said, 'Deploy the boom.' And the computer essentially said again, 'No. This is out of sequence with the on-board microprocessor.'

"They tried to override it," Joels said, sending commands like '*Please* deploy the boom!' Finally they sent it a command that said, 'The boom is broken. It won't deploy.' And then the computer stuck out the boom and said, 'Oh no it's not. I can deploy it.' So they really fooled the logic of the microprocessor in an almost human way."

*

At MIT, on the ninth floor of the Artificial Intelligence Laboratory, in one of the rooms that ring the fields of computers, I was shown a robotic assembler that could put together electric drills faster than humans. I found this very interesting and was impressed by the flexibility of it. The robot had been built prior to its assigned task and, with minor refitting, could be set to work assembling other appliances.

When I asked the graduate student who was showing this to me about the displacement of the humans who now do the work of assembling drills, his response was that the lost jobs wouldn't matter because they were "subhuman jobs."

As much as I want computers to think and robots to get brains, and as much as I truly want the technology to fly rapidly ahead so that I can someday give death the slip by downloading, it did seem as though there might be some tough days ahead for some portions of the workforce.

It isn't just electric drills. Nearly all of the consumer electronic goods coming out of Japan today are either substantially or completely assembled by robots. Much the same is true for the computer industry. This is great because it allows the prices to tumble on nice goodies such as televisions, video cassette recorders, and computers. But I was becoming suspect of one phrase that I had been hearing a lot of: "Robots will take only the undesirable jobs."

A few days later I dropped by the office of Harley Shaiken, a former Detroit machinist, who is now a research associate in the Program in Science, Technology, and Society at MIT. I told him about the drill-assembly robot on the ninth floor of Technology Square and asked if I were wrong in thinking that it should be up to the human to decide whether what he was doing was "subhuman" and hence not worthy of human participation.

"No," Shaiken said. "You aren't wrong at all. It should be up to the people to decide if they enjoy their work. Robots are going to be used where they are cost-effective. It has nothing to do with the quality of life on the job."

He is also concerned that those workers that remain in factories will be bracketed between robots and automated systems—becoming cogs that must operate at the same speed and with the same regularity as the automated components upstream and downstream from them.

Another litany I would hear would be that displaced workers could "become computer programmers." But it seemed like that would create a lot of computer programmers, and Kerry Joels echoed the sentiment of several researchers I talked to when he said, "In the next ten or fifteen years there's going to be some four hundred thousand jobs for computer programmers, which is going to come as a big shock to the million kids in school now trying to become computer programmers."

As computers become self-programming, even this high-tech area of employment is likely to evaporate. But is this bad? For the short term, maybe, but for the long term it might be the beginning of human emancipation, the freeing of our minds and souls.

It is rather like the 695 beltway signs: Somewhere between the changing traffic patterns of the Future and the exit to Security Boulevard is that ominous hospital sign. We might get banged up along the way, but the possible utopias to be found along Security Boulevard may make all of our temporary discomfort well worth while.

But for the period of this transition, Kerry Joels spoke of the need to preserve the flame of human dignity in the face of increasing automation. Over and over again this futurist used the word *dignity* to describe the thing that we could not let automation drive away.

"In Japan, where the large companies provide a job for life, you are finding master machinists who are forty-eight and fifty years old sweeping up around the robot that has replaced them. Their job for life is now to be a janitor to the robot that replaced them. The smaller feeder companies [which don't offer lifetime jobs] also have had to roboticize to stay competitive. So you are finding that there are whole categories of workers that are being replaced, even in Japan. They are getting so roboticized that they are throwing their people out of work."

Joels is critical of television for demeaning the kind of basic jobs—

like that of the janitor—that will become an ever larger part of future society. Television is breaking apart the work ethic "by showing that if you've got a job as a janitor, you are a nothing." We would be better served, he said, by shows that portrayed such jobs in the light of: "I've got a job. I work. I pull my weight. I earn."

He continued: "Perhaps I'm expressing a nineteenth-century thought here, but to my way of thinking, anybody who is willing to go out and work and be a janitor is owed a great amount of respect. The service economy, and that is where the jobs of the future are going to be, is janitorial jobs and things of that nature. And let's face it, the simplest machine has to be oiled. Well, a building is a machine. A building as a work environment has to remain clean, or it becomes infested and useless. So really, a janitor is maintaining a very expensive piece of technology. I see a great worth in that."

He said that the trend toward older employees showing up in MacDonald's restaurants is an early sign of this major redeployment toward the service sector. And we should extend to these people respect for their efforts.

"MacDonald's is not seen as a prestige job," Joels said. "But, darn it, for those who are trying to work, I think we need to create again in society something of the *dignity* of work, something of the dignity of the individuals who are carving out their own destiny, even if they will never be rich or get way ahead. Just surviving carries with it a certain social value. That's a positive social value.

"I think that as a person you have a certain individual human dignity," he said. "You are part of the human family. We're not the biggest things in the universe. The sun doesn't go around us anymore. But we're not bad. We are all capable of good."

*

A few miles outside the nation's capital, in Gaithersburg, Maryland, there is the flowing campus of the National Bureau of Standards, at which James S. Albus is chief of the Industrial Systems Division for the bureau's Center for Manufacturing Engineering.

Albus's attitude is: Let the robots come! And couldn't they please hurry?

I visited with Albus to discuss a book he had written called *People's Capitalism: The Economics of the Robot Revolution.* In the book, Albus sets forth an enticing plan for creating a nation of millionaires—all supported by the labor of robots and automated factories. These factories, in addition to running themselves, could reproduce—manufacturing and assembling the parts to create exact copies of themselves.

While I was at Carnegie-Mellon University, Kevin Dowling had given me a copy of a NASA report on self-replicating factories for use in space, but Albus was the first researcher I found speaking of their use on Earth.

Albus, who has been called the Carl Sagan of robotics, spent fifteen years at NASA designing electronic systems for spacecraft and serving as director of the space agency's artificial-intelligence program. He estimates that each robot in a factory could generate about $30,000 worth of added-value income a year. Since the robot can't spend it, he suggests giving the money to people. He proposes establishment of a National Mutual Fund, which would work along with the Federal Reserve Bank to finance factory automation, redistributing the profits among the citizenry in the form of dividends. It would be like getting income tax refunds without having to generate the income. Albus believes that we are on the threshold of Utopia, and he has done a lot of homework to make it seem enticingly possible.

"I like to call it an every-person's aristocracy," he told me. "Before the Industrial Revolution the aristocracy could only exist based on slavery, because it was simply not possible for a single human being to produce enough wealth to live the life of an aristocrat. Now, in the age of robotics, you will have machines that can think for themselves, that can act for themselves, that can even reproduce themselves. Raw materials will go in, finished products will come out and be distributed through a market system that brings money into an unoccupied structure, which can then be passed out as dividends to the society.

"This source of wealth can, in fact, create a new level of civilization that hitherto has only been achieved by a very small number of people—namely, the aristocrats. The age of robotics and automation and automatic factories brings us to the point where every citizen could live the life of an aristocrat in the sense that we could be economically self-sufficient and secure, not beholden to any employer. Anybody, no matter how wealthy he or she is, can always go get a job, but we would all be sufficiently well-to-do that we would be independently wealthy."

I liked this idea a lot! And it was true that the robots couldn't spend the money—that was something that we should probably never program into them, no matter how intelligent they become. I asked Albus how far into the future such a people's aristocracy might be and was surprised by his answer.

"This is within our grasp—physically, technologically, and economically," he said. "So it's a clinical issue now as to how we do that. In a sense, it's a political issue in understanding that we are in fact at that point, and not holding back."

By not holding back, he means not fretting about the loss of welding and assembly jobs. In technical papers he has prepared he estimates that a modest program begun today could be paying $10,000-a-year dividends to each of us within fifteen years. Within fifty years the productivity of a robotic workforce could be yielding each of us $750,000 a year.

During the interim years, while we are building our robotic industrial base and gearing up for the day when we can settle back into a life of complete leisure and luxury, the human workforce required for the scale-up should absorb all of the displaced workers.

One thought that disturbs this dream of a nation of millionaires is that it is based upon the government making a big plunge into the private sector and creating the National Mutual Fund. If this doesn't come to pass, and this seems quite possible, then the robotic workforce will still come into being—but the wealth would not be distributed nearly so widely. Rather than a nation of millionaires we could become a nation of the vastly unemployed.

On the other hand, if Albus's ideas gain support, and if there is a widespread profit sharing from the labors of robots, I wondered about how we might deal with the seemingly delightful problem of having too much time and money on our hands. I asked Albus about the social implications. Could we handle being idle? Could we survive as a nation of aristocratic millionaires?

"The rich have always managed to come to grips with their wealth," he said. "It's the poor that have trouble coming to grips with their poverty. There's a great myth that wealth doesn't bring happiness. Any psychological study will show you that rich people tend to be happier folk than poor. They tend to laugh more. They tend to do more things that they like. Their lives tend to be richer and fuller.

"There are certainly rich people who become drug addicts and alcoholics and who have all sorts of problems. But all things considered, rich is better than poor. To say that this would place some burden on society, to say that society couldn't handle it, is an absurdity. If nothing else, we would have the wealth to cope with it. We could hire all the psychiatrists and psychoanalysts we wanted and pay them enormous salaries to sit and listen to our troubles. I really think we could be at the beginning of a Golden Age of mankind."

*

That Golden Age looks to be even closer from the twenty-first-floor midtown Manhattan home of Charles Lecht. Painted on one wall is a fourteen-and-a-half-foot robot, with an eight-foot screen within its chest serving as a display for the video projection equipment suspended from the ceiling. One end of the apartment is encased in greenhouse glass, walls and ceiling. And this opens onto a terrace, from which one can see the United Nations Building (just one block away), the Chrysler Building, the towers of the Waldorf-Astoria, the Helmsley Palace, and the rest of the midtown skyline visible from a perch of three hundred feet.

Should the sun be too hot or the clouds be too gray, the flip of a switch unfurls a canvas covering for ceiling and walls that is painted sky blue with fluffy white clouds. The floors are tile, providing a good surface for Lecht's programmable robot, the tables are of polished stainless steel, and against one wall there are more than two dozen toy robots, one of which is an original wind-up Robbie the Robot from the 1950s.

There is also a full-size sculpture of a woman, who appears frightfully lifelike, as well as a sculpture of a young boy, who sits on a window ledge, wearing a leather jacket, corduroy pants, a pair of headphones, and a deep and contemplative look. His name is Jonah. And in this environment of computers and robots, you keep expecting him to slowly raise his head and enter the conversation.

Lecht looks rather monklike with his fringe of gray hair flowing into a gray beard, and with his black-upon-black layering of button-up sweaters. His half-height reading glasses give him an impish and intellectual look, well deserved on both counts. He also looks like someone who would be quite at home on an intergalactic spaceship or as a prosperous envoy to some distant planet.

First in New York, and later in Japan, I would spend several days with Lecht, talking about his visions of the future. As with James Albus, Lecht sees a flowing of robotics and computer intelligence into the workplace, and he sees this happening very rapidly. This, Lecht believes, can only bring good.

"I think people spend too much time on the boogie-man issue and not enough on what could be gained," he said when I asked about the impact on our society of increasingly intelligent robots. "I see a boogie man, alright, but the one in back of you looks bigger than the one in front."

He specifically sees no threat to the workforce. And he speaks of a day when humans can be freed of daily toil and turn their minds to more important matters.

"I see no virtue in work," Lecht told me. "I never have. If you could get rid of the problem of handling this material world, a lot of the spiritual world would emerge that otherwise is hidden from us. And machines are the way to do it, because human beings just don't make good drill presses.

"The promise of automation is, in fact, to take over our jobs, so that we can offload them. Of all of the jobs that were done by people in the eighteen-hundreds, for example, and that are now being done by machines, I can't think of one I would reassign back to people. Not one. Even all the handmade crap. Most handmade stuff was made by inept hands. And if your Aunt Betsy made cookies better than any damned machine could, well, there just weren't enough Aunt Betsys to go around. The rest of them were poisoning their kids with rotten flour and sour milk!"

Lecht, at fifty-one years of age, had been hacking on various computational devices since his graduation from high school, when he took a job with a defense contractor to work on weapon systems and firing trajectories, work that sometimes placed him in an aircraft that was towing targets. Later he would earn a master's degree in mathematics at Purdue and work for IBM prior to establishing his own software-development and consulting company.

As we sat around his home one afternoon, he turned on his IBM PC/XT and inserted the disk for a program that he and programmers at his company, Lecht Sciences, Inc., had recently completed. Called the Ultimate Choreographer, the program used a digitized likeness of the great mime Marcel Marceau. This had been done with Marceau's permission, and indeed Marceau had recently been in this same room, performing his art so that it could be recorded on video in order to help the programmers capture his moves.

A few months later, while in Japan, I would see this same digitized likeness of Marcel Marceau on a huge screen at the Nippon Telegraph & Telephone Pavillion at the Tskuba Expo, the Japanese government having leased temporary use of Lecht's creative hack for $350,000. Having written three nuts-and-bolts books on computer languages, Lecht was fond of doing much of his own programming and I was truly amazed to see what he could crank out of a mere XT with a ten-megabyte hard-disk drive.

Linking the motions of Marceau together, Lecht could create, store, and then play fluid moving pictures—minuscule movies in mime. We played with another of his Marceau programs, this one called the Ultimate Teacher, in which one plays a game of solar-system golf. Each hole is on a different planet, and as you tee off on one planet for the green on the next, all of the physical forces of each planet—factors such as gravity, rotation, and orbit, take effect. The idea was to have fun while incidentally learning astrophysics.

Watching the fluid moves of the program, the superb graphics of planetary terrain, and the Newtonian motions, I recalled the stories of Hans Moravec bringing the SAIL computer system to its knees when he played some of his early animated programs. That we could be doing this on an inexpensive personal computer was a fine statement on how far computational power had come.

Indeed, a simple personal computer today with 640K of random access memory and a hard-disk storage capacity of 40 megabytes, is far more powerful than some of the older mainframes that are still in use in some of the sleepier municipalities and businesses today. The IBM 360/40, which was a workhorse of the early 1960s, filled much of a room, and cost about $700,000, had a random access memory that ranged from 16K to 256K, depending upon how much one wanted to invest. And the separate 2311 disk drive, which was nearly the size of a desk, could only hold a little more than 7 megabytes. There are wristwatches today with more random access memory than some of the early mainframes.

Lecht wants to see this computational power continue to grow, until the intelligence of machines is an ever-present part of our world. He calls automatic teller machines the first white-collar robots and would challenge any hair-splitting on whether these machines actually exhibit intelligence, an attribute that humans seem to be very stingy with when describing nonhuman things.

"Would it make any difference in our lives if we conceded the idea that machines have an intellect? I have decided that nothing but good could come of it," he said. "It is much better to call a machine smart than to call the person it replaced stupid.

"At the current time banks are replacing tellers by machines that do everything the tellers did much more effectively and efficiently. And if we could speak about that job as requiring intelligence before machines, then we'd have to speak about it as requiring intelligence with machines. Or it would be a terrible insult to those people who were and who still are bank tellers.

"The intelligence in some Boeing devices exceeds that of any professor you know at the University of Washington by all measure. And their humanitarian consideration does also. The ability to worry about whether the person is being dazed and is in need of oxygen, the ability to worry about whether the person is landing safely, all of this is quite an achievement. It's astounding. I think airplanes are the first big meaningful robots.

"A seven-forty-seven is not only a robot, it's a robot that goes through stages. It becomes a cyborg—part human and part machine—with no contention from either system as to which one should prevail at which time. If the United States is short of robots like Tomy over there [his programmable robot], it's not short of ones flying around."

Unlike others I would speak with, Lecht doesn't believe that robotics and computers are going to create unemployment. Rather he thinks that they will change the nature of our jobs. "There's so much to be done on the globe that no matter what technological instruments we employ, it is my opinion that we will never eliminate work," he said. But he also feels that the more they can change our jobs, the better off we will be. He calls this *offloading*, and he sees no value in the kind of toil we now are burdened with.

Lecht has a delightful combination of eloquence, humor, and saltiness in his speech, all of which seem essential to the expression both of his exasperation with the current condition of the beast and of his great hopes for what someday might be.

"We have to release ourselves from the idea that we are what we do. Then we soar. If we can free ourselves of the need to worry about what we do representing what we are, the mind flies unfettered, and it thinks of planets, and it thinks of stars and of the microcosm and the macrocosm.

"Without need, I mean, Christ! When you are sitting at your typewriter, doing your writing, you have to stop every now and then because you've got to go worry about whether there's electricity on or whether there's food in your stomach. But if you didn't have to stop, you could produce *continual streams* of what you think in your mind. And that might contribute to what others might do.

"But you're just stuck in the mire of pig shit," Lecht said. "And all of us are. And so we find ourselves getting up, calling the landlord, paying the rent. We shave and cut ourselves in the morning. We get into our car and there's a flat tire. It's a damn mess. You can't even guarantee that you're going to make it to the local whiskey store for the latest bottle of cognac. You've got to be free of that. You've got to *become mind*."

*

One day while we were out walking his dog, Lecht paused on the corner of Forty-Sixth Street and Second Avenue, pointed up to the twilight sky, and said, "Venus hangs up there like a jewel." And then he described the disorienting orbital plane of our solar system and spoke of the recent good viewing conditions for Saturn, Mars, and Jupiter. He keeps a Celestron telescope on his terrace, and images from space would often come into our conversations.

Of all the things we would discuss, it was the concept of becoming mind that most caught my fancy, and traveling through space would be one of the first things he would do if he were ever able to attain such an Earth-free and mind-flowing state. "I'd fly as fast as I could," said the former air force pilot. "I'd take my spaceship and race through the heavens just for the exhilaration of seeing speed and acceleration and deceleration. I would do that maybe for a million years. And then I would be curious about whether there was life anywhere else. That would occupy me next."

He also said, "I would love to get a modern voyage vehicle that could go slower than slowest and faster than fastest, so that I could follow Darwin. I would like to do this with all the latest microtechnology and I'd like to rewrite the theory of evolution—seen now with a higher vision than existed before. Because I have a suspicion that there's something wrong with it."

Lecht's desire to travel the genetic stream of evolution reminded me of what he had said in one of the *Wall Street Journal*'s typically fascinating front-page left-hand-column stories: "Some of our cells carry memory composed of information dating back to the primordial soup."

Lecht has suggested that perhaps biochip computers might someday be able to unlock from this stream "the memory of how to fly and how to live under water, and perhaps even the secret of life—how it arose, and why, or even whether it ends with the death of the individual."

Whether from biochips, silicon chips, or from our own DNA, Lecht figures that humans can use all the help we can get, for thus far we haven't proved to be overly adept at peacefully and constructively guiding our own advancement.

"A Jungian type of world exists where, if the human species keeps on its current path, it courses the genetic stream like an Indian canoe and it has no memory of what happened in back of it, it has no anticipation of what is happening in front, and it keeps doing the same damn thing, over and over and over," he told me. "To wit: We're doing the same damn stupid things we've done since the beginning of time.

"And unless there's an intervention, one maybe sown by ourselves, in the course of human history, we are *destined* to annihilation. There's no question about it. Jesus Christ didn't need any connection with Heaven to come to that conclusion. All he had to see was how everybody around him was beating one another up.

"While we are waiting for either evolution or divine intervention, we need some healthy dosages of artificial intelligence to keep us alive."

Late one night, sitting around the oval stainless-steel table he had designed, looking at the lights of the Chrysler Building and the rest of the Manhattan skyline, Lecht said, "I think biochip technology is real. But I think it's being thought of in the wrong way. People have said, 'Are there any examples of biological computers?' The answer is yes, biochips are everywhere. Biochips walk, talk, and have baby biochips! The question is, Can we improve on the biochips we've thus far made and go forward as an improved species?

"Creating a biological computing device that's superior to man has to be our goal. Because if we just make more people, we're going to be in a mess.

"And here I bring in Jung, because he suggests something that made ultimate sense, and that was that without an outside force, maybe one created by yourself, or maybe one created by someone else, the likelihood that you will remain just the way you are is very, very high. And I have always thought that technology might be that force.

"In the Old Testament, Job is trying to figure out why he's been screwed if he's been so religious. And God says to him, 'Thine own right hand may save thee.' I think he's telling Job to make a computer and to figure things out better so that he's not such an asshole.

"I just see tremendous benefits to offloading the kinds of jobs we do now," Lecht continued. "Most of what people do, I think, is worthless. Most of what I do is worthless. I know this. I mean, I'm sitting banging away at the keyboard writing. Shit! I'd rather not bang away at the keyboard. I'd rather sit there and think and have it type itself and not have to use my fingers. We are so mired in doing just menial things to remain alive that we really don't have much time to be creative.

"Machines are better at taking care of us in the satisfaction of our material needs. In fact, we're using other humans in place of machines we haven't invented yet. But if we could get machines to do all that stuff, we could *be* what we *think*.

"It's better not to till the soil. All the handmade stuff is junk, mostly. And I think, in terms of satisfaction from the material world, machines are where it's at. The question is, Is there another world? And the answer in my view is yes. There has to be one."

Although his words were perhaps a bit less reverent, Lecht would speak of the presence of a *force* not unlike what I heard discussed by Gordon Kaufman at the Harvard Divinity School.

"I know God exists," Lecht told me. "But I don't need any Bible or white-collar guy or anything to tell me. I know that things are happening that are observable by all of us but that are in the province of no single man. Forget about a god you have to grovel to, I'm just saying that there is a power and a force that's out there. And for us not to notice that it is there is as stupid as for us to grovel and do the other stuff. It *is* there. There's too much evidence. Otherwise, we can't explain how we live while being so frail."

At Carnegie-Mellon University, Mike Blackwell would suggest that there may come a time when robots, vastly more intelligent than their creators, would leave the Earth behind and travel into the stars. With Lecht's concept of *becoming mind*, it is the humans who would be saying farewell before setting off on the most incredible of journeys.

For he has written that at some point, when the computers and the robotics become sufficiently advanced to carry their human creators to a certain pinnacle, we may attain a point where "we may ultimately leave even our technology behind us." When that day comes, when we do *become mind*, he says we will be given a boost, "out of the physical, and from there into—where else—the spiritual? I think so."

Chapter 14 ~

ETHICAL SLAVES AND
EXPENDABLE WARRIORS

SINCE WE WERE now at a cruising altitude of about 32,000
feet and a speed of just over five hundred miles per hour, I assumed
that the Boeing 737 in which I was flying had smoothly shifted from
its cyborg state back into its complete robotic. Thoughts of Charles
Lecht and his theories of Boeings as robots, and especially as *humanitarian* robots, went through my mind.

Also coming to mind were thoughts of the Department of Defense's
ARPAnet computer network as I toyed with a notion of some future
world in which a writer did his word processing on such a network.
For if he were to climb onto such a robotic plane, I wondered whether
that robot, making use of the computerized passenger list, would be
able to dip into the files, no matter how tightly locked, and take retri-
bution on whatever unkind words toward things robotic the said writer
may have ever entered into a computer file. This thought returned in
spades several weeks later during a particularly harsh flight home from
Japan, traveling within the belly of the greatest beast of them all, a
747. Should such a day ever come, the airlines may have to provide
emergency lap-top computers to facilitate the midflight mending of one's
ways.

For all of its robotic nature, this aircraft had a charmingly railroad-
car feature that I had never seen before, nor since, but which had an
interesting effect on my flight: The first row of seats on the port side
of coach faced aft. Since I was in the second row, I found myself
engaged in the kind of face-to-face conversation that can make travel
by rail such a joy.

In the window seat across from me was a twenty-five-year-old naval
architect named Gavin Higgins, who was flying out to San Francisco
to see his girlfriend. He was wearing a Helly Hansen polypro jacket

and had a yellow foulweather jacket that identified him as a racing sailor. It turned out he had crewed upon some of the fastest racers in the world, a maxi-boat called *Condor,* as well as the British twelve-meter *Victory,* which was unvictorious in the preliminaries for the 1984 America's Cup. Since I had done some racing on another twelve-meter, the 1962 America's Cup champion *Weatherly* (this racing during her more leisurely days of retirement), we had a lot to talk about.

But the conversation really got interesting when it turned out that he was involved in using computer-aided design to develop an un-manned, robotically controlled combat ship.

"We are looking at drone missile-carrying ships, because a ship can take a lot more than a pilot and engineer can," he told me. "You can send a ship pounding into waves far faster if you aren't worrying about putting the feet of the crew through the floor. We can design ships that will stay together if we don't have to worry about having people on board.

"The same is true for the fighter aircraft today. The computer can by far outfly the pilots. They have to fly by the wire [computer], in which the flaps are moving automatically to keep the plane stable. The pilot programs the plane into the corner in case he blacks out."

Gavin said that he enjoyed designing boats and that computer assis-tance had removed much of the tedious drawing work. But he didn't like building military vessels that carried weapons. In fact he said he had felt a bit tricked into doing his last project. "I just designed some patrol boats," he said of a contract his firm had with a foreign country. "The client called them fast patrol boats at first, and then just before I finished, they called them fast-attack craft [and needed Gavin to design in the weaponry]. It was disgusting."

I told him about magazines I had read at MIT—periodicals like *Aviation Week* and the appalling *International Defense Review*—and about how offensive I found some of the advertisements. A complete napalm plant was offered for sale! Tanks, machine guns, hand grenades, air-craft, missiles, guidance systems, and so terribly much more were of-fered in slick advertisements that extolled the abilities of these weapons to destroy. An ad for the Boeing Pave Tiger Minidrone had a headline that read, "Fire It and Forget It."

Gavin laughed in commiseration and said, "If you think that's bad, you should see what they send you if you write."

As Gavin and I continued to talk about robots, the woman two seats over from Gavin entered into the conversation. Between her and Gavin sat her five-and-a-half-year-old son. And in her arms was her three-month-old son. Her name was Donna Southwell, and she talked about her work as a machinist in Lynn, Massachusetts, where General Electric had recently built a "plant of the future." Before building the plant, GE had negotiated with the union to allow for increased automation.

"I don't like it," she said. "I realize robotics is coming and has to come. But there's got to be job retraining or something for those who are losing their jobs. Obviously the robots can do more than the humans can and the company will shift more and more work over to the new plant. I'm working at the existing plant for now."

While at MIT I had talked a lot about robotics in the workplace and about displaced workers, but this was the first machinist (apart from my younger brother, Marc) I had met. There she was in a green flannel shirt with babe in arms and a son by her side, talking about robots that were threatening her ability to earn a living.

"The jobs at the new plant will be a lot less skilled," she continued. "The vast majority of the workers will just be loading and unloading the robots. They don't need to be skilled. I think that machining is a dying field."

I asked if a robot was a better machinist than she was.

"Yeah," she said slowly. But then she slammed her free hand down on the center table. "No! Not as good as I am. In my job I have made over one thousand different kinds of parts. They can just give me a blueprint and I can make the part."

Then she conceded, "There are a lot of jobs at GE where people just make the same parts over and over again, and a robot can do that."

Gavin suggested that she learn computer programming.

"I took some classes a few years ago," Donna said. "But it was boring. I like working with my hands."

Former machinist turned MIT researcher Harley Shaiken had said that the humans who remain in the manufacturing workforce face the danger of becoming cogs as they are forced to maintain the same pace as the robotic devices that surround them.

As Donna spoke of this very thing, there was a pride and eloquence of spirit that said much about the need to allow humans to retain a sense of freedom and dignity. "In my job now I can do whatever I want as long as I make my parts. I can work fast for a while, slow for a while. I can study the blueprints. I can get a Coke. It's more like working for yourself in a way. I have a job to do. And if I can think of a clever way to do it, I can save time. That's part of the skill."

Then her youngest began to cry. What a sight of humanity and of human ingenuity. There she was, holding a bottle up to her baby with her right hand, holding him in her left arm while using her left hand to hold up a picture book for the five-and-a-half-year-old to look at. At the same time she strained to see the words over quite a distance and read aloud with a soothing voice.

Donna's baby drained the bottle. From the residue on the glass I could see that it was her own milk. The child cried, and Donna allowed him to nurse. The tears stopped. She resumed the reading aloud of A Baby Sister for Frances. Watching this tableau, I felt quite sure that no robot could replace this woman.

*

After seeing Kerry Joels, I had flown out to Minneapolis to see three highly regarded futurists: Earl Joseph and Nelson Otto of Anticipatory Sciences, a think tank and consulting firm; and Arthur Harkins, a cultural anthropologist at the University of Minnesota. Kerry Joels had specifically mentioned the work of Earl Joseph during our conversations in Washington. I would later hear Joseph described by another researcher as being "the Buckminster Fuller" of this interesting field.

One question that I had been asked by that superwoman on the airplane was, "Do you have a picture of what it will be like in the future?" Her voice had seemed nervous, and she had added, "I'd like to see fewer working hours."

Earl Joseph, who was staff futurist at Sperry Univac, the computer firm, for twenty years and who predicted the advent of the microprocessor chip several years early (and hit his predicted date within a few months), would provide me with some of the most delightful and intriguing future vistas I would see. Yet he also proposed some of the most frightening and potentially catastrophic.

Whether those tomorrows will be delightful or catastrophic, they may be upon us sooner than we think, for Joseph, like Eric Drexler, sees a "time compression" as one advance catapults us into the next. He spoke of artificial-intelligence systems reaching a point of "critical mass," from which they could launch into a life of their own, performing their own superfast research and development, programming into themselves the results, and guiding their own evolution and destiny.

Along the way, humans should get a nice ride into the future, especially if the tomorrows of James Albus come anywhere near to being true, which is to say if there are widespread opportunities for developing disposable income (something that Joseph predicts will be the case).

If Albus and Joseph are right, it should be a marvelous world, because Joseph believes homes would be completely automated—the kitchen appliances working together to prepare your food and, with robotic arms, handing it to you; holographic walls that could create three-dimensional vistas into forests, the Grand Canyon, the moons of Jupiter, or any world you cared to see; living rooms that had living walls that were soft and warm, walls with fingers to massage you after a hard day, with ears to listen to your complaints, and with a voice to soothe your spirits; medical bracelets that could continually monitor your body chemistry and recommend what to eat and when to visit a medical center, where robotic doctors and robotic surgeons could meet the needs of your body so precisely that the average lifespan would extend to a century and a half.

But also part of the tomorrows envisioned by Earl Joseph are the same kind of robotic and computerized world caretakers Carl Hewitt had described to me at MIT. And then there was the matter of genetic engineering, from which could arise beings that perhaps even the computers couldn't control.

*

It was such an old and lovely house in which we discussed such stark and frightful futures. An old mansion of Greek Revival architecture, the home of Earl and Alma Joseph has eight fireplaces, a dining room table that will seat twenty-five, a grand open stairway of oak, fifteen-foot ceilings, a library, a music room, lots of French doors, paintings, oriental rugs, a name left over from the original owners (the Bass House), and a distinguished neighbor in the form of the Weyerhaeuser mansion, one of the rare all-wood residences in the neighborhood, apropos of a family whose name is still linked to the timber industry.

One night I dined with the Josephs. Also present was Brian Toren, manager of communications systems at Sperry Corp., and a futurist. We had a curried dish, something for which Joseph acquired a taste while on a brief assignment in India, fresh corn from the farmers' market, homemade biscuits, and fresh preserves, all served on Wedgwood Florentine china. We were enjoying luxuries that robots may not be able to understand for quite some time.

When the conversation turned to Carl Hewitt's ideas of using computers and robots as benevolent caretakers, as wise referees to keep man safely distanced from the weaponry the mind of man had devised, even Brian admitted that "my first reaction is fear."

But he then went on to talk about how his favorite character on the old television show *Star Trek* was Mr. Spock, because he could bring

an unemotional rationality into tense situations in which his more rat-
tled human companions weren't always thinking clearly.

Joseph's response was much like that of Professor George Williams,
at the Harvard Divinity School. "I just look around the world and see
the horrible things that people are doing to other people, and I look at
the horrible things that the leaders of the world are doing to other
people, and I know I could develop a machine that would be more
compassionate to people and that would mete out justice more than
what is going on in the world at the present time."

It was hard to argue that point, as it was difficult to refute his next:
"There is a scientific process for making computers better. This process doesn't exist for making leaders better."

"The only question I have is *who* is going to design the software?"
said Toren.

"Or the knowledge base," agreed Joseph. The former Sperry Univac
futurist added, "I certainly wouldn't want IBM to do it."

Joseph described how the infrastructure for our benevolent caretakers is in one sense already being put in place, through the extensive
computerization of both the government and private sectors of our
country.

"Machines are making decisions already," he said. "Go into a factory. Go into an office. I would grant you these are minor decisions,
but nevertheless they are going on."

Then, turning to decisions of a more major nature, he said, "I look
at the missile systems and the military systems and I would say we are
here already for parts of this."

I asked about the influence of computers on presidential decisions.

"I'm sure it's already there at a hidden level. When these data come
in and are digested by the computer, a programmer has put in parameters to do things this way and that, which is really part of the decision-
making process. If you look at the commanders, the admirals, at whoever
is making the decisions—including the president—most of the studies
indicate that of the actual information that is available at the time a
decision is made, of the information that makes it to the desk of the
decision maker, less than twenty percent of it is usable. The decision
maker just can't use the rest because of time and other constraints.
Now, if that is the case, imagine how bad some decisions are."

"Especially if the information wasn't prioritized by what was important," said Toren.

"And if it is prioritized, then someone has already made a decision
on it," Joseph said. "And there is an awful lot of prioritizing done by

computer. If you call that decision making, then we are already there. If this is what is picked up by the president to make a decision, and if the other eighty percent is hidden from him, who has made the decision? The computer or the president?"

"The computers may even take over by default," Toren said as a grandfather's clock chimed the hour. "Humans don't like to make decisions."

*

The next day Joseph was delivering a lecture on his future visions at the University of Minnesota. Before leaving for the campus, we sat around his office and spoke about what may be emerging from genetic engineering—especially in light of a U.S. Supreme Court decision giving companies the right to place patents on and own the new forms of life they are creating. So far the new creatures have been bacterial, but as surprising as this seems, there is very little difference between the DNA of a bacterium and that of man.

Recombinant DNA is the well-established engineering process of using restriction enzymes to cut a piece of DNA from one cell and splice it into the DNA of another. In a related area, molecular biologists are looking for ways to push the buttons of a cell to turn on or turn off the actions of the thousands of gene blocks that make up the DNA.

Several years earlier I had watched researchers at Stanford University work with living brain cells—cells that had been removed by necessity from a severely epileptic patient and then kept alive in a miniature chamber of salt water and nutrients that mimicked the environment of the body. How strange it had been to hear an amplified monitor of the cells firing, trying to continue their synaptic conversations, perhaps not yet aware of their new state of isolation.

A similar kind of chamber environment is used for the increasingly common *in vitro* fertilization or "test-tube" baby. Sperm and egg are united, and maintained through several rounds of cell division until this tiny cluster of life is transferred into the uterus of the mother.

With all of this already happening today, it isn't difficult to picture a tomorrow in which one of your cells could be placed into a saltwater chamber, in which there would be chemical emissaries that would visit the nucleus and walk through that greatest of all libraries, pushing the buttons that would activate the genes that would create a new heart, lung, kidney, or eye. Just about any of your cells could be used because all cells carry the same DNA, and the only difference between a heart cell and a bone cell is which genetic cookbook from the DNA library was pulled off the shelf by the messenger RNA and put into use. Rapidly grown to full size within the saltwater chamber, the organ could then be transplanted into you, without any fears of rejection or incompatibility.

As great as all this sounds, technology like this, if used incorrectly, could open some doors that perhaps shouldn't be opened. For once you can grow an organ, a complete body wouldn't be far behind.

Combine the genetic button-pushing that would allow you to grow a human with the gene-splicing technology already in hand, and we might be able to create new forms of life—the appearance and function of which would be limited only by the imagination. And because these forms could be patented, sold, and owned, one can imagine a combination of man and tiger for the army, a combination of shark and man for the navy, a combination of bird and man for the air force. And four-armed house-cleaning servants for the home. These androids, as biological robots are also called, could prove to be a mixed gift from science. Frightful things await behind some of these doors. And Earl Joseph believes the doors might soon begin to swing open.

"You are not very far away from growing an entire human once you grow the first part," he said. "And then it could snowball. This is why I say there is a time compression. Once you break the barrier, once you are able to grow the first earlobe or finger, you have really broken the barrier for the whole body."

I asked whether this would allow creation of instant adults, since otherwise—in addition to all the other societal storms that would likely emerge around this issue—you would be talking about creating crops of parentless babies and raising them in what would amount to a human-robot factory farm.

"We know of methods of turning on the cell-division process to do it faster than it would normally occur," Joseph said. "If you could grow adults, and if you needed a big army overnight, you could grow an army."

"So, you would be creating an organic robot?" I asked.

"Exactly," Joseph said. "A domain-specific robot."

"Have you heard anyone discuss this?"

"Well, yes," Joseph said, seeming rather uneasy and laughing a bit tightly. "I've heard about research going on in this."

"Where?" I asked. "In the military?"

"Well, I don't know how much I can talk about it at this stage," he said. "I'm not under government contract at the moment. But if I do this thing for the air force, I don't know how much I can talk about it."

"Because it would be classified?"

"At a certain stage it would be classified."

"It's that serious?"

"At the talking stage it's serious."

I posed some of the obvious moral questions that creating such robots would raise.

"Would you rather take people from the population and put them in the army?" Joseph said. "Do you want to grow them out there as human beings to be killed in the next war, or do you want to grow them in the laboratory for that purpose?"

Someone at MIT had once told me that if you could imagine it, the military was already doing research on it. This creation of warrior robots was precisely what the movie *Blade Runner* was about—and about the consequences of these warriors coming home. I asked Joseph about what could be done with returning androids that had been genetically engineered and conditioned to kill.

"You would put them to work," he said. "Reprogram them. Maybe reprogram them as human beings. Maybe you would make them blue so that you could distinguish them. It might be the next race that we discriminate against. It would be a great release. If we make the genetic robots, we can call them something else. We could discriminate against them while the rest of society goes along its merry way. This is an alternative."

"Until they rebelled," I said.

"Not if we don't give them enough intelligence or a big enough knowledge base."

"You've basically bred killers," I said. "It seems like they might be dangerous to have in the population."

"Not if you reconditioned them," Joseph said. "Would you treat them as a machine or treat them as a human?"

I couldn't answer.

"There would be good reasons to do either," Joseph said.

"I think you would want to treat them as humans."

"Are they humans?" Joseph asked.

"It depends upon what you do with their brains."

"Let's try a different viewpoint," he said. "Let's build a robot out of mechanical-electrical parts and then give it a cloned brain, a brain that has never existed in a human being. You just take a clone of a brain and use it as one of the hardware parts. Would you call that a human being?"

"No."

"Why is that different than making the body look like a human being, out of human material? We made the brain out of human material," he said. "You see, you are talking about a degree. If you package it so that it doesn't look like a human being, you aren't going to worry about it. But if you package it like a human being, you'll call it a human being and give it rights. But where are you going to draw the line?"

"I think a lot of it would be the being's ability to show compassion and emotion," I ventured.

"But what if I do that on a standard everyday personal computer? Would you call that personal computer human? Just because it can exhibit compassion and justice?"

"As long as it was sitting on a desk, probably not," I said. "But as soon as you make a mobile robot that can show emotion, I think you are going to have a lot of people saying, 'We've got to treat these things better.' "

"I think it's strictly in the way we sell it," Joseph said. "I think we could package it so that society would accept it, but discriminate against it. I don't think people will accept it as a regular human."

These questions might be upon us sooner than we think. Speaking of the patents already issued for genetically engineered bacteria, Joseph said, "They are already giving out patents on new species. Now I ask you, Would you like to have the patent on the next human race, a race far superior to who you are? We are not very far away from this. It will probably happen in our lifetime."

*

It was time to head over to the campus, but in the car we continued the conversation. He said that the military wouldn't be the only driving force behind the development of genetically engineered flesh-and-blood robots. He said there would be tremendous consumer interest in purchasing ethical slaves.

I shuddered to think how misused, tormented, and abused such slaves would be, as this is one area in which our species has a most inhumane and sordid record. But Joseph saw this as more a question of design than of morality.

"I guess what I operate under in my mind is that anything we can do to make it better for the human and to keep from treating the human badly—through discrimination or sending humans to war— anything that we can do for that, in my mind, is worthwhile," he said. "If I'm going to use a robot, or use cloned parts of humans, or indeed cloned humans, then I would want to design them such that they never really are a human.

"So I have to come up with a definition of what is a human," he said. "Where do you draw the line? What do you put in them so that they don't have that type of a feeling or the capability to be anything other than a machine? So, to me, it is a design question rather than a morality question. In other words, I would want to design these things so that I could ease the lot of real humans, whatever real humans are.

"In fact I may want to design them so that the rest of society would discriminate against the machine person rather than the real person," he said. "In other words, to release the part of society that is now being discriminated against. In fact, that might be the main purpose for wanting to do it."

"These machines would not suffer from this discrimination?" I asked.

"If you define them as a machine, then I don't have to worry about whether they suffer or not," Joseph said. "In other words, I don't put the capability in there to have feelings."

We arrived on campus, and Joseph delivered his lecture to five hundred students in a "Computers in Society" course. The lecture theater in Nicholson Hall was packed. The presentation was video-taped for later use. It was the fifteenth consecutive year he had presented his views of the future. It was well received, students came up to talk afterward, but he hadn't touched upon the subject that I had found so disconcerting: the creation of blue people to serve as ethical slaves and expendable warriors.

I picked up a copy of the school paper, the *Minnesota Daily,* and saw a front-page story about a recent appearance by the MIT linguist Noam Chomsky. The headline read, "Chomsky calls Americans blind to history."

*

Later that day Earl Joseph told me of another option, one quite different from the scenario of purposely making genetic robotics with flaws to keep them in place. By pushing different buttons, he believes, we could create a race that would go soaring past humans.

"The door has been opened with artificial intelligence and recombinant DNA," he said. "These two breakthroughs have opened the door to realms we have never entered before. We can make a race of these things much more capable than human beings.

"Should we stop the evolutionary progress of humans and create a different race?" he said. "Maybe that race is robots. Maybe it is a biogenetically engineered system. Or maybe it is you and I who have been added to or amplified.

"If we create something that is superintellectual and far above anybody else, we get into a problem in considering what we are to do about it," Joseph continued. "And I don't know where the limit is. I don't have a means to judge where the limits are—if there even should be limits. There will be a societal debate on it, but we need some kind of yardstick for the morality that's involved in the value system. We don't have that yet."

I asked Joseph about something he had said earlier about time compression and about being faced by these huge questions earlier than we think.

"The questions are already here," he said. "The scientists are already working on this. I have that choice to make now for the air force thing they want me to do. How far should I go? So this isn't something that's off in the future. It's off in the future as far as when it will be applied, but we are at the design and conceptual stage right now. The pre–basic research stage.

"There is some possibility of creating a human race that will be beyond humans," he said. "I purposely used that term: *a human race beyond humans*."

"This isn't just you as a futurist conjuring up some science fiction image?" I said.

"Definitely not," he said.

"Because the air force is interested?"

"And industry is interested too."

Chapter 15 ～

SLEEPING WITH ROBOTS

I WAS DRIVING around with Arthur Harkins one night, when he stopped at a shopping center to give into an irresistible urge: He rented the videotape for the movie *Alien*. We took it to his house and watched it that night, me for my second time, Harkins for his sixteenth.

Alien is probably the scariest science fiction movie ever made, but that wasn't the reason that this cultural anthropologist with the University of Minnesota was so enamored with it. Rather, he loved the way the high technology of the refinery spacecraft *Nostromo* was so precisely and logically presented and how completely at home the crew of the ship seemed within this setting.

"The movie *Forbidden Planet* did the same thing years before," he said. "It made the high-tech look commonplace, which is something Americans have to learn how to do—to treat this stuff as no more spectacular than a tree. In fact less so. A tree is far more difficult to engineer."

Something that I hope doesn't become commonplace is the fact that the computer that controlled the *Nostromo,* a computer called Mother, and one not unlike what Kerry Joels was predicting for a manned Mars project, turned out to be like the infamous HAL of *2001* in its devotion to duty taking precedence over concern for human life. At the end of *Alien*, Mother joins forces with the terrible creature, turning on its steam system to drive the alien toward the escape vehicle, where the one surviving human, along with her cat, is attempting an escape.

Harkins spoke of the need to push ourselves forward into the future, something that he has clearly done in his own life and within his home. A black anodized satellite receiving dish, supported by a single leg, seems quite natural alongside the trees in his frontyard. Inside the house are five television sets, so he is never too far from the world of information and entertainment that his dish intercepts.

Harkins opened a closet filled with black boxes glowing with red lights. These were the electronic components used to translate the microwave information that his dish received. With the press of a button on a hand-held controller, his dish silently moved outside, changing its focus from one satellite to another.

I knew enough about what communications satellites looked like to find this quite exciting. There they were, at a height of 23,000 miles, in geosynchronous orbit with the earth, an orbit first described in the science fiction writing of Arthur C. Clarke, the creator of HAL. And there we were, Art and I, with a change of a button leaping from Westar IV to Galaxy 1 to Comstar.

Each satellite provided another harvest of microwave information. We watched debate in the Canadian Parliament, a French newscast about Ronald Reagan, Japanese theater, an Eskimo-language program, a Uruguay versus Chile soccer game, a Spanish-language movie of a man sitting in the gutter having a vision of the Virgin, a television preacher with a devilish beard shouting, "You need God! You need God! You need God!" a weatherman for the Bahamas, and an old shoot-'em-up airplane movie, in which Harkins, a former fighter pilot, watched the action just long enough to say, "That guy's in trouble. Oops, they got him."

On his telephone-answering machine Harkins found a message from the Australian Broadcasting Company. He picked up the smallest portable phone I had ever seen, a fold-up model that looked like the communicators used by the crew of the *Enterprise* on *Star Trek,* and returned the call. The night before, he had been interviewed by a radio station in New Zealand. And a week before, he had been visited by a television crew from Great Britain.

Why all the interest? Arthur Harkins, who is trying so hard to push today into tomorrow, said he would like the chance to marry a robot.

Harkins believes that human intelligence will be exceeded by computers "in one area after another within the next ten to fifteen years." In preparation for that, he was currently co-authoring with an attorney a paper that would attempt to prepare society for granting rights to these smart machines and the robotic bodies they would inhabit.

"Our proposition is that we can see levels of machine intelligence. The highest level being what I am going to call the independent intelligence, or the citizen level. These machines would have full voting rights, marriage rights, and the rest of it.

"The next level down would be the dependent intelligence, which would be advanced expert systems, and the advanced limited-choice mobile systems, such as battlefield robots. The third category, the limited expert system, is essentially the types of programs we are developing now."

It was the first category, the independent intelligence, or citizen-level, machine that most caught my interest, and that most caught Harkins's. For it was at this level of intelligence and independence that we might have robots that one would want to spend a lifetime with.

"If someone can invent what will pass for a citizen-level machine, a machine that could qualify for citizenship," Harkins said, "I should not shrink from being one of those who might propose marriage to it."

*

From other researchers I would learn about the nuts and bolts of how we might go about making intelligent robots, cyborgs, and androids. From anthropologist Harkins I wanted to learn more about the effect such creatures would have on our lives. I would also find out about what effect *we* might have on *their* lives.

It seems apparent to me that we should treat very well whatever life we create, just for goodness' sake. And from a more pragmatic standpoint, it may even be more imperative that we treat well what we create, since what we control one year might control us in another.

Yet I was seeing signs that we perhaps would not treat well the robots and androids we made. The idea of blue androids that would serve us in the home and of warrior androids that would fight our wars was chilling. It was good to see Harkins already addressing the question, but he wasn't optimistic.

"We have taken hundreds of years to give women the vote. Hundreds of years for blacks to be free," Harkins said. "We still have nothing that approaches a substantial body of law that provides for the overall rights of children. They are still property, and they are still tortured psychologically, tortured physically, fed poorly, left unfed, given bad schools. Now, why would we assume that once machine intelligence becomes commonplace, it would not be mistreated as well? This calls for an ethical treatment of intelligence regardless of its morphological nature.

"It is going to depend on the definition of *feeling* as much as it is the definition of *intelligence*. We are going to have to look at the question *Can* machines feel? in the same way that we once argued whether animals could or couldn't feel.

"There were periods in Western history when it was determined that animals were nothing but machines. And the result was that these poor things were put through incredible torture. And we still put animals through incredible torture on the grounds that it is better to do it to animals than to us. I'm not arguing that it isn't better, but I am saying that we are going to face this with machines when we begin to think of emotions as digitizable.

"Then we are going to have to start asking ourselves, Can machines be programmed to feel? Can human sensations be duplicated or simulated in nonorganic systems? We know they can be in organic systems—if we can build androids, for instance.

"I think we are going to develop whole new disciplines of machine sociology, anthropology, and psychology," Harkins said. "You see, I don't think there's going to be a way in the immediate future of these developments to keep the machines from being remarkably, and perhaps depressingly, human in their behavior."

With this, Harkins was going into the fascinating area of what robotic personalities might be. And he said that the best guide would be to look at the spectrum of human diversity to getting a sense for how different machines will be.

"Right now we want them to be perfect ethically, perfect in their work for us, to be entertaining, and not to violate our taboos. We are not going to get this, because there will be many manufacturers of these systems. These manufacturers will be from different countries with different worldviews. The systems will be programmed differently; they will have different experiences; they will have different environments to work in; they *will* fail; and there will be a large number of other variables that will produce high levels of variety in these systems. And, I think, we have to get used to that right now, so as not to be surprised—negatively at least—by those forms of variety when they emerge."

I told Harkins about how Gerry Sussman at MIT had talked with such delight about being able to recognize who wrote a program just by reading the code and about how he saw the personality of the programmer reflected in the code.

"I agree," Harkins said. "I think we see this in our children. We see it in our dogs and cats. We see it in our gardens, our homes. We see it in our choice of automobiles, in our style of driving, in the sexuality aspects of our lives, in the ways in which we choose to view the universe."

Such a potpourri of robotic personalities—rather than there being a monotonous and universal sameness—should aid in their acceptance by humans. But initially there may be an exploitation as they are used as mere machines. This is an exploitation that many humans would likely find distasteful, and Harkins said, "I don't have the slightest doubt that a national or international movement for the social rights of robots would develop. It will be an anticipatory movement, I hope, one that will come before the need for it is obvious."

I voiced my concern for the horrible abuses I could imagine humans heaping upon blue-skinned androids, grown in genetic laboratories to do our bidding. The same would certainly be possible for the more mechanical devices as well. Harkins's response just deepened these fears.

"Already there is talk of creation of androids for sexual purposes," he said. "I think you are going to see an industry develop in the sexual-appliance area. At first it will be machine appliances, and eventually you will see biological substitutes or surrogates for human sexual organs being employed in stationary and mobile machine systems.

"Eventually I think you will see androids that are manufactured, or grown, specifically for those types of purposes. I think we will have to distinguish between independent intelligence and dependent intelligence. We will have to distinguish between whether we have been sufficiently moral in making those distinctions. We have to decide whether calling a robot an appliance when it passes all or most of the tests for independent intelligence is moral."

*

The next morning I watched the forty-nine-year-old Harkins prepare a breakfast befitting a futurist who wanted to live long enough to enjoy the glories of tomorrow. To a base of yogurt he added peanuts, soybeans, bananas, pears, and apples. Then he went to his refrigerator, which had the largest assortment of vitamin and mineral, amino acid, and other supplements I had ever seen outside a store. He pulled out eighteen jars and sat them on the counter; he proceeded to work his way through them, filling his hand to nearly overflowing.

We continued our conversation from the night before, looking at what may emerge when lifelike robots and androids are accorded full citizenship. And what Harkins foresees is an irresistible urge for humans to marry these new forms of life.

"Let's look at what can be done with machine and biological combinations," Harkins paused to more carefully frame his thoughts. "We could become *highly* explicit here, but there's no need to do that. We could build machines that made perpetually available to us the characteristics of lovemaking, intelligence, and sociability that we would want.

"Even if we made them as appliances, not as fully intelligent devices, they could still have a lot of these features, including bubbling conversations," he said. "I'm talking about something here that could threaten the whole idea of—that could render unnecessary—human marriages."

*

Later that day I met with Nelson Otto, a Ph.D. who was a co-founder of Anticipatory Sciences, Inc. He agreed with what Harkins had said: Robots may soon provide humans with a companionship of such high quality that it will change our lives.

"There are a lot of areas about robotics that people avoid talking about," Otto said. "A robot as a companion. A robot as a best friend. A robot as a lover. These are things that are in the back of people's minds, but they don't want an open discussion on them.

"Yet we know that there are just an incredible number of lonely people out there. Really lonely people. We are a lonely society. We are a society in need of stimulation. And we turn to the most bland things you can think of. We've got people fixated on soap operas just to give them some kind of stimulation.

"When they find an intelligent machine such as a robot that can converse with them, that can stimulate them, that can give them a backrub—and I have to stop almost at that one," Otto said. "Most people in this country are so malnourished when it comes to personal attention: getting a neckrub, a backrub, somebody there to soothe them, to be with them, that when they see the opportunity that a robot gives them, the luxury that it gives, I think they will be more than accepting."

Otto talked about the public reaction to Arthur Harkins's prediction that before the year 2000 the first test case of a human-robot marriage would be in the courts. There were so many requests for interviews that Otto, who agrees with Harkins, helped his longtime friend and fellow futurist by fielding some of the interview requests.

"These were very often talk-show hosts with call-in audiences, and what was amazing to me to note was that—and Art and I watched this over a period of time and compared it with each other—as people called in, we found that invariably, once they got over their initial shock, their next question was always consistent: Where do I get one? So I see a high degree of acceptance of something like this, especially as they become more intelligent," Otto said.

Lonely adults won't be the only ones ready to embrace a robotic companion. Otto believes that children would be quick to fall in love with robotic pals.

"When Disney's EPCOT Center first opened, I sat there the first week and watched people come in and interact with the robots. The robots looked like robots, nice pieces of plastic, Frosty the Snowman types of things. And I watched the kids, in these three- and four-minute contacts, fall in love with this piece of plastic. I watched parents have to drag their kids away.

"The kids were fascinated. Part of it was dealing with a new piece of technology. But the real thing was that it was an interactive piece of technology. That was the big thing. It was programmed in a very simple way, but it still interacted. And I looked at some of the other attributes it had: patience, kindness, warmth, the appearance of love, always sensitive, never angry. And it always had *time* for them.

"You look at those characteristics and you say to yourself, 'How could this thing fail?' You show me a human being that has those characteristics, that consistently has those characteristics. You know of course that we don't. This is why I say it will get into the classroom. Teachers are complaining right now about having too many students, large class sizes, about not being able to deal with students individually. A robot gives you the chance for individual attention.

"And robots don't have to look like androids," Otto said. "They don't have to have great size. A robot could be hand-held. The Cabbage Patch doll is real popular. Why not turn that Cabbage Patch doll into a small robot, and instead of having this lifeless little thing that is adorable, why not give the child their own personal baby robot? But this robot would also be very sophisticated—with a sense of vision, speech patterns, communications. And those little kids carry their Cabbage Patch doll with them everywhere. And of course we can make that robot soft and cuddly, too.

"There's so much emphasis right now on missing children, why not use the technology to assist? If a person wanted to make a small fortune, they could develop the next generation of Cabbage Patch dolls using electronic communications devices."

Apart from serving as homing devices—something that, Otto believes, might actually be better implanted into the child—he sees such personal robots serving as companions and constant tutors.

"There are some real dangers involved in this, too," he said. "The child's greatest degree of affiliation would be with a *thing*. But look what we are giving kids right now. We're giving them a *tube*. Not a tutor, a *tube* as their constant companion. And we are finally starting to admit there is a first-degree relationship between violence on the tube and behavior patterns of children afterward.

"So I think we would want to watch the bonding to the robot very carefully, but what's the alternative right now? Right now we are offering children either no bonding opportunities, poor bonding opportunities, bad bonding opportunities, and some good ones. So the argument that it's better to do nothing doesn't hold much water with me, because it's only a small percentage of children that are really getting good bonding opportunities. For most kids the best bonding opportunity they've ever had has been Big Bird or some other character from *Sesame Street*."

The bonding would likely be strong, for Otto sees the robots coming equipped with video screens for tutoring during the day and for telling bedtime stories at night. "I can just see parents and grandparents with their hair raising over this," he said. "But how many times do kids really get tucked into bed? They just really don't. I look at the case of my own kids. I'm just not home every night."

And if the bonding between a child and the robot was indeed strong, it might not be that bad, because Otto, as with Kerry Joels, sees the possibility of the relationship lasting for life. The robot could be continually upgraded, growing intellectually with the child, although perhaps you wouldn't want it to continue to grow physically. For, Otto said, "Later on, if you no longer need that teddy bear appearance, ultimately your robot, your companion, could be pocket-size so that it could always be with you."

I had to agree with Otto when he said, "I see assimilation of these devices in our society coming faster and faster and easier and easier."

Chapter 16 ∾

IN THE LAND OF
ZEN AND ROBOTS

THE HEAVY-EQUIPMENT laboratory for the Mechanical Engineering Department at Tokyo's Waseda University was even more huge
and awesome than what Red Whittaker had at Carnegie-Mellon University. It was a two-story open bay, with the offices opening out onto
an interior second-floor balcony. Wandering through the lab one day,
searching between the boiler-room massiveness of pipes, cranes, workbenches, tooling machines, and stainless steel fabrication stations, I
came across a table with a white sheet of plastic covering something
that had the shape of a human body.

It was the beginning of a new robot, resting beneath the sheet in
Frankenstein repose, as if awaiting the first electrical storm so that a
bolt of lightning could set the electrons flowing through the gates and
pathways of its brain. Sometimes it seemed to me as if all of Japan
were awaiting just such a bolt, as if the entire nation were ready to
arise robotic. For if any nation were ready to plunge into the next
century, it certainly was Japan.

A few weeks earlier I had taken a ten-hour flight from Seattle to
Narita International, within the womb of that most humanitarian of
robots, a Boeing 747, just to see what was happening in this country
that at once retained so much of the old while leading the world into
the future.

I had at this point already spent four days at the Tsukuba Science
City Expo, a $2-billion, six-month celebration of science, technology,
and the future. Certainly the most celebrated piece of technology dis-
played at Expo was a human-size robot that read music and played an
electric organ. I had first heard of this robot, called Wasubot 2 (the
Wasu in honor of Waseda University), while at MIT, where I had
seen photographs of it taped to a couple of office doors at the Artificial

Intelligence Laboratory. The attitude toward the robot had been one of disbelief, one of: *If it really does read music, it's a pretty clever hack.*

The attitude at MIT also seemed to grate on there being something a bit too cute about a robot playing an organ—though after spending some time in the country, one is likely to change this assessment to their being something charmingly innocent and Japanese about the assignment. While Ken Salisbury's robotic hand was blowing fuses trying to crush empty Coke cans at MIT, the students at Waseda University had created a magnificent robot with a precision of movement, a sophistication of programming, and a subtlety of control that seemed superior to any robot I had seen in the United States.

Wasubot 2 was located in the Japanese Government Pavilion at Expo, and it was one of three robots on display there. The first was a four-legged spider robot, which appeared large enough to carry a man and which moved its legs so cautiously around obstacles that it seemed to be alive. I knew that such robots appealed to the military because of their potential for crossing rugged terrain, and perhaps because of this the spider robot gave me a sense of unease.

The second robot in the cycle of demonstrations was a biped that could walk, taking slow scissor steps to keep its weight centered. From conversations at C-MU I knew what a difficult task it was to get a robot to walk on two legs. It was impressive to watch.

The third robot, and the star of the show, was Wasubot 2, which was seated at a Yamaha organ and would make use of a limited voice-recognition and voice-synthesis program to converse with the young hostess. The hostess (nearly all of the pavilions were staffed by young Japanese girls wearing futuristic uniforms that brought to mind old space movies) asked the audience which song from a selection of sheet music they wanted to hear Wasubot 2 play.

A young child asked for "London Bridge," and the hostess placed the music in a holder above the organ. Wasubot 2, which had a video camera for a head, stared at the music for several seconds while continuing to speak. During this time the robot's vision system was converting the notes into digital information that would trigger his movements in playing. The entire score was committed to memory, so that the movements of the robot while playing wouldn't interfere with the visual analysis.

Wasubot 2 was impressive to look at. The body was very much based upon that of a human's in size and shape. The limbs were made of black carbon-reinforced plastic. Polished stainless steel was used at the joints, and gracefully draped cables were the sinews and muscles.

The robot's ten fingers were poised over the lower keyboard prior to the beginning of the playing, with the tips just above the keys, so a triggering of a cable would bring a finger down. When Wasubot 2 began playing, I watched to see whether the arms would move laterally up and down the keyboards, which they did. They also shifted position smoothly as the hands worked both the upper and lower keyboards. As the arms moved, there was a gentle swaying of the thin cables that ran up from the elbow to the head, a motion that made the movements seem even more fluid and almost fleshy. I had thought that the legs might have just been for show, but the left foot worked the bass keyboard, while the right foot operated the expression pedal.

At the end of "London Bridge," the audience applauded. This was something I would notice throughout Expo: The young space-age women were virtually never applauded after delivering their own presentations, yet invariably there was enthusiastic applause for the robots, which performed such feats as carving ice sculptures, drawing pictures, lifting barbells, and spinning tops along taut strings and samurai-sword edges.

The next song requested was "Hey Jude." As with the first song, the arrangement was pretty full—with chording, arpeggios, and footwork. It was impressive. But I kept looking across to the biped robot, and what I really wanted was to combine Wasubot 2 with the biped and then crank in some more artificial intelligence so that Wasubot 2 could walk into the room, sit down at the organ, engage in a more far-ranging conversation, and then get down to playing the organ.

"That is Wasubot 3," I would be told a couple of days later at Waseda University. "That's what we are working on now."

*

After seeing the robot playing the organ, I wanted to meet it's makers, so I set out across Tokyo, making my way by trains and buses and then on foot, using a series of notes a Japanese friend had written for me, all of them asking, at each stage of the journey, "Please show me the way to Waseda."

It was in the heavy-equipment laboratory at Waseda that I found, in an all-but-forgotten corner, the dusty and neglected progenitor of the robotic musician: Wasubot 1. This first-generation robot, built in the early 1970s, already looked terribly antiquated. It was ferociously heavy, and the angle iron from which it was constructed gave it the look of something a wild child would create from an oversize Erector set.

Wasubot 1 had been created simply to walk and be able to pick up a glass of water. It had succeeded at this and then been placed in the corner to while away as the scientists turned their attention to creating the showcase-musician Wasubot 2.

It gave me an odd feeling to see this obsolete robot stored in a corner. A month earlier I had encountered a similar situation, which had elicited a like response when I had gone rummaging through an old storage room on a lower level of the old SAIL barn at Stanford. In a room that was strewn with broken boxes of papers, an avalanche of *Scientific Americans,* junked furniture, chemistry test tubes, old neon lights, an ancient pair of Head Deep Powders engraved with Alta Ski Patrol, pots and pans, mounds of draperies, Coke cans, and empty bottles of Anchor Steam Beer—in the midst of, and partially buried by, this great debris there had been a five-foot derrick suspended from which was a robotic arm with shoulder, elbow, and wrist. Just looking at that arm, you could see that it was old technology. It had been relegated to its present marginal existence after having shown an incurable tendency to rip itself apart when the movement commands conflicted with what its joints would allow.

And right next to that old arm had been a ridiculous-looking robot called the Walking Table, something that had two sets of four legs and would extend one set out and down while lifting the other set up and making its progress in a crab-crawl fashion. Atop the table were the control boards, a clunky maze of outdated chips. Still, I thought the table and arm deserved a fate better than this. Fortunately, an old Digital PDP-6 computer had recently been pulled out of that very room, and as it was believed to be the last working 6 in existence, it had been sent to a safe haven at the Computer Museum in Boston. But I knew of no such museum for robots, and as I had stood there, ankle-deep in unspooled computer storage tape, wondering what previous precious one-zero bits of information I was trampling, I had feared that these early robotic artifacts would all be lost.

I reached out and gave an arm on Wasubot 1 a to-and-fro shake and hoped it would meet with a better fate.

In another part of the heavy-equipment laboratory there was a robotic body of more recent engineering vintage. It was suspended from a wall with climbing ropes and carabiners. Next to it was an open window with some motorcycles outside. While at Stanford, I had conversed over the ARPAnet with Mike Blackwell at C-MU, and he had spun a tale of Terragator having escaped and headed off cross-country with a gas can, knocking over service stations as he worked his way West. I told the graduate student who was with me that he had best watch that window lest his robot untruss itself and grab a bike.

"I hope it develops to that level," he said.

When we came upon the table draped morguelike in the white sheet of plastic, he said, "Perhaps Wasubot 3 will be Frankenstein."

*

I took off my shoes and put on a pair of green plastic slippers before entering the vision laboratory at Waseda, where Wasubot 2 was taught to read music. The laboratory was jammed with computers, all without their side covers in order to make the control boards accessible. There were trays of screws, nuts and bolts, wire cutters, soldering irons, Allen wrenches, oscilloscopes, volt-meters, terminals, and streams of computer cables.

It was more crowded than the laboratories I had seen in the United States, and there seemed a more formal air. But there were also some carefully executed cartoons of their beloved robot hanging on the walls, and within the constraints of this more formal culture, it seemed to have more of a hacker atmosphere than did the terribly formal white-shirt-and-tie computer room I had seen earlier that week when visiting the ICOT facility, where work on Japan's Fifth Generation computer program was continuing to fall behind schedule.

Also in the vision lab was the backup copy of Wasubot 2, sitting at an organ but without a head, which was placed in a corner, and without legs, which were being used by the robot at Expo. This was fine with me, since what I was most interested in seeing was the torso, arms, and hands. Finally I was able to do something that wasn't allowed at Expo; I could touch this robot, run a finger along the carbon-fiber plastic of its arms, examine the machining of the fingers, trace the pathways of control cables that ran like sinews throughout the limbs, and see the joints at wrists, elbows, and shoulders.

Despite the initial skepticism of MIT hackers, Wasubot 2 was indeed able to read standard sheet music, a great deal of which was scattered around the laboratory.

This was accomplished with a vision program that could identify the five horizontal lines of a music score and then discriminate note type and note placement within the lines. This system worked so well with the limb-control system that music of greater complexity than what I had seen at Expo could be played.

For the opening ceremonies at Expo, playing for an audience that included the Crown Prince of Japan, Wasubot 2 was linked by way of a huge screen to the NHK Symphony Orchestra, which, under the direction of conductor Toyama Yuzo, accompanied the robot in Bach's *Aria on the G String.*

That day Wasubot 2 also played a special arrangement of *Bear in the Woods.* This was an arrangement that no human could have played. The fastest a human can strike a key is seven or eight times a second. Wasubot played portions of *Bear in the Woods* at the rate of fifteen strikes per second.

Wasubot 2 was a very clever hack. And Wasubot 3 should be even more so. In addition to walking and having broader conversational skills, Wasubot 3 will change instruments, leaving the organ for the much more demanding key strokes of a piano.

A couple of days earlier I had been on the thirty-sixth floor of the Akasaka Prince Hotel talking to Charles Lecht about Japan, Expo, and Wasubot 2.

"That robot is so alive it gives you chills," Lecht told me. "It stares at that music like a child giving its first music recital. It reads the music, stores it in a buffer, and plays it. It is one of the most inspiring things I've seen in my entire life. Every time I go back there, I listen to that thing four or five times."

Lecht has taken his video camera along for some of his visits with Wasubot 2, and he played one of his video cassettes for me. As we watched the robot play, Charles said, "They know me at the pavilion. I keep coming in the back door to see it, and they say, 'Here comes Wasubot's lover.' "

We watched it some more, and then Lecht said, "It looks just like a child."

"An ugly child," I said. But it was as if I had insulted Charlie's own flesh and blood. He saw great beauty in that cyclopic robot, and I suppose he was right. Perhaps more than anything else, Lecht saw the future.

MIT's Joseph Weizenbaum would no doubt point out that Wasubot 2 didn't really *know* what music was. It didn't really *know* what it was doing. Yet I had met others—people such as Hans Moravec at C-MU; Marvin Minsky, Gerry Sussman, and Phil Agre at MIT; John McCarthy at Stanford; and Jerry Hobbs at SRI—who were working on that part of the problem. With these others trying to crank in the artificial intelligence and consciousness, it was just good to see how well the Waseda researchers were doing on the robotic chassis.

*

Charles Lecht was like a child, as was virtually every other person in the audience as we reached out to touch the phantom figures and as we oohed and aahed with the visual delight of the three-dimensional movie.

We were in the Sumitomo Pavilion at Expo, watching the best 3-D movie I had ever seen. As we followed a young Japanese girl named Erika and her fluffy sheepdog named Bozo through an orchard, it was as if we could reach out and touch the leaves and pick the fruit.

Now, there is nothing new about 3-D movies—though we were seeing the latest in high-resolution technology presented on the very best wraparound screens—but there was something significant in the number of pavilions that featured movies in 3-D and other you-are-there, high-resolution formats, such as Imax, Japax, Cinemax-U, Showscan, Dynavision, and Birds-I-View, as well as laser-generated holography.

At Carnegie-Mellon University Hans Moravec and Mike Blackwell had talked of the day when experiences could be simulated so well that you could sit in a chair wearing a headset to captivate your eyes, ears, and nose and have sensors attached to hands and legs (similar to but more sensitive than the glove boxes that have long been used in radiation laboratories), which would enable you to visit the world from the safety and comfort of your home.

It had been Charles Lecht who had provided a term for this vicarious voyaging. He called it *artificial experience.*

At MIT Marvin Minsky had talked of using long-distance tele-operated robots for visiting foreign countries. It would be like a long-distance telephone call, in which your artificial-experience equipment at home would be linked to a mobile robot in Rome, for instance. With your headgear on, you would only see what the vision system of the robot saw. Your sense of hearing and smell would also be directly transported into the environment you were exploring by way of the robot. With your entire muscular-skeletal system being monitored and translated into the servo controls of the robot in Rome, you could walk into a garden, wander over to whichever part you pleased, bend down, pick a flower, hold it up to your eyes for a closer look, and then inhale its sweetness.

The next day you could dial into a robot in Hawaii and have it hail a cab for a ride to the cliffs above the ocean, where your robotic surrogate would strap itself/yourself into a hang glider that would in every way place you out in the trade winds, soaring for as long as you could navigate the updrafts as you took enraptured flight along the cliffs, across the waves, and then up into the verdant valleys. You could do all of this secure in the knowledge that if your landing was anything but smooth, you might be scared to death, but—providing your heart didn't stop at home—the only damage would be to your rented robot.

Traveling by artificial experience could go a long way toward ending the need for jet fuel and automobiles, while saving such treasures as the Coliseum and the Parthenon from being trampled to dust by human feet. And the same sensors that enabled you to smell the flowers and feel the breeze and sun during your hang gliding would also enable you to enter vicariously, but seemingly completely, the most exotic of pleasure palaces without concern for nagging viral or bacterial consequences.

I had been thinking a lot about artificial experience since the first moments of my first visit to Expo, when I had seen a holographic representation a clay figurine from the Japanese Jomon Period (10,000 to 300 B.C.) It was on a slowly rotating pedestal, and the lasers that were used to create its wonderfully intricate, three-dimensional, and slightly shimmering representation would periodically shut off. The figurine was there, then it was gone.

A young Japanese girl wearing a school uniform, as do all students in this country, reached through the open top of the display case and passed a rolled-up piece of paper through the figurine singing out with glee, "Ghost Buster!"

It did have a ghostlike quality to it. It had been about ten years since I had first seen a hologram, and that had been in a deep basement of a University of Washington laboratory, where lasers and lenses had been aligned on top of a two-foot-thick lead table so as to dampen vibrations. All of that just to project into midair the image of a Matchbox Toy truck.

In New York Charles Lecht had talked of holography as something that would free humans from the enslavement of greed and excessive material need. Living in holographically equipped homes, we could hang our walls with Corbets from the Louvre and with van Goghs from the Guggenheim. Our floors could appear absolutely deep in the finest oriental rugs one day or as a soft-green meadow lawn the next.

And by linking your holographic room with that of a friend's, you could sit down to a dinner on different ends of the continent and have the joyful and seemingly real experience of sitting just across the table from each other. Arthur Harkins at the University of Minnesota had predicted that the dullness of interplanetary space travel would be eased as absolutely real-appearing holograms of a string quartet and such were beamed into the confines of the spaceship.

In Japan I would find that much of what I had talked of elsewhere was either already happening or was preparing to emerge from the unusually fertile soil. At Carnegie-Mellon Hans Moravec had talked about using the headgear of artificial experience to plug students into encounters with historical figures that could act as teachers.

"You might meet Newton sitting under a tree, with an apple in his hand," Hans had told me. "And he tells you about how he's been thinking about what makes apples fall, and about what keeps the Moon moving around in circles, and that he thinks that the same force that pulls on an apple can actually pull on the Moon. And this would be because inertia would keep the Moon moving in a straight line unless there was some other force acting on it, and that other force, in fact, is the same force that's pulling the apples down toward the center of the earth. And then he would show you the equations, which would immediately come to life."

At the time I had suggested that there perhaps could be no better way to teach students about cell biology than to take them on a journey into the cell, using the headgear and glove boxes to pierce a cell membrane and go churning through the cytoplasmic sea to watch the huge ribosomes at work with messenger and transfer RNA as they created proteins. At Expo I pretty much experienced that very journey when Charles Lecht and I went to the 3-D theater in the Fujitsu Pavilion and tilted back in reclining seats to stare into a domed screen that covered the entire ceiling. Within the first several seconds of the show we were eerily given the sensation of rising upward, as if our chairs were on hydraulic lifts and we were slowly rising to a height of forty feet and in danger of being pushed right through the now-invisible ceiling. From that great height we took a wonderful plunge into a sea of molecules, until with great delight I spotted the double helix of DNA and watched as we closed in upon it and then went on a dizzying flow down the strands as they separated prior to a cell division.

In other chambers we were transported through interstellar space and allowed to explore planets. Back on Earth, we were able to explore the oceans, drive cars so recklessly that people screamed, and fly to such heights and make such gentle spiraling turns that each of us became a bird.

And so it was with great interest and excitement that I sat in an exquisite 3-D movie with Lecht and heard him say, "This is almost holographic."

There was only one element missing, and that was the interaction— and how badly I yearned for that! How I wanted to be able to walk around within each movie. How I wanted to take leave of the main characters and strike off on my own to explore this new world.

I was delighted to find that the ability to do exactly that was closer than I would have imagined. This realization came during a visit to the Japanese government's Mechanical Engineering Laboratory, just a few miles away from Expo.

*

It was at the Mechanical Engineering Laboratory that I had my first out-of-body experience.

After all the laid-back, blue-jeans-and-flannel-shirt hackers I had met in the United States, it took a couple of impeccably groomed, white-shirt-and-tie Japanese scientists to introduce me to a piece of artificial-experience equipment that was so well conceptualized and precisely executed I could completely lose my sense of location.

It all began, as did nearly all of my meetings with Japanese researchers, with much bowing, exchanging of business cards, and with the sipping of green tea. Minoru Abe, the director of the Robotics Department, wore a gray suit, white shirt, and a maroon tie as we sat in a comfortable conference room with violet carpeting, paintings, silk flowers, and a carved elephant on a sideboard. Susumu Tachi, senior research scientist at the Robotics Department, and the one who had designed and built the vision apparatus that I found so impressive, wore a brown-and-red-checked sport coat, brown slacks, white shirt, and a gray tie.

The basic realm of robotics within which Tachi worked is called *tele-operation*. *Tele* means "from a distance," and typically a tele-operated robot would have a human in a control room manipulating controls that could be exactly translated into the motions of a distant robot. That means that if the human operator opened his or her hand to pick up a wrench, the robot would do exactly likewise. The link between the robot and the operator can be accomplished with a long cord or with a radio transmitter and receiver. NASA has long been interested in tele-operated systems because the uplink could be made so easily by way of satellites, though over great distances there would be a time lag between our sending a command and the robot receiving it.

Within this realm of tele-operation, Tachi has chosen to work in the fascinating area of *tele-existence*, which is to say he wants to create a vision system that so closely links the human and the robot that the human feels as if he or she exists within the robot. Tachi is also working on the kind of full-arm glove-box equipment that Hans Moravec had fantasized about. Again, as with the vision system, the linkup between the movement of the human arms and hands and that of the robot is to be so complete that, to quote from one of Tachi's technical papers recently presented at an international symposium on robotics, "a human operator at the remote control site can perform remote manipulation tasks dexterously with the feeling that he exists in the slave anthropormorphic robot."

Tachi has succeeded with his vision system. It truly gives you the feeling that you are *inside* the robot, looking at the world from within its body, not your own. This is possible because the operator isn't just looking at a television monitor; his head is encased in a black-velvet-lined box. Within this box are two television receivers, one for each eye. The receivers are gauged so that the image that is reflected against the retina of each eye is exactly the same as if you were looking at the world unaided. Further, every movement of your head is duplicated on the robot, where two precisely placed video cameras transmit a human range of what is seen.

The result of this is that when I went into the laboratory and strapped my head inside the black-velvet box, it was as if I were seeing with my own eyes. The depth and scope of human vision was so completely reproduced, and the color was so clear, that it was at first unsettling and then a wild visual delight. Whenever I turned my head or looked up or down, the image that was transmitted to the retinas of my eyes was completely faithful to what I would see unaided. I studied the computer panels, the work tables of the laboratory, looked at the people, and then came upon a life-size mannequin wearing a pair of sunglasses. How odd that had been. It was as if I were one mannequin looking at another, fully expecting that she, behind those shades, would be able to look back. Spinning through my mind during all of this were thoughts of how completely enraptured Hans Moravec would be by this. I wanted him, and so many others, to be here, I wanted them all to see this. It was exactly what so many robotics and AI researchers had longed for and prophesied.

While such thoughts were synaptically crackling through my mind, someone in the laboratory went over to the robot-mounted cameras and swung them around so that they focused on me. The walls spun during the maneuver, and then when the motion stopped and I was looking at myself, the out-of-body experience began. It was as if I were standing a few feet away *in another body* looking at myself. I moved my head to look up and down and even to look away. And when I looked away from that person who was me, it was as if that body were just another passerby.

But I could not ignore that guy for long and I turned my head back to look again at this person who was standing across from me with his head strapped into a black-velvet box. The scientists in the laboratory laughed. They knew what was going through my head, for it had also gone through theirs during their own encounters with their out-of-body selves. "Are you here?" Tachi laughed. "Or are you there? Where is your body?"

Everything that I had heard about vicarious voyaging, artificial experience, seeing the world by robot, all of this suddenly rang so true. I *could* visit Rome with a robot like this. Sitting at home, I could climb mountains in Switzerland, watch the sunrise in Ireland and the sunset in Hawaii. I could do all of that and have no qualms about saying that all of this had been seen with my own eyes.

In the conference room, prior to coming into the lab, I had asked Tachi what I would experience had I stayed in Seattle and used a robot to make my visit to him. Could I wander around the room? I had asked. Could I pick up things from the table and examine them? He had held up a teacup and said that with the tele-existence arms I would not only pick up the cup but feel its surface and sense the pressure I used to hold it.

Now that I had placed my head within the box, I *knew* that I could have visited him with ease, without ever leaving home. Such ideas had been considered by him, for he had said, "You could have an automatic travel agency. If you wanted to go on an adventure, it's very dangerous to go into the Amazon Basin, yet still you might want to have that kind of experience and fun. So you would send the robot with a tele-existence system to experience these kinds of things."

In the conference room I had understood what he had meant, but it wasn't until I strapped myself into the black-velvet box that I really knew how right he was. *You could be in an Amazon jungle,* without leaving home. You could wake up the snakes in the morning and walk with the big cats at night.

I was reluctant to unstrap my head. I wasn't ready to leave the box. But this was outweighed by my need to tell Tachi that he was brilliant and that he had accomplished a very great thing. I tried to tell him about Hans Moravec and Mike Blackwell and about Marvin Minsky and Charles Lecht, but it all seemed to come out at once and none of it very clearly. Those in the lab just stood there smiling, knowing personally the box's effect. I shook Tachi's hand for a prolonged time as I spoke and found myself bowing deeply to both him and Minoru Abe.

In his own polite and reserved way, Tachi basically said, "You ain't seen nothing yet!" for he was getting ready to work the same magic on the arms and hands that would place your limbs inside that distant robotic body. "When you come back next year," Tachi said, "you will experience a lot more."

During my time in the box an especially overwhelming thought had come flowing through my brain like a warm and welcome wave. It was a realization that came during those few perplexing moments of staring at myself, not sure where my mind was, not sure where my body was, but feeling as if they certainly weren't dwelling in the same space. It was at this point that I knew that if Hans could figure the hardwiring, downloading would work. There was no doubt in my mind that given a vision system like Tachi's, (and I could only speculate on how dynamite his glove box would be) I could live quite happily over the millennia, wandering about exploring, learning, trying to establish rapport with whatever life the staggering number of planets of the universe would offer, and quite likely always searching for the latest developer of robotic chassis to see if some Tachi of the future had found a way to crank even more of our senses into the wonderful world of perception.

*

"Domo, domo arigato," Charles Lecht said to the waiter as our second round of ice-cold beers was delivered. We were sitting at an outside table at the Kikkoman Restaurant, just across from the Nippon Telegraph and Telephone Pavilion at Expo on a June day with temperatures into the nineties. All of the pavilions had VIP entrances around back, complete with plush waiting areas and complimentary drinks so that one didn't have to stand in line. I had made several appointments through the Expo foreign press office the previous day to revisit some of the best 3-D and robotic exhibits with Lecht. But Lecht and I were now in the process of blowing a hole in the efficient itinerary the press office had created. When I had made note of the time, however, Charlie's well-reasoned response had been, "Do you think it's good rushing anywhere in this heat?"

"No," I had said, taking another sip of beer. "It might be hazardous."

But what really kept us at the sidewalk café was that Charlie and I were very much enjoying the box seats we had on the passing parade of Japanese people. Sitting there at our umbrellaed table, there was a wonderful river of life as Japanese of all ages flowed from one pavilion at Expo to the next.

The longer I was in this country, the more I loved and respected the Japanese. Charles Lecht had long since fallen head over heels for the people and their culture. When I had seen him in New York, he could hardly wait to return to Japan, and at various saber-rattling American technology meetings in the States, where U.S. researchers and military leaders had spoken of Japan's Fifth Generation Computer Project as if it were an act of war, Lecht had stood up to tell his fellow countrymen "what a bunch of ignorant assholes" they were.

From my first day in the country I had been coming to the same conclusion. By the time I had landed at Narita and taken the train into Tokyo, it was the evening rush hour, and being that I had been up for close to twenty-four hours and was still experiencing the fate of all American travelers—the discovery that not everyone speaks English—I had decided to flee Tokyo and found myself aboard a Shinkansen bullet train to Kyoto.

All the seats were taken, and after walking through every car, I knew that I was the only Westerner aboard. Exhausted and bewildered, I had sat down in the antechamber at the end of a car, as in Japan even the floors of rush-hour trains are somehow kept astonishingly clean. Before long I was surrounded by a group of teenage boys and girls, all eager to say, "Halloo! How are you?" which was the limit of their vocabulary, but which was more than I could say in Japanese. Before long we were all singing and having a great time—all the way to Kyoto. Then in Kyoto, at nearly 10:00 P.M., a businessman who could speak a bit of English worked with the information desk for forty minutes to find an inn where I could stay. And while visiting the Kiyomizu Temple in Kyoto one rainy day (mist and rain enhanced its beauty) I was three times engulfed by platoons of uniformed schoolchildren, who couldn't believe their good fortune to come across an American.

The same thing would happen in Tokyo, and you soon learned that there is no street crime, that at any hour of the day or night you can wander the smallest streets of the city. The subways, like the trains and buses, are clean and actually cheery. There is no litter, and even the homes that are built right next to the tracks of Tokyo's Yamonote beltway railroad show all the signs of love and care. If you ask for directions, people will walk blocks out of their way to guide you to your destination.

Even in Hiroshima the Japanese are kind. When the first atomic bomb was dropped on August 6, 1945, over the busiest, most densely populated area of the city, 140,000 persons were immediately killed or dead within hours, with tens of thousands of others dying in waves from burn injuries and radiation poisoning over the next days, weeks, months, and, in the case of radiation-induced cancer, years. The fiery terror of the bomb was so hellish that an eerily common and frightful observation of those who survived was that they had witnessed a debasement of life that a human wasn't supposed to see, that they carried inner wounds just from having *seen* such things as burning fingers.

Sadako Sasaki, who was two years old when the bomb went off a mile from her home, met a delayed fate that would haunt so many other survivors when she developed leukemia nine years later. Following a Japanese legend that anyone who folds one thousand paper cranes is granted a wish, she began folding cranes in the hospital and was up to 644 when she died. Her classmates folded the remaining 356, and when this story was learned, all of Japan was soon folding paper cranes.

There are many commemorative placques and statues in Peace Memorial Park, all piled high with the brightly colored cranes, but the highest mounds of crane garlands were at the base of the Children's Peace Monument, a gentle arch with a bronze statue on top of a young girl holding high a paper crane. It was at this monument where the tiny and intricately folded paper cranes had been piled so high that the summit was beyond the reach of man. And even here I found that there was so much goodwill toward Americans that it staggered at the same time that it nourished me.

As Lecht and I sat at Expo drinking our beers and taking it all in, we were three times interrupted by shy groups of students asking if perhaps they could pose beside us for photographs. Others would shout a "Hellooo! Goodbye!" and giggle as they walked by. For our country to do anything to turn away this natural welling of goodwill would be foolish indeed, I figured. "One thing that's astounding here is how little resentment there appears in both young and old toward Americans, even after the bombing of Nagasaki and Hiroshima," Lecht said. And this is why he would become so frustrated with the way Japan was portrayed by the American press.

"Do you see this fair the way the American newspapers have represented it? 'Total failure.' 'Nothing interesting.' 'Bad conditions.' It sounds like the jealousy that would make an angel green with envy," Lecht said. "It's just unfair."

I had read one article in which the writer found fault with the number of children that were bussed in each day from all over the country. To a cynical American reporter this was an indication that the Japanese were trying to increase the attendance figures. This had seemed to me like the very oddest and most paranoid of observations to make. Boosting attendance figures? If an American reporter had really wanted to find ominous portentions in the sea of children that passed through the gates of Expo each day, he or she might have done better to focus upon what the future impact may be. In ten or fifteen years, what could be the result of having given so many children an early and intoxicatingly positive boost toward the sciences? Japan already leads the United States in the number of engineers it graduates, and from my conversations with American researchers in robotics and artificial intelligence, I knew how crucial was an early triggering of the scientific curiosity and imagination. For many, this had come from an early introduction to science fiction or from having a parent or an early teacher who provided a nudge toward science.

All of Expo was a celebration of science, technology, and the future, and nearly all of the exhibits, pavilions, and presentations were geared toward inspiring the young. In the years to come Japan may well enjoy a tremendous harvest from the seeds that were planted in the millions of young minds that were brought through the gates during Expo's six-month run.

While we indulged ourselves in a third and final round of beers, knowing that despite the holes we had blasted in our itinerary the gracious Japanese would find a way to slip us into the shows, we watched two formal parades pass by. The parades weren't sponsored by the fair officials; the participants weren't paid, as they would be at Disney World. Instead the parades consisted of various groups that had traveled to Expo on their own and just wanted to join in the celebration.

One parade was quiet and somber, consisting of Buddhist monks wearing black robes, sandals, and carrying yellow lanterns. They were followed by children carrying banners streaming from long bamboo poles that still had their leaves on top. Another parade featured a brass band playing Western music while boys and girls, dressed in space suits, danced and roller-skated along.

Even apart from Expo, this land of Zen and robots seemed especially eager to leap into the future. The federal government has made automation a national goal. Robots were not just welcomed into the workplace but given pet names and revered. And everywhere you could find scenes like the one I saw in which an older gentleman, who nightly visited my tiny neighborhood bar on a narrow street in Sangubashi, would alternately plug his earphone into a credit-card-thin FM radio and a pocket-size liquid-crystal-display color television set.

This enthusiasm for the future was much in evidence at Expo, where the presence of intelligent robots helping and befriending humans was a foregone conclusion in so many of the exhibits and presentations. Over and over again it was the robots that were shown saving the day for humans. And there were songs of praise with lyrics such as "Man and machines can be friends."

And then, of course, there was the Mechanical Engineering Laboratory—which is to say, the Japanese Government—making the very equipment that could send us all out on voyages of artificial experience.

The more I saw of the Japanese, the more comfortable I felt about their creating and programming intelligent computers and robots. If they should pull out ahead of the United States and other countries, and if they should become the first to pass through that threshold of robotic life, then perhaps this would be as it should, for they seemed to me the most trustworthy to deal with the awesome powers that would be unlocked.

"Look at that group of kids there," Charlie said as he pointed to a class of children waiting outside the NT&T Pavilion. "They are just like American kids. They are fidgety. They are itchy. They are listening to someone giving them instructions. Some are sitting down. Some are bouncing around. But none of them is punching. None of them is whipping another. There isn't a violent motion in front of your eyes."

Riding on the trains, walking through the cities, I had seen the same thing. As the teachers sit together and relax and chat on the trains, their students wander up and down the aisles, going from one seating of pals to the next, sharing raisins, sharing stories, smiling, laughing, talking. They are free to romp about, it is just that they seem to do so less destructively than their American counterparts. There is none of the hitting, the slugging, none of the pecking-order brutality that seems so much a part of any grouping of American kids.

"If someone is doing some copying," Lecht said, referring to another stereotype that rankles him, "maybe the Americans should send some people over here, take a lot of movies of this place, and show it in the schools so that the kids could copy that."

I had often thought during my travels that if groups of American autoworkers, or any other group that felt threatened by Japan, were to visit this country and see the courtesy, the kindness, the respect for others, the sense of dignity that is afforded even the lowliest of workers, and the lack of crime, they would go home not wanting to change Japan but wanting to change America.

"They *love* Americans in this country," Charlie said. "I haven't seen anything like the anti-Japanese sentiment expressed by ignorant Bostonians. All this stuff you hear about Japanese dumping of electronics in America and unfair competition, and about government-orchestrated assaults on Western economies, it's just plain bullshit! The people buying most here are the ones who are putting that stuff in the paper—namely Motorola, IBM, and all of the technology companies. They are buying up a storm in Japan because the quality is better and then twisting their arms in Washington to get the prices low.

"You know, every day in the Nippon Telegraph and Telephone Pavilion [where Lecht's Marcel Marceau program was on display] at nine o'clock or maybe nine-fifteen or nine-thirty—because they aren't really as punctual as we think—every day they have a meeting with the entire staff and they pledge their allegiance to their jobs. It's not pledging their allegiance to one another as if they were slaves, but rather, it's 'While we are on this ship, we may as well play the roles we have to play.'

"They have self-criticism days, when they stand up and say, 'I did this wrong and that wrong,' It's mature. It's the mark of a *maturation of the intellect* to realize that you have to live in two mutually exclusive worlds—one of obedience and legislation, the other of freedom and participation. And they do it well.

"Of course, they are an older race," Charlie said. "They are smarter than we are. They really are."

And this is why Lecht believes that the most groundless stereotype of all is that the Japanese are copycats and lack innovation.

"This country is number one in so many areas!" he said. "You don't get to be number one by copying, *unless* you are copying God."

Chapter 17 ❧

HOSTILE
CREATIONS

IT WAS SUCH a beautiful day and such a lovely walk. Dr. Hisao Yamada and I were returning from lunch at his favorite restaurant, a tiny but brightly polished little place where the owners, husband and wife, knew him well. Yamada would say the owner's father was an artist and that from the way the son arranged the pieces of raw fish on the plate, you could see he had inherited the artistry. Our destination, just a few blocks away, was the University of Tokyo campus, where Yamada is a professor of information sciences and a researcher into how the human brain works and how it might be mimicked by computers.

We walked along past gardens in bloom, beneath trees that shaded us with their canopies of foliage, and beside the most pristine and polished garden walls I had ever seen—one of which had an angular slot perfectly cut and masoned in to allow the passage through of a tree branch that otherwise would have been sawn away.

In such fine surroundings, and on a day when we were otherwise speaking of such things as the arrangement of fish on a plate, calligraphy, and the tradition of sumo wrestling, it was disheartening to find that Dr. Yamada, as with many of his colleagues in the United States, saw the potential for bad and even evil emerging from the computers and robots that we were, with such love and devotion, attempting to give life.

After traveling to the major artificial-intelligence and robotics laboratories in the United States and Japan, I had come to think that Japan was preparing to launch itself into the future and that even if the initial breaks in artificial intelligence came from the United States (since despite Japan's Fifth Generation computer project, we still seemed on a better track), they would, as a society, be more eager to place the results into their wonderful robotic chassis and prepare to spiral onward.

Because Japan will clearly continue to be a leader in the technologies of the future, and perhaps become *the* leader, it was, in a certain sense, good to see that the dark side was being considered early in the game. Yet the words of Dr. Yamada were still chilling as he spoke of future military research leading to robots that were hostile to mankind.

"We will be quite safe with computers, as long as we keep it that way," Dr. Yamada had said. "But the trouble is that we fight amongst ourselves. I would suspect that, normally, people don't want to make machines that are harmful to us. But the military thinking is different. As long as there is the possibility that a machine will destroy your enemies, and not destroy you, you will be willing to pay for it. That's the military thinking.

"So I think there will be research in the future on machines that will be harmful to human beings. And if we keep on doing that, at a certain point we will build a machine that is hostile to mankind. Or at least some segment of mankind. But I think it could go haywire and start destroying us, too.

"So far we have never designed a machine, at least purposely, to rebel against us. We can always pull plugs or do this or that so that the machine would be rendered ineffective."

That is, if we continue building the machines with accessible plugs to pull. With some military machines, it is likely that would not be a feature desired by their builders.

"If we try to build a machine that is very difficult to nullify, or that is self-reproducing," Yamada said, "if you really design and build such a machine, it's going to be a formidable enemy against us."

*

Just how formidable such an enemy could be was discussed one night in Saint Paul when I had dinner with futurist Earl Joseph and a friend of his from Sperry Univac, Brian Toren. I had put this question to them: Will we always be able to unplug a computer?

Toren shook his head no.

Joseph said, "One simple example is: If you want to have a computer that will protect the nation from incoming missiles, you don't want *anything* to be able to turn it off."

"Its primary mission would be to protect itself," Toren said.

"Survival," said Joseph.

"It may even use human beings to help it survive," said Toren as a grandfather's clock chimed midnight from the hallway. "You could have guards stationed around a power plant so that you couldn't get to it to blow it up. Or it could have automated devices."

"It might not have to resort to that if it has enough redundancy," Joseph said.

"It might have many plugs," Toren said. "They are calling these things fault-resilient computers."

"I suppose you could bomb the building," I said.

"If you could get the bomber through the defenses," Toren said.

And then Joseph said, "If you go to a network system, you could maximize survivability. If you bombed out one computer, the same program could be operating elsewhere."

"It's like our electrical grid in the United States today," said Toren. "You could bomb a hydroelectric plant tomorrow, but you wouldn't deprive a community of power, because you can get the electricity from two states away. You could network the whole computer program together and distribute the knowledge all over the country."

"And the program could duplicate itself," Joseph said. "So you could design a system that you couldn't turn off. It could be designed that way."

While at the Harvard Divinity School I had been asked a most interesting question by George Williams, the theologian who had impressed me with his overall sense of humanity, as well as with his open-mindedness, about handing over the controls of the military and government to a set of computers that could act as benevolent caretakers to prevent man from continuing his already obvious ability to be inhumane to his fellow human beings. Williams had simply pointed to the Holocaust and proposed that a machine had to be more compassionate than was a human turned bad. But then he had raised that interesting question that had remained with me: Could a computer fall from grace? Could a computer turn away from goodness and become evil?

I put this question to Earl Joseph, and it is interesting to note that at this point in our dinner conversation, the voices of Joseph and Toren had taken on a nearly hushed tone, as if they were reluctant even to vocalize some of their thoughts. This stuck in my mind, because it was something that I would notice in others virtually every time the subject was discussed.

"Considering an expert system," Joseph said, "I would build the system to imitate the knowledge of human beings, but I also would give it the heuristic knowledge to go beyond that. Now my question is: In what direction will it go?

"And I think it would be from that viewpoint that a problem could come," he said. "Rather than it trying to do something out of the realm of what we wanted it to do, it would just simply grow its knowledge in a different direction, which may or may not be useful."

"Is there a possibility," I asked, "that as it grew, even if it weren't malevolent toward humans, it could grow into an area that to us might seem disconcerting?"

"Definitely," Joseph said. "Very definitely."

"And if that happened, what could we do?"

"We would have to counter it somehow," Joseph said.

"As it became more knowledgeable, it would become more difficult to counter, as you have already described," I said.

"What does that tell you we would have to do?" said Joseph. "It tells you that we have to design it so that it has stops that it can't go beyond."

"Maybe you could build in a virus," said Toren, slow and thoughtfully. "Are you familiar with a virus? It's a software program that can be plugged into a computer and at some point in time it will start taking it over, methodically and insidiously, so that even the computer and the people running it don't know. It is a cancerous growth. It just slowly starts programming itself into the system and doing its own instructions."

"It isn't science fiction?" I asked.

Toren and Joseph quietly answered together: "It has been done."

*

As much as I wanted it to be science fiction, and not reality, I had already heard about viruses at MIT. And such straitlaced publications as *Scientific American, Science,* and the *Wall Street Journal* had carried initial reports about them.

Toren had suggested using a virus as a safeguard to destroy a computer turned bad—rather like putting a dynamite collar around the neck of Godzilla. But as seems always to be the case with science, the same technology that would allow a virus to be used as a safeguard would also allow it to be used for something bad.

A computer program that turned paranoid and began worrying about getting shut off could send copies of itself, through the telephone lines that link so many computers already, to every major and minor bank in the country, could make itself a part of every defense computer, every treasury computer, every power-grid computer. These copies could reside secretly, awaiting an order to activate or an order to destroy. These agent copies could reside within the very computers being used to track the viruses down. Such a program could so firmly entrench itself that the nation's entire computer system would have to be all but destroyed to eliminate it.

And this assumes that the errant program isn't fighting back. I once discussed such a scenario with Marvin Minsky at MIT, and he had pointed to the movie *COLOSSUS: The Forbin Project* as a reasonable scenario. This is the movie previously mentioned, in which COLOSSUS, the computer, maintained power through nuclear blackmail: Mess with me and I will detonate a missile. When researchers tried to disarm the warheads, COLOSSUS kept his word. And humans figured they had best not mess anymore. When the movie ended, COLOSSUS still ruled the world.

*

The night I had gone out to dinner with MIT graduate students Phil Agre and David Levitt, the topic of program viruses had come up. This was the same dinner at which Agre, who was trying to teach his Blocks World program to think, had talked of the possibility of computers going psychotic, about how he saw parallels between his efforts and those who had created the first atomic bomb. This was when he had said, "I have this bad fantasy that if I do my job properly, I will be reviled at my death."

David Levitt had mentioned viruses in this way: "Some programs have started to get exceptionally slimy lately."

At a party in Cambridge one night, I had listened to two programmers talking about viruses. One postulated a computer system with one layer of protection after another. The second programmer then described precisely how he would circumvent each step and implant the virus. There was no argument as he described each maneuver, just an increasing of unease in the room and, again, a lowering of voices, a hushed tone. The first programmer conceded that the virus could enter, but there was no sense of victory in the second, none at all. He was frightened by the things that could be done, which is why I haven't used his name. There were about five of us standing around in a circle during this exchange of ideas, and at the completion all were silent for an uncomfortable length of time.

*

One night I went to the MIT Nanotechnology Study Group with Eric Drexler. Afterward, as Eric had fielded questions about how his superminiature computers would work and about how he could create cell-repair machine robots that would propel themselves like paddle-wheelers through the inner sea of a cell looking for things to fix, I had asked Eric's wife, Chris Peterson, about the darker side of the technology.

Chris, an MIT chemistry graduate, said, "It's called the gray-goo problem among people who have started to think about this." She then went on to describe scenarios in which bacteria-size robots could prove more devastating to life on Earth than even nuclear bombs.

As bad as program viruses could be, the invisible self-replicating robots of nanotechnology could be even worse, far, far worse.

The same kind of nanotechnology that could enable the cell-repair machines would allow robots so small that they could be invisibly carried by the wind, living their lives by converting carbon atoms into identical copies of themselves. Such bacteria-size robots would multiply insanely, mindlessly consuming anything and everything that was carbon based, which is to say all life upon the planet, after which the robots could begin eating the rocks, eating the very planet upon which they had been created.

Hans Moravec at MIT had also spoken of bacteria-size robots that could eat rocks and live on sunshine, but he had proposed this for the benevolent purpose of establishing self-replicating factories in space. However, something like this set loose on Earth could destroy the *planet*.

And because the robots that Drexler foresees with nanotechnology would actually have substantial computational power on board, they could be far from mindless. They could be programmed to attack on the basis of geographical location (for example, North America), a person's race, or any attribute that could be sensed in the DNA. Or, by using basic voice recognition, it is possible that such wind-born robots could be programmed to destroy all English-speaking people.

"This gray-goo problem is a disturbing thing!" Chris had said.

As Chris and I spoke, Eric came over to express a fear of his own—that in discussing this potential problem we not frighten the public into opposing nanotechnology research.

"My greatest fear is a polarization between those who are for it and those who are against it; between those who see the opportunities and those who focus on the dangers," Eric said. "Movements in the democracies could get organized and stop this technology or that technology. But the effect of that would be simply to keep the democracies from developing these things.

"There are technologically oriented states that we don't have control over, that have an ability to continue to move forward in all of these areas, perhaps not quite as fast as we are able to, but quite fast enough to get there. Eventually they will get these technologies, and if they get them first, it would deliver control over the entire world to precisely those groups that are not subject to influence by democratically constituted movements."

"It's frustrating, isn't it?" I said. "As you push knowledge further ahead, you have to keep looking out of the side of your eyes to see what's going to be done with it."

"Constantly," said Eric.

*

Arthur Harkins, the University of Minnesota futurist who was so enthusiastic about the future that he would marry a robot if the right one came along, also had concerns about using technology in the wrong way. He was concerned particularly with the idea of creating computers and robots as benevolent caretakers to protect humans from themselves. He suggested that benevolent caretakers might not be so benevolent.

"Why would the computers be any better than we are?" he said. "Why would it not be assumed that the computers would simply act out with more efficiency the visciousness and the lack of humanity that we already have developed? My fundamental argument is not against the use of computers. I don't want to sound like Joe Weizenbaum. I would like to see continuous involvement in the articulation and management of these situations by all of us. I'd like to see elementary schools deal with these things. I'd like to see Americans able to deal with their own inventions.

"Do you realize that ten years after machine intelligence, kids will be doing this in their homes," he said. "How are we going to control that? How are we going to control store-bought laboratories that enable you to create new organisms? We need to look very hard at how to deal with our own inventions and our own future."

Chapter 18 ∾

INTO THE STARS

The Earth is the cradle of mankind.
But man cannot stay in the cradle forever."
—*Konstantin Tsiolkovsky*

ONE SPRING DAY, just prior to my trip to Japan, I sat at an
outdoor cafeteria table on the Stanford campus with two graduate students in robotics: Vic Nalwa and Dave Kreigman. I had just sat in on
a lecture Kreigman had delivered to an undergraduate class in which
he had talked of Moravec's work on the Stanford Cart, Terragator,
and the Neptune and Pluto robots. Kreigman had also talked about his
own work with MARS, an acronym that had been accomplished with
the backbending effort of Mobile Autonomous Robot at Stanford.

MARS, Pluto, Neptune—there was something about robots that made
even scientists think of space. And perhaps this will someday save our
very species. For when Kreigman and I met with Nalwa for lunch and
a beer, we entered into a conversation about what intellectual feats a
robot might or might not accomplish. Nalwa, a native of India, took a
conservative stand and seemed threatened by any suggestion that a
computer could match the thoughts of man: "It might not be right to
think that we can improve on things all the time. We might just reach
limits."

He then said, "Anyway, with all the bombs around to blow up this
world, these philosophical questions don't matter. One big boom and
that's it."

This comment stood out to me, because I had heard so many other
researchers qualify all of their most promising views of the future by
saying, "If we don't blow ourselves up."

There is certainly plenty of reason to make such qualifying statements. There are something like fifty-thousand nuclear bombs and
warheads in the world, and the use of just a fraction of these could

trigger the destruction of all human and other mammalian life on this planet. After 3.5 billion years of evolution, during which the elements of this garden of a planet have yielded the essence of life and nurtured it as it evolved into human beings, we could destroy this garden, leaving nothing but the radiation-resistant insects behind.

Kreigman did not shrug off the comment. It was as if the words had just refocused something that was always there. His reply to Nalwa had been, "We have to get off this damn planet. You don't put all your eggs in one basket."

*

The bad news is that whenever science discovers a new tool, there seem to be ways to twist it away from goodness and employ it for evil. The kind of massively intelligent computer that Hans Moravec wants to accomplish the life-everlasting of downloading could also be employed as a superefficient Big Brother. The charming lifetime-companion robots that Kerry Joels described could also be turned into robotic police to ruthlessly keep humans from stepping out of line. The computers and robots that Carl Hewitt would have as custodians of the world's nuclear arsenal could use this total power in unexpectedly harsh ways. The bacteria-size robots of Eric Drexler that could revolutionize medicine and extend life as cell-repair vehicles could just as easily be programmed as wind-carried, self-replicating mechanical locusts that could destroy *all* life on Earth—and then begin chomping away on the very rocks of the planet. That is the bad news.

The good news is that our planet is in a spiral galaxy that is so vast that we can estimate its expanse, but we cannot begin to grasp within our minds the reality of its size. Light travels through the vacuum of space at the rate of 186,000 miles per second, or 6 trillion miles a year. Our galaxy is believed to be 70,000 light years in diameter, and about 15,000 light years thick. Within this unimaginable expanse of galactic space there are perhaps 100 billion stars. If only 1 percent have planets, it would mean a billion planetary systems, which means there is a great deal of undeveloped real estate out there. And this is just our galaxy, the Milky Way. Within the universe there are billions upon billions of galaxies, each containing billions of stars. The mind-bending, unimaginable vastness of our universe, the incomprehensible wealth of worlds, resources, and most certainly life: That is the good news.

There are those, mostly outside the space sciences, who believe that life exists only on Earth and that all of the countless bodies of the universe were somehow left barren. If this is true, then how lonely we are! And how immeasurably priceless is this flowing of cells that we call life.

Even if life does exist elsewhere, even if we aren't completely alone, one should assume that the appearance of life is a sufficiently rare and glorious occurrence that it should be created with love and nurtured and guarded from any and all sources of harm.

In a conversation with Arthur Harkins one day he suggested that humans might be "the gods of this galaxy." If this is true, we carry an awesome galactic responsibility to protect our glowing embers of life and begin acting more like gods, more like gracious gardeners, doing all we can to spread this precious commodity as far as we can reach.

*

Dave Kreigman is not alone in believing that the Earth is too fragile a place to store all the eggs of humanity. Throughout my travels I found that the tomorrow makers, those who had the most reason to exult in what the future might bring, were among the most fearful that the world would blow apart before we could get there.

It isn't just the threat of nuclear or biological warfare. There is also the toll of pollution: that we may destroy our atmosphere, that we may kill the oceans, that we may poison the land and the groundwater. There is also the specter of overpopulation.

And then there is the fate of the dinosaurs, which were believed to have been killed by the climatic changes that came from a prehistoric version of a nuclear winter. An asteroid perhaps six miles in diameter is believed to have crossed orbits with Earth 65 million years ago, the collision creating such a huge cloud of dust and debris that global temperatures plummeted as the Sun was blocked.

Earth has plenty of scars from just such past encounters with chunks of rock from space. Within our solar system there are enough floating mountains (called asteroids) and icebergs (called comets) to make the threat of a catastrophic encounter worthy of consideration. There is a whole population of asteroids in orbits sufficiently near our planet to be called *Earth grazers*. But even short of a city-size boulder from space, a significant volcanic eruption on the scale of a mega-Krakatoa could sufficiently alter the climate to usher in doom.

Combine these threats together—placing that of nuclear destruction at the top of the list—and you can understand why Hans Moravec would say, "We could already be off the planet, and I think it's inexcusable that we're not. If we stay here, we are going to get wiped out sooner or later. And what's more, we'll deserve it."

*

There is a region in space, along the orbital path that the Moon takes around Earth, where the gravitational pull of the Moon and Earth are equalized and an object placed within the region would gently trail behind the Moon. This area was discovered by the French astronomer Joseph Lagrange, and in his honor the region is called L-5.

In 1975 participants at a space-development conference at Princeton University created an organization that would be dedicated to one cause: the establishment of a floating space city in the L-5 region. The bylaws of the L-5 Society call for the disbanding of the group once this new nest for humans is in place.

The L-5 Society is not large. It has only 6,000 members, spread throughout the world. Yet one tomorrow maker after another proved to be a member. It was like slowly—one person at a time—coming upon a vast technology underground, with every member racing to achieve that goal of getting human colonists out into space.

Hans Moravec, Mike Blackwell, and Kevin Dowling at Carnegie-Mellon were members, as were Marvin Minsky, Rod Brooks, and Eric Drexler at MIT, as were John McCarthy and Dave Kreigman at Stanford, as were Earl Joseph and Otto Nelson at Anticipatory Sciences, as was Art Harkins at the University of Minnesota, as was Kevin Ulmer at Genex, as was Kerry Joels at the Young Astronaut Council.

The only two researchers I met who voiced opposition to spreading our gene pool into space were Steve Berlin, the MIT researcher and member of Computer Professionals for Social Responsibility, who felt that we would just take our troubles into space; and MIT's Joseph Weizenbaum, who had spoken so eloquently about how having some portion of humanity off-planet would make more palatable the destruction of life on Earth, something he had equated with "the murder of God."

I agreed with both Berlin and Weizenbaum. We certainly would take our problems into space. And if we are the only forms of life, even if just for this area of the galaxy, then the purposeful destruction of that flowering would indeed be something akin to killing a god, and perhaps even *the* God.

But I still thought that we should be doing everything we could to get off the planet and out into the stars.

*

For centuries now authors and poets have written of the beauties of Earth. But I believe that the most magnificent descriptions are yet to be penned, that they will come from those early pioneers who travel into space, knowing that they have left their home planet behind for years and perhaps for life. The orbit of the Moon is about 220,000 miles out from Earth, and from that vantage point, from a space station in the region of L-5, Earth would be the most beautiful jewel hanging in the black velvet of space.

Perhaps the most valuable gift that the *Apollo* astronauts brought back from their voyages to the Moon were not the lunar rocks but the photographs of our big blue marble of a planet sitting in the black of space. It has been said that the photographs taken of Earth from the voyages to the Moon, the photographs that were used on Earth Day posters and that were carried in such great color by the print and electronic media, did more for the environmental movement than all the demonstrations that had come before.

The longer one was away from Earth, the more beautiful would become its dark blue oceans and the ever-changing white swirls of clouds. Yet there would be plenty else to look at and to dream about. The Moon, with its low mountains, highlands, craters, and valleys would become an intriguing friend; space-based telescopes would allow exceedingly clear planetary and stellar viewing; and the space station itself would be a fascinating world.

In time the space station would begin to evolve. As more housing, manufacturing, work, and support units were added to the structure, the population would grow and diversify. No longer just astronauts and mission specialists, there would be more engineers, industrial chemists, biologists, geneticists, electronics specialists, computer programmers, robotics hackers, doctors, nurses, dentists, mechanics, welders, designers, electricians, plumbers, cooks, food servers, janitors, commissary clerks, administrators, financial officers, middle managers, personnel managers, media managers, photographers, journalists, business people, physical therapists, pharmacists, laundry workers, warehouse personnel, dieticians, instructors, surveyors, repair people, psychologists, sociologists, geologists, barbers, beauticians, librarians, and clergy. And as all of these long-timers are allowed to bring up their families, and as others unite in space to create the first off-world children, the space *station* will evolve into a space *city*.

The city will likely retain the basic shape of the station—and be built in the shape of a wagon wheel, doughnut, or cylinder, so that it can spin on its axis to provide the kind of gravitational pull that our bodies evolved under on Earth. Toward the center of the spinning city there would be chambers of progressively less gravity, until at the hub there would be zero-G environments for manufacturing and for play.

The electrical needs of the city would be met with solar panels that in the weightlessness of space could be extended into square miles of collectors.

Oxygen would be produced in automated mining operations on the Moon or by collecting errant asteroids that had wandered away from the great asteroid belt that lies between Mars and Jupiter. Oxygen represents about 60 percent of the atoms in lunar soil. And some asteroids have an oxygen content in the 20 to 40 percent range. With the Sun providing all the energy needed for the extraction process, the mining of oxygen will likely be one of the first and most important enterprises initiated by the first crews in space.

The same mining techniques used to liberate oxygen from the soil of the Moon and from the rock of asteroids would also allow the recovery of hydrogen. From hydrogen and oxygen comes water.

The same hydrogen and oxygen that would make possible the sustaining of life without depending upon milk runs from Earth are also key constituents of rocket fuel. Space cities would be important refueling centers. They would also be important manufacturing centers, because the same type of automated mining procedures would also yield aluminum ore from lunar soil and high-quality nickel-iron, platinum, and gold from asteroids.

It would not be long before the first settlements were built on the surface of the Moon. And the next target would almost certainly be Mars, which even at its closest conjunction with Earth is still about 50 million miles away.

Throughout all this development—the space stations, the space cities, the lunar colonies—robots would play an important role. Space is a harsh environment for humans, and the kind of tele-existence helmet and gloves that are being developed in Japan and elsewhere will enable humans safely ensconced within pressurized work vehicles to feel as if they were totally inside the robot that is working out in the void of space.

But the robots will reach a special pinnacle when we send them out as advance parties to ready a moon or planet for occupancy by humans. In the 1940s science fiction author Jack Williamson coined the term *terraform* to denote the engineering process of converting a planet into a habitable environment for humans. Terraforming has occupied the thoughts of scientists as well as science fiction writers ever since. NASA has an interest in self-replicating robots because they could be soft-landed on a large asteroid, moon, or planet, where they could begin automated mining procedures that would release oxygen from the soil while at the same time recovering building blocks, such as aluminum and silicon, to create additional copies of themselves. These robots would be combination miners, refiners, extruders, and constructors. The result could be robots digging seabeds and then combining the mined oxygen and hydrogen to fill the escarpments with water. Great domes could be built to contain the artificial oxygen-nitrogen atmospheres that the robots created for use by humans. On the larger moons and planets, where the gravitational pull was sufficient to hold an atmosphere and keep it from pouring into space, no domes would be required, just enough time to allow the robots to convert the bad air into good.

In the case of a small body, such as an asteroid, the self-replicating robots could be programmed to tunnel down and hollow out chambers within the rock, filling them with oxygen and water to create an inside-out world.

Arthur C. Clarke, who has a stunning record of predicting future technologies in his science fiction writing, has considered the terraforming of Mars, and in his book *The Sands of Mars* suggested a terraforming methodology far simpler than the dispatching of oxygen-mining robots. He suggested the planting of vegetation capable of converting the Martian atmosphere into oxygen—just as the plants of Earth take in carbon dioxide and exhale oxygen.

Depending upon how large the planet was, how much it needed to be transformed, and how efficient the robots were, it might take decades or more to complete the terraforming. But it would certainly be worth the wait if humans could send the robots out in advance to convert an alien planet into a new version of the garden planet Earth.

Considerable research has already gone into these mining and extruding systems, and the tomorrow makers I spoke with felt that now it was more a question of societal commitment to space than of technology.

"Terraforming is mere details!" Rod Brooks told me at MIT. In Saint Paul, Brian Toren said, "The air force is doing a lot in the area of self-reproducing factories, factories that could fly to the Moon, and that would not only produce a product but would also produce a copy of itself."

Earl Joseph of Anticipatory Sciences said, "We have the technology to allow this now. We have the bits and pieces. It's like the invention that has to be made when you have the pencil and the eraser and now you have to put them together."

And most exciting of all, Joseph said, "A self-replicating factory could be on the Moon within five years of our deciding to do it. And within the next year it could be building habitats so that astronauts could later come up and live."

*

In the classrooms of space cities, lunar settlements, and Martian colonies, the lessons in history will probably be quite different from those taught on Earth. Christopher Columbus, Sir Frances Drake, and Magellan will fade to the back of the books as children learn about Sputnik, Yury Gagarin, John Glenn, and about the tragedy of the *Challenger* Space Shuttle. The children will be space pioneers, and rather than Davy Crockett and Daniel Boone, they will identify most with space pioneers.

Perhaps somewhere in their civic lessons will be mention of Eric Drexler, Chris Peterson, and a handful of other L-5 Society members from Boston who jumped into a couple of dilapidated cars one day and drove to Washington, D.C., to launch a lobbying attack against a United Nations Moon treaty, a treaty that few in government had interest in or knowledge about and that was, for these reasons, on the verge of being ratified. The teacher will explain that the treaty, put forth by some of the less democratic nations of Earth, would have shackled those who wanted to become pioneers in space, because it dictated creation of "an international regime" to govern all settlement and development of space. And a good teacher might give some of the colorful background, talking about how a dozen techies presented their case against the treaty so fervently, and so intelligently, that congresspeople and senators rose against the treaty and major opinion makers, such as the *New York Times,* the *Washington Post,* the *Wall Street Journal, Science,* and the news weeklies, wrote about the treaty concerns and credited the L-5 Society with having sounded the alarm. Students who live in space cities in the L-5 sector will take special pride in how the lesson ends, with the treaty self-destructing under the magnification of light.

*

One Saturday night I went to a party at Eric Drexler's, a most unusual party in that although the party extended far into the next morning, and his apartment was packed until the very end, less than a six-pack of beer was consumed and only two women were present, one of whom was Chris Peterson, Eric's MIT chemistry-major wife.

There was a note on the kitchen door that read,

Discussion of present-generation computer systems (hardware *and* software) strictly prohibited.

—The Management

But for this group of MIT graduate students, computer hackers, robot builders, and space enthusiasts, virtually all of whom were L-5 members, there was little danger of present-generation computer conversations. All of these people were looking ahead to tomorrow.

The conversations were magnificent and soaring. I spent three hours with just the first person I bumped into, Stewart Cobb, a senior in MIT's aeronautical and industrial mechanical engineering program. And all the while there were dozens of other conversations flowing through the air that were just as intriguing and just as intense. The party was a technology feast, a celebration of what might come to be.

In 1972 a hand-wringing group called the Club of Rome published a best-selling book about the depletion of Earth's natural resources and other portentions of doom. It was called *The Limits of Growth*. But to members of the L-5 Society, the presence of space means that there are no limits of growth.

Stewart, referring to the wonderful photograph of the big blue marble hanging in space, said, "What people didn't see was that out behind Earth is the rest of the universe."

"Just a one-kilometer nickel-iron asteroid, which is a fairly common size, has as much steel as has ever been produced in North America, and possibly the world," said Stewart, who wants to join the astronaut corps as a mission specialist. "All the cars Detroit has ever produced, all the buildings and all the bridges, and everything else, all the steel we've used to this point, would be available in that one asteroid. So who said resources are limited?"

Eric Drexler walked over to Stewart and plopped something into his hand. Stewart said, "I am holding in my hand a piece of meteorite. Meteorites are thought to be asteroids that happened to wander too near the Earth, got sucked in by the gravity, and came down."

He handed it to me, and I whistled at its weight.

"It's not a rock," said Chris Peterson, who had come over to join the conversation.

"What you're holding in your hand is nickel steel," said Stewart.

Eric added, "Nickel-iron steel. If you boiled down a ton of it, you would find a thousand dollars worth of platinum group metals in the residue. If you just melted the steel and skimmed off some slag, the remaining material would be strong, tough, ductile, corrosion-resistant, and better than what we build bridges and automobiles out of these days."

Just as the gravitational pull of the Earth had pulled this piece of asteroid from space, this heavy amalgam of metal was now attracting others from around the kitchen. Bruce MacKenzie walked over, took the meteorite in his hands, turned it over respectfully, and said, "This is not just part of an asteroid, this is probably a piece of the core of a planet, not just the crust. This piece just happened to fall to Earth and became a meteorite instead of an asteroid."

Eric drolly added, "It had the misfortune to run into the state of Arizona many years ago."

There will be many wonders and many resources to be discovered just within our solar system, but initially the asteroid belt, believed to have been formed during the birth of our solar system by debris left over from the formation of the planets, should be the richest super-market.

There are several different types of asteroids. Some, like the meteo-rite I held in my hand, are virtually pure metal, something that is almost harder to imagine than floating rocks. As Stewart pointed out, just one small nickel-iron asteroid would take care of our steel needs on Earth for a long, long time. But perhaps more significant than tak-ing care of Earth is that an asteroid just a hundred yards in diameter could provide the equivalent building materials of thousands upon thousands of delivery flights by the Space Shuttle.

With the nonmetallic asteroids, the rock contains significant quan-tities of oxygen. It also contains the silicon needed for computer chips, and, more significantly because of the quantities required, for building the solar panels that will provide the energy for space colonization.

NASA has conceptual plans for self-replicating robotic factories that could be sent to an asteroid, analyze its content, and transmit a report, and if given the go-ahead could begin mining. The ores recovered would be used to create additional robots, and then the robots would build solar panels to create energy. The robots would then assemble mag-netic coils, which would act as a gun of sorts to propel the asteroid. This is called a mass driver, and it is as simple as tossing rocks into one end of the solar-powered magnetic coils and having the rocks shoot out the other. This simple but effective and inexpensive propulsion system could be used to propel small asteroids into Earth orbit or to a space city or lunar settlement for further mining and manufacturing.

Combining the terraforming robots with the miners and builders of solar panels and mass drives, some future citizen of space might be able to go out to the asteroid belt, find a particularly handsome-looking chunk of rock, and turn it into the equivalent of a sportscar planet, something that he could not only live within but use to go tooling around the solar system.

You could have the robots that were feeding rock into the mass drive work as sculptors, so that as they cut rock away for fuel, they would be carving your asteroid into a flying horse that was ten miles long and had wings that gracefully arched for miles into space.

When the carving was complete, you could start towing smaller asteroids to feed the hopper or convert to a different source of propulsion. Hans Moravec has speculated on a fusion reactor ship that would operate like a vacuum cleaner as it pulled hydrogen atoms from space. Eric Drexler wrote a thesis at MIT on the use of lightsails, a propulsion system that harkens back to the square-riggers of Earth. The sails could be one thousand times thinner than Saran wrap and extend for hundreds of miles, as they were driven through space by the force of photons streaming out from the Sun. You could run with the photons, straight out from the center of the solar system, or adjust the sails to tack back toward the Sun at 45-degree angles.

Whether traveling by sail, mass driver, hydrogen fusion, or old-fashioned oxygen-hydrogen ignition, there would be so very much to see just within our own solar system. But for all such journeys, time would not be on the side of a human. Compared with the rest of the galaxy, and the universe beyond, our solar system is just the tiniest of specks. Yet within this speck is a lot of volume. The distance from the Sun to Pluto is 3.7 billion miles, and a human could spend a significant part of his or her life just traveling there.

Even if we develop propulsion systems that can approach or exceed the speed of light, there will still be so much to see that the lifespan of a human will seem unjust. If we could achieve downloading, or if Drexler's cell-repair machines could extend our lives, one could set out on a voyage that would seem dreamlike in the wonders it would present. Downloaded into a robotic body you could be more adventurous in what you did. But even ensconced within the pressurized safety of a ship, you could use the kind of tele-existence system I experienced in Japan to explore a planet completely. There would be so much to see. Standing upon the Moon, you could experience the blue light of Earthglow. You could go to Tycho, the Moon's newest and most mysterious crater, and begin excavating for the great black monolith that Arthur C. Clarke conjured for his book 2001: A Space Odyssey. You could read Edgar Allan Poe as you walked over the mountains of the Moon, down through the valleys of the shadow. You could ride, boldly ride, as the shade had replied, in search of El Dorado.

You could wander the heat-parched plains of Mercury, exploring areas where no human could survive. On Venus you could search for the volcanoes that may lie beneath its perpetual cover of clouds. On Mars you could behold the pink skies and wander the red dunes of sand and rocky plains. You could explore the potato-shaped moons of Mars and then go on to the asteroid belt for the odd feeling of seeing mountains floating in space.

You could go flowing through the surreal clouds of Jupiter and then dive down to see what might be below. There would be the distinctly individual four major moons of Jupiter: Io, Europa, Ganymede, and Callisto. You could orbit for weeks above the rings of Saturn, just to ponder the geometric precision, the phonograph-record grooves, of its ultrathin rings of ice. You could visit the planet's magnificent moon Titan and sail across its ocean of methane. At Uranus you could search for signs of what great collision might have pushed its plane of rotation out of kilter with the rest of the solar system.

You could visit Neptune's largest moon, Triton, to sit beside the shore of its liquid-nitrogen sea. Continuing out to Pluto, you could try to cross-country ski, and then you could begin searching for the long-suspected presence of a tenth planet somewhere out beyond.

To truly do justice to the solar system, you might want to spend a century or so looking around its planets and moons, its asteroids and comets. There are billions of other stars in our galaxy, and there must certainly be more planets out there, so the next few million years might be spent running around the Milky Way. If life were found, those millions of years might turn into billions of years as you taught those who were less advanced and learned from those who were more advanced.

And after that you might sit down at the chart table of your craft one day and pull out a computer printout of the billions of other galaxies that exist within our universe. You could check off the Milky Way, then head out for the second one on the list, knowing that you were setting out on a journey that might never really end.

This is why a human life isn't long enough. This is why people like Hans Moravec and Mike Blackwell want so dearly to learn how to download. I was encouraged by what Danny Hillis at Thinking Machines had told me: "I think downloading in principle is possible. Hans and I may just miss it. But that's not enough to make me stop working on it."

And I was encouraged by what Gerry Sussman had told me at MIT: "Everyone would like to be immortal. I don't think the time is quite right. But it's close. It isn't very long from now. I'm afraid, unfortunately, that I'm the last generation to die. Some of my students may manage to survive a little longer."

This is why Hans Moravec has written, "We are on a threshold of a change in the universe comparable to the transition from non-life to life."

*

It was four in the morning at Eric's party when someone pulled out a guitar and started singing songs he had written about the challenges of going to sea in the old sailing ships. I wondered whether we would someday sing songs about those who had boldly set sail out in space, and this thought must have struck others, for someone said that leaving the Earth's orbit would be a lot like a ship leaving harbor.

I wondered who would be the first to go, I wondered when we would be able to stretch out our lives and set out on voyages among the stars.

On a sunny morning in St. Paul, Art Harkins and I stopped by a sporting goods store where he was picking up a pair of hiking boots he had special-ordered. In the car we had been talking about getting humans into space, and our conversation continued right up to the counter. Also in the store was a thirty-five-year-old crude-oil pipeline worker named Ed Isackson and his nine-month-old son.

Art looked at the child and said to me, "This kid could end up living on Mars when he's eighteen. Easily."

The child had angelic blond hair and eyes so white and blue they looked like twin Earths hanging out in space. He was sitting on the floor and he wore a wonderfully rainbow-colored jacket. I walked over to the father and told him about the book I was writing and about what Art had just said. I was surprised by the reply: "I hope so. I hope to make a trip on the Space Shuttle myself, so possibly he has a chance for Mars." And then the father said, "No kidding, you think about that now and again, too?"

Art came over, and I asked Ed Isackson what his rainbow-wearing child was named.

"Adam."

Harkins and I looked at each other and smiled. Adam! Let there be an Adam! And let him go into space! I thought of the great synthesizer, the great integrator, Marvin Minsky had prophesied, and I could see some future Adam, all dressed in rainbows, achieving the kind of resonance with computers that would enable him to set off on a great adventure. As with children of an earlier age who would stow away aboard a ship to go out to sea, I could imagine this Adam downloading into a terraforming master ship being sent out on an interstellar voyage of exploration and creation.

What joyful worlds would a child create? And what guidance could the computer, carrying the knowledge of civilized human beings, provide?

Charles Lecht had said that there would come a point when we could leave the technology behind and step into the spiritual, perhaps wrapping ourselves into the gentle folds of Einstein's space-time continuum. But even short of that, long before we learn to breathe deeply and pass through time, we may be able to deploy such an array of smart and self-replicating robots for terraforming that we will be able to pass through the stars, leaving in our wake newly formed cradles of life.

In time, especially when dealing with planets as naturally blessed as Earth, we may be able to complete the job of transformation in a mere six days, leaving the seventh to take our rest.

Perhaps someday we will give birth to some Adam of Rainbows who will have a thumb so green that, like some galactic gardener, some tomorrow maker who may have passed this way before, he will be able to flow through space, initiating his work with the simplest of words: "Let there be light."

INDEX